Geology of ... Coalbrookd...

C000103316

Telford new town continues to develop, and the surrounding district continues to be exploited for a range of mineral products, including opencast coal, and aggregates for the construction industry. In an area such as this, up-to-date geological information is vital for planners faced with conflicting demands for land use, as well as for those involved in the construction and mineral extraction industries. The memoir is intended to satisfy this need and to indicate where more detailed information is available in the Survey's extensive database.

The district described in this memoir is dominated by Telford new town and the Coalbrookdale Coalfield, and extends from Sheinton, in the valley of the River Severn in the south-west, to Lilleshall in the north-east. The solid rocks at outcrop include some of the oldest in Britain, including the Uriconian volcanic rocks, the Rushton Schists and the Primrose Hill metamorphic rocks, all of Precambrian age. The youngest solid strata preserved are sandstones and conglomerates of the Sherwood Sandstone Group, formed in near-desert conditions during the Triassic period. A wide range of rocks of Cambrian, Ordovician and Silurian ages adds variety to this fascinating microcosm of British geology, but it is the Carboniferousage Coal Measures of the Coalbrookdale Coalfield which form the immediate substratum of most of the new town. The rocks are heavily faulted and this adds complexity to the planning both of mineral extraction and of land reclamation. The whole of the district was glaciated during the last ice age and glacial deposits still cover most of its surface, also occupying a series of buried valleys cut by meltwaters beneath the retreating icesheet.

The memoir concentrates largely on the Coal Measures because of the problems induced by earlier generations of underground and opencast mining. The area was chosen for new town development because of its high proportion of derelict land, a legacy of the industrial revolution which was founded on the mineral wealth of the coalfield. Old mine workings have to be stabilised for development, and coal is still worked opencast. Both the glacial deposits and hard rocks are worked for aggregates, and the Sherwood Sandstone Group and Bridgnorth Sandstone provide a valuable aquifer in the north-west of the district.

Cover photograph
Abandoned Crawstone Ironstone mine at Ironbridge, worked by the advancing longwall method. The Main Road in the mine (right) is about 1.7 m high. Its base has been sunk lower than the working level (a practice known as 'bating' or 'dinting') to provide sandstone blocks ('pack') to fill the empty space ('gob' or 'goaf') remaining after the mineral had been mined. The mine was abandoned in the early 19th century. (A12198)

The Tar Tunnel at Coalport

Natural bitumen collecting in a sump in a branch of the main tunnel, draining from the Thick Rock sandstone of the Coalport Formation. The wall behind the tar pool is 2.1 m high of which the lowest 0.3 m is stained black with tar. The Tar Tunnel was originally driven as a canal but was not used as such since commercial quantities of bitumen continued to drain from the walls for many years. The tunnel has been incorporated in the Coalbrookdale Museum and part of it is open to the public. (A12188)

BRITISH GEOLOGICAL SURVEY

R J O HAMBLIN and
B C COPPACK

CONTRIBUTORS

Palaeontology
M A Calver
M Mitchell
B Owens
A W A Rushton
D E White

Geophysics
M R Henson
E A Atitullah
P Freeman

Geology of Telford and the Coalbrookdale Coalfield

Memoir for parts of 1:50 000 geological sheets 152 and 153 (England and Wales): 1:25 000 sheet SJ 60 with parts of 61, 70, 71

LONDON: HMSO   1995

First published 1995

ISBN 0 11 884516 0

Bibliographical reference

HAMBLIN, R J O, AND COPPACK, B C. 1995. Geology of Telford and the Coalbrookdale Coalfield. *Memoir of the British Geological Survey,* parts of sheets 152 and 153 (England and Wales).

Authors

R J O Hamblin, BSc, PhD
British Geological Survey, Keyworth

B C Coppack, BSc
formerly British Geological Survey

Contributors

B Owens, BSc, PhD, DSc
A W A Rushton, BA, PhD
British Geological Survey, Keyworth

E A Atitullah, BSc
M A Calver, MA, PhD
P Freeman, BSc
M R Henson, BSc, PhD
M Mitchell, MA
D E White, MSc, PhD
formerly British Geological Survey

Printed in the UK for HMSO
Dd 296609   C8

Other publications of the Survey dealing with this and adjoining areas

BOOKS

British Regional Geology
Central England, 3rd edition, 1969
The Welsh Borderland, 3rd edition, 1971

Memoirs
Geology of the country around Church Stretton, sheet 166, 1968
Geology of the country around Dudley and Bridgnorth, sheet 167, 1947

Explanatory booklets for 1:25 000 maps
Wenlock Edge, 1970
Church Stretton, 1968
Craven Arms, 1969

Mineral Assessment Reports
No. 86   The sand and gravel resources around Wem, 1981
No. 90   The sand and gravel resources around Shrewsbury, 1982

MAPS

1:625 000
Great Britain South, Solid geology, 1979
Great Britain South, Quaternary geology, 1977
Aeromagnetic map (south sheet), 1965
Bouguer anomaly map (south sheet), 1986

1:250 000
Mid Wales and Marches, Solid geology, 1990
Mid Wales and Marches, Aeromagnetic anomaly, 1980
Mid Wales and Marches, Bouguer gravity anomaly, 1986

1:100 000
Hydrogeological map: Clwyd and the Cheshire Basin, 1989

1:50 000
Sheet 138, Wem, Solid with Drift, 1990
Sheet 139, Stafford, Drift, 1974
Sheet 152, Shrewsbury, Solid, 1978
Sheet 166, Church Stretton, Solid, 1974
Sheet 167, Dudley, Solid with Drift, 1975

1:63 360
Sheet 152, Shrewsbury, Drift, 1932
Sheet 153, Wolverhampton, Solid, 1929
Sheet 153, Wolverhampton, Drift, 1929
Sheet 166, Church Stretton, Drift, 1967

1:25 000
SJ 60 and parts of 61, 70, 71, Telford, Solid with Drift, 1978
SO 59, Wenlock Edge, Solid with Drift, 1969
SO 49, Church Stretton, Solid with Drift, 1968
SO 48, Craven Arms, Solid with Drift, 1969
Parts of SO 29, SO 39, SJ 20, SJ 30, Shelve Ordovician Inlier, Solid with Drift, 1991

CONTENTS

FIGURES

TABLES

HISTORY OF SURVEY OF THE TELFORD DISTRICT

The district covered by the Telford 1:25 000 sheet was surveyed on the six-inch County Series sheets Shropshire 35, 36, 42, 43, 50 and 51 by T C Cantrill, E E L Dixon, R W Pocock, T Robertson and T H Whitehead in 1915–1929. Six-inch-scale maps of the coalfield area were published, and the whole district was incorporated in separate Solid and Drift editions of one-inch sheets 152 (Shrewsbury) published in 1932, and 153 (Wolverhampton) published in 1929. The Telford district was resurveyed on the six-inch scale by R J O Hamblin and B C Coppack in 1970–1972, and published at 1:25 000 scale in 1977. Sheet 152 (Solid) was revised by B A Hains and published in 1978 incorporating Mr Coppack's surveys of the Telford district.

Geological six-inch-scale maps are listed below, together with initials of the geological surveyors and dates of the survey. These are all published except for SJ 60 SW and SJ 61 SW, which are available as black and white dyeline copies. All can be purchased from BGS.

SJ 60 NW	BCC	1970–1972
SJ 60 NE	RJOH, BCC	1970–1972
SJ 60 SW	BCC	1972
SJ 60 SE	RJOH, BCC	1972
SJ 61 SW	BCC	1970–1972
SJ 61 SE	RJOH, BCC	1971–1972
SJ 70 NW	RJOH	1970–1972
SJ 70 SW	RJOH, BCC	1970–1972
SJ 71 SW	RJOH	1971–1972

PREFACE

This account of the geology of Telford and the surrounding area is intended to be a description of the published 1:25 000 scale geological map (IGS, 1978). The area is the site of one of Britain's newest major towns and of the birthplace of the industrial revolution, which was in turn founded on the rich mineral resources of the area. The mapping resurvey was carried out in 1970–1972 by B C Coppack and R J O Hamblin, to provide an up-to-date geological basis for the development of Telford New Town. New information that has become available since the resurvey has, where possible, been incorporated in this account. However, the stratigraphical classifications used here are essentially the same as those used on the map; where new classifications have become accepted, the links between old and new are indicated in the text.

The new town was sited on the exposed part of the Coalbrookdale Coalfield, which had been largely worked out; indeed, a primary reason for the choice of this area for a new town site was that it contained a high density of derelict land. Parts of the undermined land were stabilised by opencast coal working prior to building development. The decision to develop this area provided the initial impetus for the geological resurvey, which in turn benefitted from the wealth of new site-investigation and other data produced during the new town development.

The account is weighted heavily towards the detail of Coal Measures sections, this being the information that will be of greatest value to those who live in the district, and to those who may be engaged in future town planning activities and constructional projects there. However, the surrounding areas include a variety of geological formations, both older and younger than the Coal Measures. The older suite includes Precambrian metamorphic and volcanic rocks of The Wrekin, Rushton, and Wrockwardine, and also Cambrian to Silurian sedimentary and intrusive igneous rocks, among which the fossiliferous Wenlock Limestone is the best known.

The younger rocks comprise great thicknesses of late Carboniferous to Triassic red beds, which blanket the Coal Measures in the east of the area and rest unconformably on the Precambrian rocks in the northwest. The structural history of the area is complex, with a high density of faulting particularly in the coalfield. Unconsolidated drift deposits form a patchy cover to the bedrock formations.

The economic history of the area is one of mineral exploitation and the growth of manufacturing industries dependent on these indigenous resources. Mining of coal, ironstone, fireclay and limestone, in particular, were associated with the manufacture of iron, and it can be said that the industrial revolution began in Coalbrookdale. These resources are now effectively worked to exhaustion but the remains of heavy industry have become a tourist attraction, while extractive industry is presently concentrated on bulk materials for construction, provided chiefly by the Precambrian and Silurian rocks. This account does not include a chapter on the economic geology of the area, since this has already been published (Hamblin et al., 1989); but the account is slanted towards those strata most widely exploited in the past, and which are of the greatest importance to present and future mineral extraction and land reclamation.

Peter J Cook, DSc
Director

British Geological Survey
Kingsley Dunham Centre
Keyworth
Nottingham
NG12 5GG

January 1995

NOTES

Throughout the memoir the word 'district' refers to the area covered by the Telford 1:25 000 sheet.

National Grid references are given in square brackets; except where otherwise indicated, these lie within 100 km square SJ.

Enquiries concerning geological data for the district should be addressed to the Manager, National Geosciences Records Centre, Keyworth.

ACKNOWLEDGEMENTS

In this memoir, Mr B C Coppack wrote Chapter 2, for which palaeontological determinations were provided by Dr A W A Rushton (Cambrian and Ordovician), Dr D E White (Silurian), and Mr M Mitchell (Dinantian). Dr T C Pharaoh also contributed to this chapter. Mr Coppack also provided part of the details for chapters 4, 5, 7 and 9; palaeontological determinations for the Coal Measures were provided by Dr M A Calver and Dr B Owens. Chapter 8 was compiled by Dr M R Henson from an internal report by Ms E A Atitullah and Mr P Freeman. The remaining chapters were written by Dr R J O Hamblin, who was also responsible for compiling the memoir. The editors were Dr J W Baldock and Mr J I Chisholm.

BGS gratefully acknowledges the assistance generously provided by British Coal and their predecessors, by the engineering departments of Telford Development Corporation, and by Severn Trent Water Authority, for borehole information and for access to their properties during the survey. We also thank Sir Owen Williams and Partners and the Midland Road Construction Unit for access to borehole cores for the M54 motorway. In addition we acknowledge the access and help given by numerous farmers and landowners throughout the district during the course of the geological survey.

ONE

Introduction

GEOLOGICAL SETTING

The Telford 1:25 000 scale geological map sheet includes the Coalbrookdale Coalfield, which comprises the western outcrop of the Lower and Middle Coal Measures (also known as productive measures) of the Stafford Basin, together with their down-dip extension beneath Upper Coal Measures (or barren measures) to the south-east. Farther to the east and north-east, the coal seams may continue beneath the Permian and Triassic cover rocks and connect with those in the coalfields of south and north Staffordshire (Figure 1). To the north-west the sequence is cut off by the Boundary Fault, to the west of which Upper Coal Measures rest directly on Precambrian rocks. The southern limit of the Coalbrookdale Coalfield is taken to be just south of Linley (1.5 km south of the southern margin of the Telford map sheet), where the Lower and Middle Coal Measures are cut out by the intra-Carboniferous unconformity. The coalfield comprises the strata exposed in three north-eastward-plunging synclines: the Donnington Syncline in the north-west, the Madeley Syncline in the centre of the field and the Coalport Syncline in the south. This account describes in detail the Coal Measures sequence and the structures of the Coalbrookdale Coalfield. It also deals more briefly with the underlying Lower Palaeozoic and Precambrian successions and with the Permian and Triassic cover rocks, as well as the Quaternary drift deposits that extend across much of the area.

The Lower and Middle Coal Measures form a condensed sequence in comparison with those of many other coalfields. Nevertheless, they once supported a thriving mining industry. Seams of coal, ironstone and fireclay have been worked underground since Roman times, although only one deep mine survived at the time of the resurvey. Opencast or strip mining has been important since the Second World War and the district is particularly suited to this method of extraction because the coal seams lie close together in the sequence and the intensive block-faulting repeats the outcrop of the workable seams. High-alumina fireclays have also been widely worked by opencast methods. Few resources of coal or fireclay now remain at depths suitable for opencast mining, but potentially workable coal occurs at deeper levels to the east.

The Upper Coal Measures are largely devoid of useful coal seams, but some of the red mudstones are still dug for the manufacture of facing bricks.

The exposed part of the Coalbrookdale Coalfield has been largely worked out and subsequently developed as Telford New Town. The decision to develop this area provided the initial impetus for the resurvey, which in turn benefitted from the wealth of new site investigation and other data produced by the new town development.

In the exposed coalfield, much information was also obtained from opencast sites and exploration boreholes. In the concealed coalfield, old shaft sections are the main source of data, and more modern information has been gained from two borehole programmes: the Lilleshall boreholes for Granville Colliery (at the time the only remaining working mine), around Sheriff Hales in the north-east of the coalfield; and the Madeley Wood boreholes drilled for Madeley Wood Colliery, around Shifnal, in the east of the district.

HISTORY OF RESEARCH

Early accounts of the coalfield were given by Murchison (1839) and Prestwich (1840) who, with Williams (1846), published many of the shaft sections. A relationship between the Productive Coal Measures of the Coalbrookdale and South Staffordshire coalfields was first suggested by Smith (1846). Salter and Ramsay (in Jukes, 1859, pp.27 and 58) equated the marine Pennystone ironstones of the two coalfields, and detailed seam-by-seam correlations with the neighbouring coalfields of south Staffordshire, the Wyre Forest and Clee were subsequently attempted by Jones (1871, 1872, 1894, 1895) and Cantrill (1895). Stobbs (1906) recognised three distinct marine bands in the productive measures of Coalbrookdale: the Chance Pennystone, the Blackstone and the Pennystone. Later attempts at correlating these bands with other coalfields appear to have been confused by the similarity in nomenclature between the Pennystone and Chance Pennystone, and it was Trueman (1940, 1946) who first correctly equated the Pennystone with the Amman of South Wales and the Seven-Foot Banbury of north Staffordshire. Mitchell et al. (1945) correlated the Blackstone Marine Band with the sub-Brooch of south Staffordshire, and Wills (1948) correlated the Chance Pennystone with the Gin Mine and Charles of north and south Staffordshire.

Many of the publications have been concerned with the subdivision, dating and correlation of the Upper Coal Measures. Murchison (1832, 1834, 1867) believed the upper part (Keele and Enville Beds) to be Permian. Scott (1861) realised that the Upper Coal Measures overlay an unconformity and ultimately overstepped the productive measures, and Jones (1871) produced a detailed map of coal incrops against the unconformity. Clark (1901) appears to have been the first to recognise that the unconformity was the result of intra-Carboniferous folding. Gibson (1901) recognised the presence of the Newcastle-under-Lyme and Etruria Marl groups, set up in North Staffordshire, in the Coalbrookdale Coalfield. However, the age of these higher Coal Measures

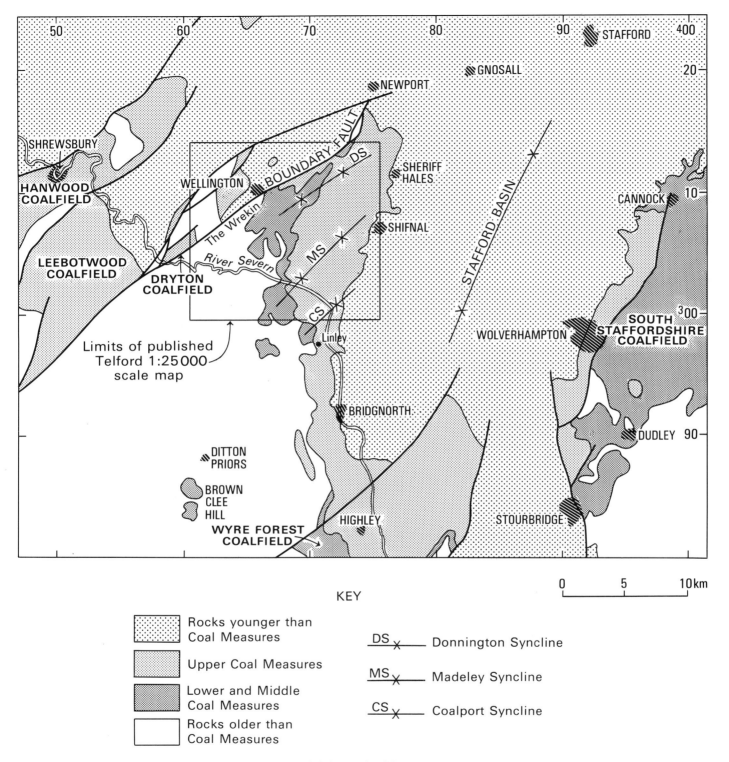

Figure 1 The geological setting of the Coalbrookdale Coalfield.

sequences remained in some doubt. Whitehead (1922) considered it most advisable to consider them all as Carboniferous and this remains the present position, though Poole (1975) believed that the entire Upper Coal Measures sequence is Stephanian, and rests unconformably on the Westphalian productive measures.

TWO

Pre-Coal Measures rocks

Rocks of Precambrian, Cambrian, Ordovician, Silurian and Lower Carboniferous ages crop out in the south-west and west of the district (Figure 2). They are overlain unconformably by rocks at various levels in the Coal Measures; in places to the north-west of the Boundary Fault, for example, the Upper Coal Measures rest upon Precambrian rocks whereas, to the south-east of the fault, Lower Coal Measures rest upon Dinantian and Silurian strata.

PRECAMBRIAN ROCKS

The Precambrian rocks of the area fall into three groups. One, almost exclusively volcanic, is known as the Uriconian volcanic group; the others, made up of metamorphic rocks, are the Rushton Schists and the Primrose (or Little) Hill schists and gneisses. The structural relationships between the Uriconian volcanic rocks and the Rushton Schists are not fully understood, but it seems probable that the latter are the older. The schists and gneisses on Primrose (or Little) Hill [617 076] underlie the main mass of the Uriconian volcanic rocks; they cannot readily be correlated either with these or with the Rushton Schists.

Rushton Schists

Poorly exposed Precambrian quartzose and pelitic schists, overlain by Cambrian strata in the south and obscured by drift in the north, occur at Rushton village on the western margin of the district. The name 'Rushton Schists' was given to them by Callaway (1884). The schists can be seen in various lane-side exposures in the western end of the village and along the footpath leading northwards towards Uppington; they show strong foliation or schistosity. Pocock (1938) considered that they represented a group of gritty shales and flags subjected to thermodynamic metamorphism of moderate intensity, while Dearnley (in Grieg et al., 1968) considered them to be low-grade regional metamorphic rocks resembling parts of the Mona Complex of Anglesey.

In 1973, the British Geological Survey sank a borehole at Rushton [6069 0822] (Appendix 1). This was drilled to a depth of 152 m and passed through extensively fractured rock which, at several horizons, readily disaggregated into a coarse gravel. The upper part of the borehole core comprises fine-grained schists with a few thin, massive layers and mafic intrusions (Figure 3). The schists are generally platy, contorted and in places overturned. Below a depth of 78 m the core consists of a more uniform sequence of fine-grained quartzite.

The core shows that the schists are more variable than is evident from the restricted outcrops. Thinly laminated pelitic schists and fine-grained quartzites predominate, with thin psammitic layers occurring within the pelites. The sequence proved in the borehole shows a tripartite subdivision possibly disrupted by tectonic slicing. The upper part, down to about 40 m, is predominantly pelitic and noticeably garnetiferous in hand specimen. In the middle part (c.40 m to c.75 m), the schists are generally more siliceous and are sparsely garnetiferous at the top. The bottom part, from about 75 m downwards, is predominantly siliceous and composed of fine-grained quartzites and quartz-schists with minor pelitic layers near the top.

The pelitic schists are finely laminated, fine-grained, dark olive-grey, porphyroblastic quartz-plagioclase-chlorite schists with or without garnets. They show relict sedimentary structures such as small-scale cross-bedding, and clastic textures. Interlayered with them are a few thin, pale, commonly pinkish, massive quartz-feldspar-garnet rocks. The fine-grained siliceous rocks in the lower part of the borehole are typically quartzitic siltstones, composed of interlocking quartz and subordinate feldspar grains with some chlorite and muscovite. Their petrography suggests that they originated as fine-grained, laminated, impure and tuffaceous sandstones, orthoquartzites and shales, which accumulated in relatively quiet waters. Thin mafic lavas or penecontemporaneous intrusions were included.

The schists suffered regional prograde metamorphism, a later retrogressive greenschist facies metamorphism and two episodes of postmetamorphic cataclastic deformation. The initial prograde metamorphism developed mineral assemblages of the almandine-amphibolite facies (biotite, grossular-rich garnet and calcium-rich plagioclase). Some brecciation evidently occurred before the retrograde metamorphism but, during the latter, the rocks were veined with quartz-albite-chlorite aggregates. Many samples contain some epidote or clinozoisite, and a specimen from an outcrop 260 m west of the borehole site [6044 0823] is now largely composed of quartz and epidote with some chlorite pseudomorphs after biotite. The subsequent cataclastic deformation produced open fractures with little cement (resulting in the fragmentary nature of the core). Mineralisation has introduced veins of calcite and quartz, while small rosettes of fibrous malachite and aggregates of pyrite occur sporadically. In the borehole core, epidotisation is concentrated along the margins of the late calcite-filled fractures, which suggests that some of the epidote developed after the main metamorphic events.

An Rb-Sr whole-rock isochron age of 667 ± 20 Ma has been obtained for samples from the Rushton Borehole.

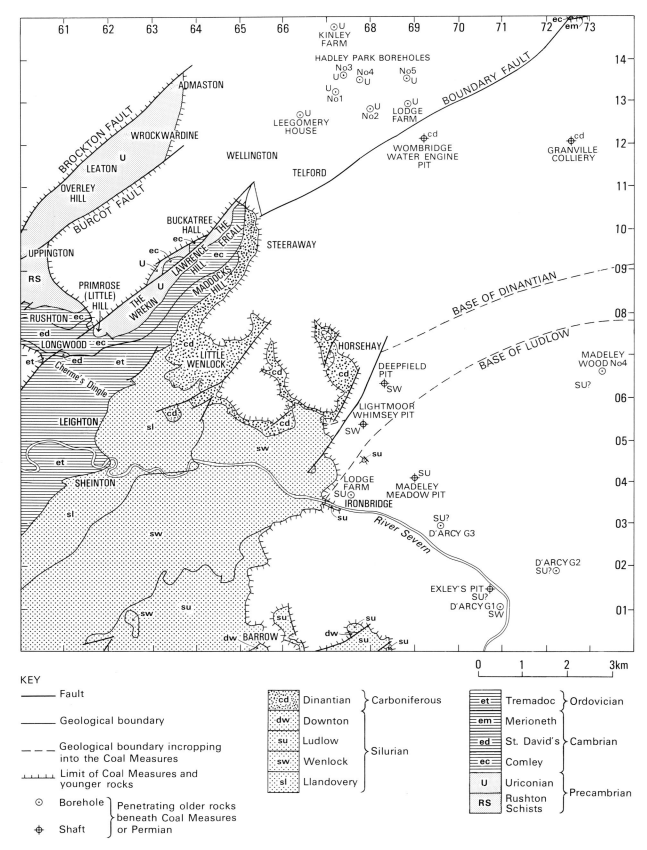

Figure 2   Simplified map of the outcrop and projected incrop of pre-Coal Measures strata.

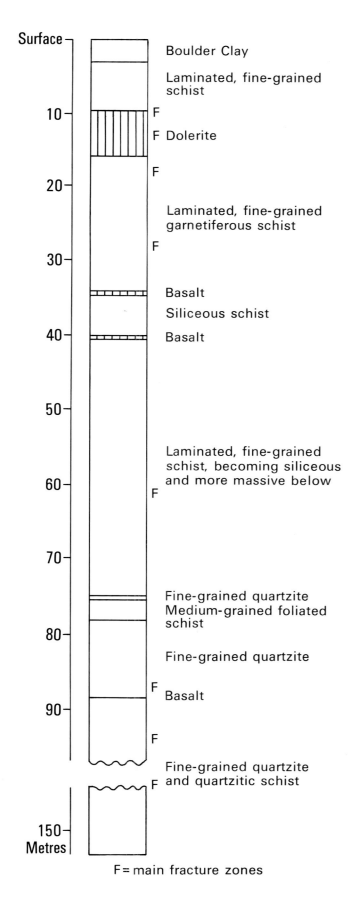

Figure 3 Rushton (Telford No.1) Borehole: graphic section showing quartzose and pelitic Rushton Schists.

This has been interpreted as the age of prograde metamorphism (Thorpe et al., 1984). Sm-Nd isotope data yield model ages of about 1300 Ma (T_{CHUR}) and about 1600 Ma (T_{MORB}), indicating the presence of a significant component of crustal material older than 670 Ma.

Apart from the mafic igneous rocks recorded in the Rushton Borehole, reddish orange, fine-grained, porphyritic granophyre is recorded from Bell Brook [6045 0895], and also from beneath the Wrekin Quartzite [6104 0798] in a quarry east of Rushton. These may represent offshoots of the Ercall granophyre (p.6). Examination of thin sections by Mr R W Sanderson revealed distorted tabular phenocrysts of turbid oligoclase-andesine up to 2.4 mm long, set in a groundmass of subsperulitic granophyric intergrowths of 0.9 mm average diameter, with a granular quartzose mesostasis. The spherulites are composed of granophyric overgrowths on stubby crystals of oligoclase. A penninitic chlorite is the only, very minor, mafic constituent. Sparse accessory minerals include acicular apatite, short prismatic zircon and opaque iron ore. Some of the latter shows alteration to leucoxene, indicating an appreciable titanium content.

Metamorphic rocks of Primrose (or Little) Hill

This hill is separated from the main mass of The Wrekin by the Primrose Hill Fault, which lies about 25 m southwest of the depression between the two features. The rocks can be divided into three groups.

The lowest group, which crops out on the southern and south-western slopes of the hill, is distinctly layered, but 'schistose'. In one layer, 15 m south of the summit, the rock is composed almost entirely of uralitic hornblende, whereas other layers are made up of a quartz-feldspar mosaic with laminae of brown biotite and aggregates of white mica.

A group of 'gneissic' rocks crops out at the summit and down the western slope. These rocks are, in places, very largely composed of feldspathic material, which bears a strong resemblance to the Ercall granophyre, although the 'granophyric' texture is generally coarser and much of the feldspar is microperthite. Evidence from thin sections suggests that the gneissose appearance may result from the streaking out of an original granophyre.

The uppermost rocks, which crop out on the northern and north-eastern slopes, are composed of acid igneous material, some also with a granophyric texture, but all showing pronounced cataclastic structures. They may represent crushed and altered acid crystal tuffs.

All three groups are veined with pink feldspathic material. The Primrose Hill rocks might have been produced by the injection of granophyre into a sequence of tuffs and lavas, followed by moderately intense dynamothermal metamorphism. It is evident that these rocks suffered some dynamic alteration before injection, but renewed stress produced a later set of cataclastic and schistose structures. The schistose group is more akin to the sheared and metamorphosed igneous rocks of the Malvern Hills than to the metasedimentary Rushton Schists.

Uriconian volcanic group

Uriconian rocks crop out in two fault-controlled, elongated inliers each 5 km to 6 km in length, aligned NE–SW, to the west and south-west of Wellington; these are the Wrockwardine Ridge and Wrekin inliers. Both include rhyolites, tuffs and basic volcanic rocks; in the former, they dip generally south-westwards, while at The Wrekin they dip fairly steeply to the north or north-east. In addition, Uriconian rocks are recorded at relatively shallow depths beneath the Bridgnorth Sandstone and Keele Beds, north-east of Wellington.

THE WROCKWARDINE RIDGE

The ridge, which includes Admaston, Wrockwardine and Overley Hill, is bounded by the Brockton Fault to the north-west and the Burcot Fault to the south-east. The main central and north-eastern sections of the ridge are dominated by tuffs; the south-western section contains a large section of rhyolites now forming Overley Hill.

Around Admaston village, tuffs were recorded in shallow trenches and wells. South of the village, a sequence dominated by rhyolites is exposed for about 150 m in a railway cutting [6322 1265]. Farther to the south-west, an old quarry [6305 1251] formerly showed rhyolites on its southern face and basalt on the north. Numerous exposures can be seen in the village of Wrockwardine. All the outcrops are of green pyroclastic rocks (vitric vesicular tuffs) commonly invaded by dykes and veins of cryptocrystalline felsite. An old quarry [6278 1170] south-east of Wrockwardine shows blocks of flow-banded rhyolite. A major sequence of rhyolites crops out to the south-west of Wrockwardine and several old quarries [6220 1172] at David's Bank also showed flow-banded rhyolites.

A major quarry [6180 1120] at Leaton, which exploits the tuffs for roadstone and general aggregate exposes more than 150 m of strata, mainly green and blue basic tuffs, commonly showing well defined upward-coarsening graded bedding. Several dolerite dykes associated with east–west faults occur in the northern part of the quarry, and basaltic sills have caused baking of the tuffs along their margins. At the northern corner of the quarry, a 10 m sill of basalt shows curved columnar jointing in its upper parts.

At Overley Hill, a disused and partly infilled quarry at Lea Rock [6100 1080] shows excellent sections of rhyolitic rocks varying from flow-banded to spherulitic and nodular types. On its western side the main quarry shows beautifully banded purple rhyolite, with small phenocrysts of albite and with perlitic, spherulitic and fluxion structures. The rock is completely devitrified and largely silicified. Highly spherulitic varieties can be seen in older workings [6108 1075], and about 100 m to the south-east

[6110 1067], a projecting mass shows rhyolite with nodules varying from the size of a pea to that of a cricket ball.

Flow-banded rhyolite lava from temporary exposures north-east of Overley village [6128 1112] have yielded zircons dated at 566 ± 2 Ma by the U-Pb method (Tucker and Pharaoh, 1991), in good agreement with a previously published Rb-Sr age of 558 ± 16 Ma for felsic tuffs at Wrockwardine (Patchett et al., 1980).

THE WREKIN INLIER

The Precambrian rocks of the Wrekin inlier include the rhyolitic tuffs and flows of the main mass of The Wrekin, the dominantly basic tuffs of Lawrence Hill and Forest Glen, the Ercall Granophyre in the north-east and the 'gneissose' and 'granitic' rocks of Primrose (Little) Hill in the south-west (see above). They are all overlain by the basal Cambrian quartzites along the south-eastern flanks of the Wrekin hills and, apart from an isolated area south-west of Buckatree Hall, all are bounded to the north-west by the Wrekin Fault.

The Wrekin

The main central mass of The Wrekin is formed of 600 to 700 m of rhyolitic rocks, which occur as a succession of flows with a northward dip of 40° to 60°, although the direction of flow banding does not always coincide with this. The rhyolites are hard and compact, breaking with a splintery fracture, and vary from pink and purple to greenish grey; they are largely silicified and devitrified. There are numerous large crags showing fine examples of various lava types on and to the south of the summit.

The north-eastern end of The Wrekin is composed of at least 400 m of pyroclastic rocks, which generally dip northwards at up to 50°. The tuffs are exposed on and alongside the crest of the hill leading to the summit. They are intruded by at least seven dolerite dykes trending north–south or NE–SW and dipping eastward or south-eastward at 50° to 60°. The width of the dykes varies from 1.5 m to more than 15 m. Similar pyroclastic rocks are present on the north-western side of The Wrekin Fault [6330 0910]; they are overlain by the Wrekin Quartzite against the fault and are apparently overlain by the Bridgnorth Sandstone on the lower slopes.

Lawrence Hill

A fine section of 60 m or more of dominantly felsic tuffaceous rocks is exposed in an old quarry [6390 0925] in Forest Glen; they dip steeply northwards at 45°. The quarry includes a vesicular olivine basalt, but is dominated by medium to coarse vitric and lithic tuffs, mostly rhyolitic. The side walls of the quarry are formed by two dolerite dykes associated with faulting. The valley [6420 0950] between Lawrence Hill and The Ercall exposes rhyolites, many showing good flow-banding, cut by a number of thin, near-vertical dolerite dykes.

The Ercall

The Ercall comprises a granitic body, which has been variously called 'granitoidite', 'eurite', 'aplite' and 'ercallite'. In thin section it is a granophyre with a well-developed microg021ographic texture, consisting of a coarse aggregate of quartz and feldspar in a graphic intergrowth enclosing rectangular phenocrysts of plagioclase (albite–oligoclase). The granophyre appears to have intruded the Uriconian rocks, although field evidence is now limited. Nevertheless, there are many exposures in the disused and overgrown quarries [6450 1000] alongside the road leading from Wellington to Buckatree Hall where an abundance of small joints causes the granophyre to break up readily into a 'gravel'-like deposit as it weathers.

The Wrekin Quartzite (see below) rests unconformably on a weathered surface of Ercall Granophyre in Ercall Quarry (Cope and Gibbons, 1987). Zircons from the granophyre have yielded a concordant U-Pb age of 560 ± 1 Ma (Tucker and Pharaoh, 1991), interpreted as the date of emplacement. Rb-Sr whole-rock isochron ages of about 533 Ma reported by Patchett et al. (1980) and Thorpe et al. (1984) almost certainly reflect the extensive weathering of the granophyre prior to deposition of the Cambrian sediments.

NORTH-EAST OF WELLINGTON

Borings made by the Shropshire Coal Company from about 1860 onwards encountered what appear to be Uriconian rocks at relatively shallow depth over the area to the north of the Boundary Fault. Borehole No. 1 [6720 1322] records 'very hard rock or granite', from 57.61 m to its base at 60.96 m; Borehole No. 2 [6798 1281] from 119.81 m to its base at 132.46 m; and Borehole No. 3 [6738 1361] from 58.22 m to its base at 62.48 m. Borehole No. 4 [6775 1349] records alternations of 'hard rock, reddish' and 'green rock' from 51.21 m to 61.47 m and Borehole No. 5 [6884 1353] entered 'hard green rock' at 100.58 m.

Three boreholes sunk by the British Geological Survey (Appendix 1) proved Uriconian rocks beneath the Keele Beds in the Leegomery–Kinley–Preston area. In Kinley Farm Borehole [6716 1478], rich green tuffs are recorded from 39.19 m to 45.72 m; in Leegomery House Farm Borehole [6638 1268], very shattered rhyolites occur from 118.74 m to 119.35 m; and in the Lodge Farm, Trench Borehole [6887 1297], banded tuffs and rhyolites are described from 88.47 m to 91.44 m. A fourth borehole at Wrekin Buildings [6231 0871] revealed granodiorite, which is presumably intrusive into the Uriconian rocks but may be post-Ordovician (Caledonian) in age.

CAMBRIAN AND ORDOVICIAN ROCKS

The stratigraphy shown on the published Telford map is based on that recommended by Cowie et al. (1972), in which the Tremadoc Series is included in the Cambrian. That used in this account differs in that the Tremadoc is regarded, in accordance with more recent practice, as part of the Ordovician.

The main outcrop forms a narrow belt extending from the eastern flanks of the Ercall Granophyre south-westwards to beyond Sheinton. This outcrop widens from about 250 m in the north-east to nearly 4 km in the south-west. Regional dips are consistently to the south-east, but local variations result from powerful strike-faulting and complex zig-zag folding, which is common in the Shineton Shales. For this reason, estimates of thicknesses, particularly in the Shineton Shales, are at best approximate. Smith and Rushton (1993) showed that deposition was in half-grabens, with some divisions thickened locally against syn-depositional faults. The Cambro-Ordovician rocks are overlain unconformably by Silurian strata in the south-west, but in the north and east Lower Carboniferous rocks overstep on to them. A second, smaller outcrop of Cambro-Ordovician strata occurs as a fault-bounded inlier around Lilleshall and extends northward beyond the district. Cambro-Ordovician rocks have not been proved in deep boreholes to the east but could be present there, beneath the Silurian strata.

Earlier and comprehensive descriptions are given in the Shrewsbury Memoir (Pocock et al., 1938); the sequence in the Rushton area was described by Cobbold and Pocock (1934) and the Shineton Shales (Tremadoc) of The Wrekin were described by Stubblefield and Bulman (1927). The Cambro-Ordovician rocks have not, therefore, been resurveyed in detail; modifications to the earlier mapping have been made where quarries have been extended or where there are new exposures. In particular, new fossil collections were made from the base of the Lower Comley Sandstone in a quarry on The Ercall, and the relationship between the Lower and Middle Cambrian in Cherme's Dingle (Cobbold and Pocock's 'locality 7') has been clarified by excavation. A BGS borehole at The Croft, Lilleshall [7384 1505], drilled as part of this revision, is described separately (Rushton et al., 1988) because it lies outside the limits of the district.

Wrekin Quartzite (Lower Cambrian–Comley Series)

The Wrekin Quartzite overlies the Precambrian basement with strong angular unconformity. It crops out along the entire south-eastern flank of The Wrekin and The Ercall, forming a pronounced feature on the slopes of these hills. The quartzite has been extensively quarried at Buckatree Glen, and is exposed in many crags and smaller disused quarries on the flank of The Wrekin. Two faulted outliers lie north and west of Lawrence Hill, and there is a further outcrop at Rushton. The Wrekin Quartzite is a massive, white, cream or pale purplish blue quartzite, with sporadic ripple-marks and a coarse basal breccia. Apart from some undescribed trace fossils, the Wrekin Quartzite is virtually unfossiliferous (cf. Cobbold, 1921, p.369; Raw, 1936, p.238) and averages some 50 m in thickness.

Lower Comley Sandstone (Lower Cambrian–Comley Series)

The Lower Comley Sandstone generally occupies low wooded ground and is therefore poorly exposed along the whole of its main outcrop south-east of and overlying the Wrekin Quartzite. It also crops out in the Lilleshall inlier where it is faulted against the Uriconian rocks, but no exposures are recorded in that part of the inlier which lies within the district. The formation comprises about 100 m of interbedded green, glauconitic and phosphatic shales, sandy mudstones and calcareous grits or sandstones, similar in all respects to those of Comley (Greig et al., 1968). Fossils are not abundant, but the fauna collected from The Ercall (p.9) suggests that the Lower Comley Sandstone extends down to the upper part of the Tommotian Stage (the lowest division of the Siberian Lower Cambrian sequence), while fossils collected from the top of the formation at The Croft, Lilleshall Borehole suggest a correlation with divisions of the Lower Comley Limestones, especially the *Strenuella* Limestone (Ac4) of Cobbold (1921, p.371) and Cobbold and Pocock (1934).

Lower Comley Limestones

The highest Lower Cambrian strata in the district are thin sandy limestones which rest, apparently conformably, on the Lower Comley Sandstone. By excavation, Cobbold and Pocock (1934, p.314) showed that the members of this 2 m-thick limestone sequence, known as the Lower Comley Limestones (or merely 'Comley Limestones'), could be correlated from Comley to the Rushton area. However, only the lowest beds (the *Callavia* Sandstone and Limestone, Ac1–2 of Cobbold's (1921) divisions) and the highest beds (*Lapworthella* Limestone (Ad)) are naturally exposed in this area. The *Lapworthella* Limestone is a thin, black, sandy algal limestone yielding sponge spicules, brachiopods, *Lapworthella* and other fossils. It is the only unit of the Lower Comley Limestones to be identified in the Croft, Lilleshall Borehole where it comprised 0.25 m of pale grey to black, recrystallised, algal limestone. The sandstone underlying the *Lapworthella* Limestone in the borehole, though typical of the Lower Comley Sandstone, appears to be a correlative of part (Ac4) of the Lower Comley Limestones of Comley (Rushton et al., 1988).

Upper Comley Group (Middle Cambrian — St David's Series)

Rocks of the Upper Comley Group are exposed in Cherme's Dingle (p.9), where the basal beds rest with probable disconformity on the *Lapworthella* Limestone. Wherever seen, they comprise pink and grey limestones with shale partings. However, following Cobbold and Pocock (1934), the group as a whole is believed to amount to about 130 m of largely pale green calcareous sandstones and shales, with thin beds of limestone containing trilobites (agnostids, *Kootenia*, *Paradoxides*, *Solenopleura*), brachiopods and hyolithids of Middle Cambrian age.

'Dolgelly Beds' (Upper Cambrian — Merioneth Series)

In the Comley area, strata of Merioneth age comprise the *Orusia* Shales, overlain by black shales with olenid trilo-

bites (Stubblefield, 1930) known as the Bentleyford Shales (Cowie et al., 1972, p.26). In the Rushton area, the *Orusia* Shales are unknown, but the Bentleyford Shales, though unexposed and not portrayed on the Telford mapsheet, are presumed to be present because of the occurrence in Dryton Brook of blocks of fossiliferous stinkstone concretions (Cobbold and Pocock, 1934, pp.317, 391). At Lilleshall, beds of Merioneth age are not exposed but were proved by power-auger drilling. The Croft, Lilleshall Borehole proved 53.75 m of micaceous black shales with brachiopods and olenid trilobites representing the zones of *Parabolina spinulosa*, *Leptoplastus* and *Protopeltura praecursor*. These beds are correlated with the *Orusia* Shales (below) and chiefly with the Bentleyford Shales (above), though they differ from the latter in having numerous thin interbeds of cross-laminated calcareous siltstone. These are shown on the Telford mapsheet as 'Dolgelly Beds' but this term has since been redefined in the type area and is no longer applicable.

Shineton Shales (Tremadoc Series)

At the time of the resurvey, rocks of Tremadoc age were assigned to the Upper Cambrian and are shown thus on the published map; they are now regarded as the oldest Ordovician rocks.

The Bentleyford Shales are succeeded, after a presumed non-sequence, by at least 800 m of Shineton Shales. Lithologically, these are grey to blue shales, smooth to silty and micaceous, with some hard, fine-grained sandstone beds. They generally form a belt of low-lying ground; thus exposures are confined to stream sections on either bank of the River Severn. A quarry at Maddock's Hill provides a good section in the shales, which are baked to a varying degree by an intrusion. The fauna of the Shineton Shales includes brachiopods (*Eurytreta sabrinae, Lingulella nicholsoni, Palaeobolus quadratus*) and several trilobites (e.g. *Platypeltoides croftii, Shumardia pusilla, Proteuloma monile*); the lower beds yield graptolites (*Rhabdinopora flabelliformis, Clonograptus tenellus*).

DETAILS

Wrekin Quartzite

This is well exposed in the Buckatree Quarries [6430 0950], where massive, greyish white quartzite dips consistently to the south-east at 40° and shows well-preserved ripple marks on the dip slope of one of the older quarries [6425 0952]. The base of the quartzite is seen in a disused quarry nearby [6415 0946], where it rests with strong unconformity on the Uriconian rocks. Coarse angular pebbles and small boulders of multicoloured Precambrian tuffs and flow-banded rhyolites occur at the base. The thickness of the quartzite in this area is calculated at about 60 to 70 m. Considerable brecciation is associated with a fault in the quarries, and there are local reversals of dip against the fault-plane. At Ercall Quarry [644 097], workings subsequent to the resurvey (Cope and Gibbons, 1987) have shown 5 m of basal conglomerate with rare granophyre clasts resting unconformably on the Ercall Granophyre, which has been radiometrically dated (p.7). West of Lawrence Hill, an outlier [6350 0930] of Wrekin Quartzite forms a prominent craggy mound. Another fault-bounded outcrop of the quartzite occurs adjacent to Buckatree Hall Hotel [6400 0970], and crags of brecciated quartzite are seen at the entrance to the Buckatree Quarries.

The strongly unconformable base of the Wrekin Quartzite can be followed along the south-eastern flanks of The Wrekin. An old quarry [6317 0820] 730 m south-south-west of Wrekin Cottage is believed to be one of those referred to by Murchison (1839, p.223), from which stone was extracted for the manufacture of china at Coalbrookdale. Locally, dips are steep, more than 60° at an exposure [6305 0803] 270 m south of Heaven Gate. Along the flank of the Wrekin, the thickness of the quartzite rarely exceeds 40 m. Around Little Hill, the outcrop is dislocated by faulting, but the small disused quarries around the village of Rushton are now all either ponded or infilled.

Lower Comley Sandstone

The main outcrop of the Lower Comley Sandstone closely follows that of the Wrekin Quartzite. There are several small disused quarries around the Wrekin Golf Course; the least obscured of these [6493 0950], north of Newhouse Farm, exposes more than 3 m of fine- to medium-grained, micaceous, glauconitic sandstone. In another disused quarry [6462 0918], south-west of the farm, the sandstone dips south-eastwards at 30°. A much overgrown quarry [6410 0887] in Hazel Hurst shows both westerly and north-westerly dips, and the sandstone is clearly very disturbed by the strike faults in the vicinity. Fossils recorded from here include *Beyrichona* sp. and '*Aluta*' *ulrichi*. Pocock (1938) recorded a quarry 600 m west of Steeraway exposing green to almost black, highly micaceous sandstone dipping west at 46°. At the Tumuli [6424 0919], sandstone debris yielded a fragment of ?*Kutorgina*, and at an exposure [6442 0936] 220 m to the north-east, 3.5 m of sandstone are seen, dipping at 50° to east-south-east.

The base of the Lower Comley Sandstone is well exposed in the Buckatree Quarries [6445 0955], where it is seen to be both conformable and quite sharp. The Wrekin Quartzite is overlain by weathered, brownish green, sandy shales which pass up into flaggy green and brown shaly sandstones. From the lowermost 15 cm specimens of *Obolella? groomi*, *Micromitra* cf. *phillipsi*, *M.rhodesi*, *Hyolithellus pallidus*, *H? sinuosus* and *Mobergella* cf. *radiolata* have been collected. This fauna correlates with beds yielding *Obolella groomi* (Ab1) at Comley and suggests the upper part of the Tommotian Stage. A calcareous concretion about 10 m above the base yielded *Paterina* sp., '*Hyolithes*' cf. *strettonensis*, '*H*'. *strettonensis brevis* and a fragment of *Torellella?*.

The base of the Lower Comley Sandstone is clearly defined by a change of vegetation and can be followed from the Buckatree Quarries along the south-eastern flanks of The Wrekin. A disused quarry [6130 0706] south of Neves Castle formerly showed sandstone dipping south-westwards at 60°. On the eastern bank of Cherme's Dingle [6110 0705] 2 m of glauconitic sandstone are overlain by the *Lapworthella* Limestone.

The Lower Comley Sandstone is not exposed around Rushton, where a depression filled with boulder clay indicates its location between the Wrekin Quartzite and the Upper Comley Group.

Upper Comley Group and *Lapworthella* Limestone

On the east banks of Cherme's Dingle [6115 0704], 200 m west-south-west of Neves Castle, excavation of 'locality 7' of Cobbold and Pocock (1934) revealed a faulted relationship between the Lower Comley Sandstone, *Lapworthella* Limestone and the Upper Comley Group. On the upthrow side of the fault, the *Lapworthella* Limestone, about 30 cm thick, overlies the Lower Comley Sandstone and yielded specimens of *Acrothyra sera*, *Hyolithellus micans*, *H? cingulatus*, *H? tortuosus*, *Lapworthella nigra*, *L. dentata*, a problematicum, calcareous algae forming concentric phosphatic nodules and a *Bevocastria*-like organism forming a non-phosphatic algal mat. On the downthrow side of the fault is the following succession:

	Thickness cm
Unfossiliferous pink limestone	15
Pink and grey limestone (with shale partings above and below) yielding *Hyolithellus micans*, *Helcionella oblonga*, *Bailiella* cf. *cobboldi* (juveniles) and fragments of a large paradoxidid	7
Pink and grey limestone (8 cm) with brown shale (1–2 cm) at base, yielding *Hyolithellus micans* and acrotretid, dorypygid? and paradoxidid? fragments	10
Lapworthella Limestone	about 10 seen

The fauna listed is of Middle Cambrian age, equivalent to that of the Quarry Ridge Grits or *Paradoxides groomi* Beds of Comley. These limestones are probably disconformable on the *Lapworthella* Limestone. Younger strata including grey limestones yielding *Paradoxides hicksii* and *P. salopiensis* (Cobbold, 1913) are no longer exposed. Between Rushton and Longwood, the outcrop is largely drift-covered and there are no exposures; the base of the Upper Comley Group is mapped as an indistinct feature against the depression formed by the Lower Comley Sandstone.

Shineton Shales

A total of 88 m of blue, evenly bedded shales are exposed for more than 200 m in Sheinton Brook [6075 0370], of which some 44 m of strata can be readily examined. Dips vary between 15° and 45° to the south-east, but are most commonly 25°. There are further exposures along Sheinton Brook [6078 0408] north of the Sheinton-Cressage Road, and in a subparallel stream to the west [6045 0400]. The rich faunas of these classic sections were recorded by Stubblefield and Bulman (1927, p.112), and a new fauna from the highest beds by Fortey and Owens (1991). During the present resurvey, a further specimen of the annelid worm *Palaeoscolex piscatorum* was collected from Sheinton Brook, which is the type locality for the species.

Small discontinuous sections can be seen throughout Cherme's Dingle and its tributary, which rises near The Spout [626 070]. Dips vary between 10° and 80° and are almost invariably to the south or south-east, although a 60° dip to west-north-west is recorded [6128 0668] in Cherme's Dingle (cf. Stubblefield and Bulman, 1927, p.108), and another north-westerly dip is evident where the beds are faulted against the Upper Comley Group. Details from various other stream sections are given by Stubblefield and Bulman (1927, pp.109–114). At Maddock's Hill, shales with *Rhabdinopora flabelliformis* are intruded by a lenticular sill of altered lamprophyric rock, apparently of variable composition, containing albite-oligoclase feldspar, augite, serpentine after olivine, biotite and hornblende. Extensive quarrying for roadstone in this intrusion has exposed metamorphosed shales; for example, at the entrance to the quarry, steeply dipping and vertical spotted shales are exposed [6447 0865], while to the north-west the intrusion thickens and the shale is baked to a hornfels.

SILURIAN ROCKS

Silurian strata within the district form a north-eastern continuation of equivalent rocks of the Welsh Borderland. They occupy about 36 km² in the south-western part of the district, where a sequence about 650 m thick is present, with a south-eastward dip of 10°. They rest unconformably on Cambrian rocks around Leighton and Sheinton, and are themselves overlain unconformably by Lower Carboniferous strata to the north-east around Little Wenlock and, more extensively, by the Lower Coal Measures to the east, around Ironbridge and Barrow.

The district is part of the area in which the Silurian System was first established (Murchison, 1834, 1835) and is also part of the type area for the Wenlock Series. Historical aspects have been summarised by Pocock et al. (1938) and by Greig et al. (1968), and the lithostratigraphy used by them in the Shrewsbury and Church Stretton districts respectively has largely been adopted, though updated. In 1972, the Barrandian area of Czechoslovakia was designated the type area for the Silurian–Devonian boundary, which was fixed at the base of the *Monograptus uniformis* Zone, at the top of the Přídolí Series. This level lies somewhere within the Downtonian to Dittonian Old Red Sandstone succession of the Welsh Borderland (White and Lawson, 1989) and, consequently, Downtonian strata within the district are here included in the Silurian.

At the beginning of the Silurian Period, the Telford district formed part of a land mass lying to the east of the Central Wales Basin of marine sedimentation. In mid-Llandovery times, there was an eastward transgression of the sea, during which the Kenley Grit was deposited unconformably on Ordovician strata. The grit is succeeded by finer-grained sediments of the Pentamerus Beds and Hughley Shales. Continued deepening of the sea is suggested by the rarity of benthic faunas in the Wenlock Shale, but by late Wenlock times the sea was again sufficiently shallow for the development of a reef belt (Scoffin, 1971). Deepening of the sea is generally postulated at the beginning of Ludlow times, followed by a gradual shallowing that culminated in an intertidal environment at the start of Downton times.

The distribution of supposed depth-related faunal communities tends to confirm this sequence of events (Ziegler et al., 1968; Calef and Hancock, 1974). However, Watkins (1978) has pointed out that studies of modern benthic communities indicate that, where zones of similar sedimentary facies and hydrographic conditions are not parallel to coastlines and bathymetric contours, the benthic communities show a similar lack of depth relationship.

STRATA OF LLANDOVERY AGE

The probable correlation of the lithological subdivisions used here with the type succession at Llandovery, Dyfed, and with the graptolite zonal sequence, is given in Table 1, which is based on Cocks et al. (1984).

Kenley Grit

The Kenley Grit crops out between the drift-covered area south of Belswardyne Hall [6030 0330] north-eastwards to Sheinton, where it rests unconformably on the Shineton Shales. North of the River Severn, the grit forms steep, wooded scarp slopes at Hall Coppice [6180 0525], and farther north-east it occupies the lower slopes of The Wrekin in Harper's Dingle [6335 0720]. It generally comprises yellowish brown, coarse sandstone or grit, up to 40 m thick, and includes conglomeratic horizons containing rounded pebbles of Uriconian rocks. Dips are south-eastwards at about 10°, increasing locally to 20°. The only fossils recorded are poorly preserved *Lingula crumena*. This 'restricted' *Lingula* community may indicate a lagoonal environment (Ziegler et al., 1969, p.436).

Pentamerus Beds

The Pentamerus Beds rest conformably on the Kenley Grit, with a gradational contact. The outcrop is generally drift-covered and, south of the River Severn, exposures are limited to Sheinton Brook, around The Springs [613 031] and its deeply gullied tributaries. North of the River Severn, the outcrop widens but is obscured by glacial till, except for sections in deeply incised streams in Hurst Coppice [6280 0560] and Harper's Dingle [6300 0640].

The Pentamerus Beds comprise about 100 m of blue and blue-grey silty mudstones, with subordinate thinly bedded, orange sandstones and sandy limestones; they are generally finely micaceous and, at certain horizons, contain rounded pebbles of Uriconian rocks up to 3 cm in diameter. The dip is to the south-east, but local disturbances produce northward or north-eastward dips; for example, in the northern part of Hurst Coppice, disruption may be related to the extension of a branch of the Little Wenlock Fault.

Compared with the Kenley Grit, the Pentamerus Beds contain more prolific and diverse faunas, particularly in the limestones. Close to the base, *Eocoelia* aff. *hemisphaerica* is common, in association with *Eostropheodonta voraginis*, *Megastrophia* (*Eomegastrophia*) *ethica* and other brachiopods; molluscs are also well represented. In higher beds, *Pentamerus oblongus* is common, and there is local evidence of the presence of a *Stricklandia* community towards the top of the formation, possibly indicating deeper-water conditions.

An assemblage of graptolites, found during the present survey approximately 50 m above the base of the Pentamerus Beds, provides new information on the age of the oldest Silurian rocks in the district. Although not wholly diagnostic, the fauna indicates a probable *M. convolutus* Zone age. This implies that the lower part of the Pentamerus Beds, and the Kenley Grit, are likely to fall within the Aeronian Stage; associated strata contain coarsely ribbed examples of *Eocoelia* close to *E. hemisphaerica*. Cocks and Rickards (1969, p.217) have recorded the possible presence of strata of similar age in the BGS Church Stretton No. 5 Borehole [SO 4217 8912].

The higher parts of the Pentamerus Beds evidently include strata of basal Telychian age, containing *E. hemi-*

Table 1 Classification of Llandovery strata.

STAGES	GRAPTOLITE ZONES	LLANDOVERY TYPE AREA LITHOSTRATIGRAPHY	TELFORD DISTRICT LITHOSTRATIGRAPHY
TELYCHIAN	*Monoclimacis crenulata*	Cerig Formation	Hughley Shales
	Monoclimacis griestoniensis		
	Monograptus crispus		
	Monograptus turriculatus		
AERONIAN		Wormwood Formation	Pentamerus Beds
	Monograptus sedgwickii	Rhydings Formation	
	Monograptus convolutus	Trefawr Formation	Kenley Grit
	Monograptus argenteus		
	Diplograptus magnus		
	Monograptus triangulatus		
RHUDDANIAN	*Coronograptus cyphus*	Crychan Formation	unconformity
	Lagarograptus acinaces	Bronydd Formation	
	Atavograptus atavus		
	Parakidograptus acuminatus		

sphaerica, Stricklandia laevis and graptolites indicative of the *M. turriculatus* Zone (Ziegler et al., 1968, p.748).

Hughley Shales

South of the River Severn, the outcrop of the Hughley Shales is mainly obscured by drift, and exposures are confined to Sheinton Brook [614 028] and Boathouse Coppice [621 040]. Extensive temporary sections north of the River Severn have been described by Cocks and Walton (1968), and further collections were made at these localities during the resurvey. The formation consists of 40 m to 50 m of purple, bluish purple and chocolate brown to grey-brown mudstones and silty mudstones, with some thin silty to sandy limestones and calcareous siltstones.

The beds contain a prolific and diverse fauna typical of the *Clorinda* community, indicating a probable deepening of the basin of deposition already recognised in the Pentamerus Beds. Ziegler et al. (1968, p.749) have recorded *Eocoelia intermedia* from the base of the Hughley Shales in Sheinton Brook [6116 0310], indicating an Aeronian to lowest Telychian age, and in the higher beds of Boathouse Coppice [6205 0398; 6210 0379] they record *E. curtisi* and *E. sulcata* respectively, of Telychian age. Confirmatory evidence from graptolites is generally lacking, though Cocks and Rickards (1969, p.226) considered that graptolites from temporary exposures high in the

Hughley Shales in Devil's Dingle indicate the presence of the *Monoclimacis griestoniensis* or the *M. crenulata* zones.

STRATA OF WENLOCK AGE

In this account the lithostratigraphical classification of strata of Wenlock age adopted by Greig et al. (1968, p.148) is followed, with the addition of the term Benthall Beds to cover a distinctive lithology laterally equivalent to the Wenlock Limestone Reef Facies. Table 2 summarises the nomenclature in relation to that in the type area (Bassett et al., 1975).

Although there is an abrupt upward change from Llandovery to Wenlock strata, Pocock et al. (1938) considered the contact probably to be conformable, a view supported by the presence of the basal *C. centrifugus* Zone of the Wenlock. Whittard (1952) believed that there is a break at the Llandovery–Wenlock boundary in the Welsh Borderland, but Bassett et al. (1975) concluded that the Wenlock sequence in the type area of Much Wenlock is complete.

Wenlock Shale

It has proved impracticable to survey separately the outcrop of the Buildwas and Coalbrookdale beds (Table 2) in this district because of the cover of glacial drift, par-

ticularly south of the River Severn. Indeed, exposures in the Wenlock Shale are confined to the River Severn and its tributaries, such as Sheinton Brook. The outcrop is approximately 1.3 km to 1.4 km wide; south of the Severn, it floors much of a shallow depression bounded by Wenlock Edge, to the south-east, and by the outcrop of the Pentamerus Beds, to the north-west. The dip generally varies between 5° and 15°. North of the river, the outcrop widens to more than 3 km as a result of strike faulting and local folding.

The **Buildwas Beds** are 30 m to 40 m thick, and consist of grey, silty, rubbly mudstones with many thin, argillaceous limestone beds and nodules. They contain an abundant fauna dominated by brachiopods, including *Dicoelosia biloba, Eoplectodonta duvalii, Isorthis elegantulina* and *Resserella sabrinae*, species which do not occur in Llandovery rocks (Bassett et al., 1975, p.11). This assemblage represents the deep-water *Dicoelosia* community of Calef and Hancock (1974). Graptolite evidence from outside the present area (Bassett et al., 1975, p.6) indicates that the *C. centrifugus* Zone is likely to be represented.

The overlying **Coalbrookdale Beds** comprise about 160 m of blue-grey, silty, shaly mudstones with sporadic calcareous nodules, which become more common towards the top as the strata grade into the Tickwood Beds; thin beds of waxy bentonite are common. The fauna of the Coalbrookdale Beds includes fragmentary

Table 2 Classification of Wenlock strata.

STANDARD CHRONOSTRATIGRAPHY (Bassett et al., 1975)		GRAPTOLITE BIOZONES	MUCH WENLOCK TYPE AREA LITHOSTRATIGRAPHY (Bassett et al., 1975)	TELFORD DISTRICT LITHOSTRATIGRAPHY	
STAGES	CHRONOZONES				
Homerian	Gleedon	? ? ? ? *Monograptus ludensis*	Much Wenlock Limestone Formation	Wenlock Limestone	
				Wenlock Limestone Reef Facies/Benthall Beds	
		Gothograptus nassa	Farley Member	Tickwood Beds	
	Whitwell	*Cyrtograptus lundgreni*	Coalbrookdale Formation	Coalbrookdale Beds	Wenlock Shale
Sheinwoodian		*C. ellesae*			
		*C. linnarssoni**			
		*C. rigidus**			
		Monograptus riccartonensis			
		*C. murchisoni**	Buildwas Formation	Buildwas Beds	
		C. centrifugus			

* Biozones marked with an asterisk have not yet been recognised in the type area of Much Wenlock.

orthocones and trilobites, especially *Dalmanites caudatus*. Benthic forms are comparitively sparse and are represented mainly by *Glassia obovata*, *Leangella segmentum* and *R. sabrinae*, suggesting a deeper-water environment than that in which the Buildwas Beds accumulated. Within the type area for the Wenlock, but mainly outside the Telford district, the *M. riccartonensis*, *C. ellesae* and *C. lundgreni* zones, as well as the higher *G. nassa* and *M. ludensis* zones, have been established (Table 2), and evidence for the remaining graptolite zones is likely to be found eventually (Bassett et al., 1975, p.6).

Tickwood Beds

The Tickwood Beds, which represent a transition between the Coalbrookdale Beds and the local Wenlock Limestone, comprise 15 m to 25 m of grey, shaly mudstones, with bands of prominent limestone nodules. Their outcrop forms part of the scarp slope of the Wenlock Limestone feature. Bassett et al. (1975, p.4) include the Tickwood Beds within their Coalbrookdale Formation, under the name 'Farley Member', with Harley Hill [6090 0035] as the standard section.

Pocock et al. (1938, p.111) found the fauna of the Tickwood Beds generally rather sparse. However, in contrast to the Wenlock Shale, large brachiopods are present, including *Atrypa reticularis*, *Eospirifer radiatus*, *Gypidula galeata* and *Meristina obtusa*. This benthic fauna suggests a shallower water environment than that which prevailed during deposition of the Coalbrookdale Beds. Locally, *Gothograptus nassa* is common, the basal part of the *G. nassa* Zone evidently straddling the boundary with the Coalbrookdale Beds. The upper limit of the zone is uncertain, but there is evidence that, to the south of the district, a horizon 0.9 m below the top of the Tickwood Beds belongs to the overlying *M. ludensis* Zone (Bassett et al., 1975, p.8).

Wenlock Limestone Reef Facies and Benthall Beds

The outcrop extends from the south-western corner of the district, north-eastwards to pass beneath the unconformable cover of Coal Measures at Lincoln Hill [6720 0415], to the north of the River Severn. The beds dip at 10° to 15° to the south-east, but structural disturbances and reef knolls locally give rise to northward and westward dips.

In the southern part of the district, the Wenlock Limestone Reef Facies directly overlies the Tickwood Beds, the boundary being taken where calcareous nodules coalesce into limestone beds. This is well seen at Harley Hill [6090 0035], which Bassett et al. (1975, p.4) designated the standard section for the base of their Much Wenlock Limestone Formation. The Reef Facies consists of up to 30 m of nodular limestones and siltstones, containing large masses of extremely fossiliferous, unbedded 'ballstones'.

Murchison (1872) was first to point out that the ballstones resembled coral banks. A century later, Scoffin (1971) concluded that they were most likely formed at the seaward fringe of a reef belt, where the sea was probably less than 30 m deep, but where the reefs were not liable to damage by surface wave action. The fauna of the Wenlock Limestone Reef Facies is renowned for its diversity and excellent preservation. Large brachiopods and corals are abundant in these beds, in contrast to the remainder of the Wenlock strata. Brachiopods include *Atrypa reticularis*, *Coolinia pecten*, *Dolerorthis rigida*, *Ferganella borealis*, *Leptaena* cf. *depressa*, *Meristina obtusa* and *Sphaerirhynchia wilsoni*. Examples of tabulate corals include *Favosites*, *Halysites*, *Heliolites*, *Paleofavosites*, *Propora* and *Thecia*; rugose corals include *Acervularia ananas*, *Entelophyllum articulatum*, *Ketophyllum turbinatum* and *Spongophylloides grayi*. Graptolites indicative of the *M. ludensis* Zone have been recorded from the basal 6 m of the Much Wenlock Limestone Formation to the southwest of the district (Bassett et al., 1975, p.8).

To the north-east, the Reef Facies passes laterally into some 20 m of massive to flaggy, shelly, crystalline limestones, interbedded with impersistent siltstones in their lower and upper parts. The name 'Benthall Beds' is here introduced for these limestones, with a standard section [6650 0337] on Benthall Edge. Brachiopods and corals are abundant, but ballstones are not common, though some may have been quarried away in the numerous old workings along the outcrop.

Wenlock Limestone

The highest beds of Wenlock age here consist of 4 m to 5 m of flaggy to thinly bedded crinoidal limestones, referred to in this account simply as 'Wenlock Limestone' (Table 2). These overlie the Reef Facies in the south and the Benthall Beds farther north. With the incoming of nodular siltstones, the Wenlock Limestone passes transitionally up into the Lower Ludlow Shales.

STRATA OF LUDLOW AGE

Rocks of Ludlow age crop out over an area of about 6 km². There are few exposures and mapping is almost entirely based on topographical features. The lithostratigraphical classification of Ludlow strata used by Pocock et al. (1938) has been retained. A BGS borehole was drilled in 1973 at The Little Dean [6799 0006], 1.5 km south of Broseley, on the southern boundary of the district, to help correlate the local lithostratigraphy with the type area at Ludlow; Table 3 is based largely upon the results from it.

The base of the Ludlow Series has been defined (Holland et al., 1963; White, 1981) in Pitch Coppice, Ludlow. In the Telford district, it is taken at the base of nodular beds that overlie the Wenlock Limestone, and it probably lies close to the base of the *N. nilssoni* Zone (White, 1974).

Lower Ludlow Shales

The outcrop of the Lower Ludlow Shales forms a broad vale between the dip slope of the Wenlock Limestone and the scarp face of the Aymestry Group. The shales have an estimated thickness of 120 m and consist of

Table 3 Classification of Ludlow strata. Stage names shown on the published Telford map have been superseded.

STAGES	GRAPHTOLITE BIOZONES	LITHOSTRATIGRAPHY LUDLOW TYPE AREA (Holland et al., 1963)	LITHOSTRATIGRAPHY TELFORD DISTRICT
Ludfordian	*Bohemograptus bohemicus*	Upper Whitcliffe Formation	Upper Ludlow Shales
		Lower Whitcliffe Formation	
	Saetograptus leintwardinensis	Upper Leintwardine Formation	Aymestry Group
		Lower Leintwardine Formation	
Gorstian	*Pristiograptus tumescens*	Upper Bringewood Formation	
		Lower Bringewood Formation	
	Neodiversograptus nilssoni– Lobograptus scanicus	Upper Elton Formation	Lower Ludlow Shales
		Middle Elton Formation	
		Lower Elton Formation	

greenish grey to grey silty mudstones, with calcareous siltstone nodules near their base. Their upper limit is marked by a prominent seepage line, which coincides with a change in slope profile, reflecting the transition into the harder, more calcareous or nodular beds of the Aymestry Group.

The fauna of the basal nodule-bearing beds is very similar to that of the Wenlock Limestone, with colonies of stromatoporoids, tabulate corals and bryozoa. The overlying mudstones contain a deeper water, diverse, shelly fauna in which small brachiopods (e.g. *Dicoelosia biloba* and *Skenidioides lewisii*) are common, together with trilobites and ostracods indicative of the *Dicoelosia* community of Calef and Hancock (1974) and the *Dicoelosia–Skenidioides* assemblage of Lawson (1975). These strata and the underlying nodule beds are correlatives of the Lower Elton Formation of the type area (Shergold and Bassett, 1970, pp.126–130). A specimen of *Monograptus uncinatus orbatus*, found during the resurvey at about 3 m to 5 m above the Wenlock Limestone, suggests that around Much Wenlock the *N. nilssoni* Zone extends down to or very close to the base of Ludlow strata (White, 1974).

The higher strata within the Lower Ludlow Shales are not well exposed, but the uppermost 45 m of the formation were proved in the Dean Borehole; they probably correlate with the highest Upper Elton Formation and the lower part of the Lower Bringewood Formation of the type area. The strata contain layers of impure, shelly limestone set in grey calcareous siltstones. *Amphistrophia funiculata, Atrypa reticularis, Eospirifer radiatus, Leptaena* cf. *depressa, Leptostrophia filosa, Sphaerirhynchia wilsoni* and *Strophonella euglypha* are comparatively common, and *Saetograptus chimaera* also occurs.

Aymestry Group

The outcrop of the Aymestry Group forms a prominent ridge, in places higher than that of the Wenlock Limestone. The lower and middle parts of the group consist of calcareous siltstones and nodular limestones; these are overlain by massive to flaggy, crystalline limestones. In all, 25 m of strata are present.

Fossils, particularly brachiopods, are common. In the lower beds (Gorstian Stage), *Atrypa reticularis, Howellella elegans, Leptostrophia filosa, Shaleria* aff. *ornatella, Sphaerirhynchia wilsoni* and *Strophonella euglypha* are common, together with fragments of *Dalmanites* sp. In the higher beds (Ludfordian Stage), '*Camarotoechia*' *nucula, Dayia navicula, H. elegans* and *S. wilsoni* are well represented, and *Shaleria ornatella* is common in the topmost beds.

Upper Ludlow Shales

The Upper Ludlow Shales consist of about 50 m of silt-stones and flaggy sandstones: they are markedly more silty than the Lower Ludlow Shales and, consequently, the low ground along their outcrop is not so well defined.

The basal 8 m of the Upper Ludlow Shales, representing the upper part of the *leintwardinensis* Zone, have a fauna comparable to that occurring at the top of the Aymestry Group. The higher beds contain an abundant but restricted shallow-water fauna, in which *Protochonetes ludloviensis* is very common and '*Camarotoechia*' *nucula* and *Salopina lunata* are well represented.

STRATA OF DOWNTONIAN AGE

The base of Downtonian strata is taken at the base of the Ludlow Bone Bed, as defined by Holland et al. (1963, p.146) at Ludlow. The lithostratigraphical subdivisions used in the Church Stretton district (Greig et al., 1968) have been retained in the present account, although only the basal Temeside Group is present; the group occurs in three small areas along the southern margin of the district (see details). Since the Telford map was published, the term Přídolí Series has replaced Downton Series (White and Lawson, 1989).

Downton Castle Sandstone

The *Ludlow Bone Bed* consists of abundant thelodont (fish) scales associated with numerous small black horny brachiopod fragments aggregated in irregular patches up to 2 mm thick. These were noted in about 2 cm of strata at an exposure on the Willey Estate [SO 6731 9912] just beyond the southern margin of the district (White and Coppack, 1978).

This very thin basal bed is overlain by about 10 m of pale grey to orange sandstone, including flaggy to shaly siltstones, particularly near the base. Another 'bone bed', which may represent the Downton Bone Bed of the Ludlow district, occurs 3 m above the Ludlow Bone Bed in the Willey section. There, the fauna of the sandstone includes a bivalve–ostracod assemblage, associated with *Lingula*, which points to a brackish, possibly lagoonal environment.

Temeside Shales

No exposures of the Temeside Shales are recorded within the district, but the basal strata were found by augering to comprise bright green and purple micaceous marls.

SILURIAN STRATA BENEATH LATER FORMATIONS

Nine deep shafts and boreholes entered Silurian strata beneath Coal Measures (Figure 2). At the Lightmoor Whimsey Pit (Prestwich, 1840, p.475), the precise location of which is unknown, Wenlock Shale was penetrated for about 90 m beneath the base of the Coal Measures at

about 140 m. Deepfield Pit [6828 0638] is said to have entered Wenlock Shale at a depth of 216 m. All the others are believed to have penetrated Ludlow strata. Madeley Meadow Pit [690 040] entered 'Upper Ludlow Rock' at a depth of 220 m, while the Lodge Farm [6756 0370], Madeley Wood No. 4 [7332 0657] and D'Arcy G3 [6956 0295] boreholes record grey-green silty mudstones with thin limestone beds containing *Atrypa*, *Leptaena*, rhynchonellids and crinoid ossicles at the last-named. In the south-eastern corner of the district, Exley's Pit [707 014] and D'Arcy G1 [7094 0104] and G2 [7221 0191] boreholes proved green, red and purple marls. The last named also records nodules of purple limestone with corals, brachiopods and crinoid fragments, which rule out the possibility of the strata being of Downtonian age; it is believed that the reddening is secondary. It is notable that in these three sections the Silurian is overlain by red Upper Coal Measures (Hadley Formation) rather than by grey productive measures as in the other sections.

From the limited data available, it is not certain whether the incrop of the base of Ludlow strata into the Coal Measures continues steadily north-eastwards following the Caledonian trend of Wenlock Edge; or whether it swings to the east, paralleling the bases of Downtonian and Dittonian rocks, south of the coalfield. The latter hypothesis has been adopted in Figure 2. The same uncertainty applies to the incrops of the Wenlock and Llandovery strata into the Dinantian. It has been assumed (Dixon, in Whitehead et al., 1928, p.40) that Silurian rocks are absent at Lilleshall, but it is now known that the Cambrian–Carboniferous junction there is faulted (Rushton et al., 1988), so that it is possible, though unproven, that Silurian strata are present.

DETAILS

Kenley Grit

Around Sheinton, blocks of orange sandstone are noted, for example, at the entrance to the church [6110 0396] and 30 m to the east [6113 0395]. There are fragments of purplish blue sandstone in an ancient, overgrown excavation [6160 0410] east-north-east of Sheinton, adjacent to the disused railway track.

Several exposures in Sheinton Brook reveal blocky or flaggy, coarse-grained orange sandstones, dipping at 10° south-east and containing numerous examples of *Lingula crumena* [e.g. 6078 0358]. The base of the formation is exposed [6079 0363] and consists of 0.15 m of coarse conglomerate unconformably overlying Shineton Shales (Whittard, 1928, p.739). North of the River Severn there are many loose blocks of coarse gritty sandstone on the scarp slopes between Hall Coppice [6180 0525] and Leighton Lane [6235 0620].

In Harper's Dingle, flaggy and blocky, coarse, gritty, and in part pebbly sandstones occur 360 m upstream from Spout Lane [6335 0720], containing large examples of *L. crumena*. A few metres upstream, at a sharp bend [6336 0722], the junction with the Shineton Shales is again visible.

Pentamerus Beds

Several good exposures of the Pentamerus Beds in Sheinton Brook reveal grey-blue, shaly mudstones with beds of calcareous and slightly ferruginous sandstone, which dip between 5° and 15° to the east and south-east. At one locality [6118 0308] *Gotatrypa?* sp. is common and *Coolinia pecten, Craniops implicatus, Hyattidina* sp., *Stricklandia lens* and crinoid columnals also occur. On the west bank of the brook [6105 0319], *Favosites* sp., *Streptelasma whittardi, Coolinia applanata, C. pecten, Eocoelia* cf. *hemisphaerica, Glassia?* sp., *Isorthis?* sp., *Leptaena* sp., *Lingula* sp., *Resserella?* sp., *S. lens* (common), *?Lophospira woodlandi, Ptychopteria* (*Actinopteria*) sp., *Dalmanites myops* var., *Proetus* sp., *Primitia* sp. and crinoid columnals occur. Farther downstream, the fauna at another locality [6100 0327] includes *Leptostrophia* (*L.*) cf. *ostrina, Pentamerus oblongus* (common), *Pholidostrophia* (*Mesopholidostrophia*) sp. and *Tentaculites anglicus.*

The largest exposure in Hurst Coppice [6276 0562] is along the western stream, where about 8 m of shales are easily accessible. Limestone beds in the upper part are up to 0.4 m thick, breaking to form large, massive blocks. From this exposure the fossil collection includes *Favosites gothlandicus* cf. *multipora, Eoplectodonta penkillensis* and *Climacograptus* sp. In the lower reaches of the eastern stream [6291 0558], a diverse fauna was collected during the resurvey including *Clorinda* sp., cf. *Isorthis* (*Ovalella*) *mackenziei, Pentlandina* cf. *parabola, Pholidostrophia* (*Eopholidostrophia*) cf. *cocksi ultima* (common), *Resserella* cf. *sefinensis* (common), *Eunema?* sp., *Liospira lenticularis,* cf. *Stenoloron aequilaterum shelvense, Cornulites serpularius, Otarion* cf. *elegantulum,* as well as species mentioned before.

An old collection from the south bank of the stream [6280 0636], 180 m west of Morrellswood Farm, includes *Paleofavosites?* sp., *Atrypina* cf. *barrandii, Brachyprion arenaceus, Megastrophia* (*Eomegastrophia*) *ethica* and *Gyronema octavia multicarinatum.* At a point [6283 0636] 45 m upstream of this locality, several gastropods are recorded, including *Euomphalopterus* sp., *Holopella?* *cancellata, Lophospira woodlandi, Trochonema valenticum* and *?Ulrichospira similis.* An important assemblage of graptolites was collected during the present survey at a stream section [6299 0643] 50 m north of Morrellswood Farm, including *Dictyonema* sp., *Inocaulis?* sp., *Koremagraptus* sp., *Monograptus lobiferus* (common), *M.* cf. *sedgwickii, ?M. tenuis, Clinoclimacograptus retroversus, Retiolites perlatus* and *Retiolites* sp; *Encrinurus* sp., *Leonaspis erinaceus salopiensis* and *Phacops elliptifrons* also occur.

An abundant and diverse coral fauna (Smith, 1930) from the *Calostylis* Limestone, which is about 12 cm thick and which was formerly exposed in the eastern bank of the stream [6308 0663] 275m north-north-east of Morrellswood Farm, includes *Calostylis aberrans, C. roemeri* (common), *Cantrillia prisca, Favosites gothlandicus, Halysites* sp., *Heliolites* sp., *Orthophyllum?* sp., *Paterophyllum?* *praematurum* and *Petrozium dewari* (common). The hydrozoan *Clathrodictyon rosarium* was also recorded. Approximately 70 m north of Spout Lane [6320 0694], the 'Dingle Conglomerate' (Whittard, 1928, p.745) was formerly exposed, consisting of Uriconian pebbles, small quartz grains and numerous examples of *P. oblongus* cemented by calcite. A large fauna collected during the resurvey [6332 0715] included *Eostropheodonta voraginis, Liospira* cf. *uriconiensis* and cf. *Phanerotrema jugosum.*

Hughley Shales

A section [6142 0278] in Sheinton Brook of about 5 m of blue-grey mudstone contains a diverse fauna including *Cantrillia prisca, Favosites* cf. *hisingeri, F. gothlandicus multipora, Streptelasma* sp., *Aegiria* (now *Jonesia*) *grayi, Clorinda* sp., *?Eocoelia curtisi, Eoplectodonta penkillensis, Eospirifer radiatus, Pholidostrophia* sp., *Resserella* aff. *sefinensis* and *Tentaculites anglicus.*

At a section [6400 0455] 400 m north-west of Buildwas Abbey, the highest beds of the Hughley Shales consist of greenish grey, red-purple and brownish mudstones with thin beds of fossiliferous limestone and calcareous sandstone. The fauna in these hard ribs includes *Cyrtia exporrecta, Dicoelosia alticavata, Glassia* sp., *Hyattidina* sp., and *Visbyella?* sp.

Excavations at the former CEGB ash disposal site in Devil's Dingle [6410 0545], briefly described by Cocks and Walton (1968), are now severely degraded. The sequence consists principally of purple mudstones with thin, but very persistent limestone and calcareous siltstone beds. During the present revision, a section on the south-facing hillside was measured in 1970 and large faunal collections were made. Subsections G, H and J probably represent equivalent horizons along the face:

		Thickness m
J	Mudstone, weathered purplish brown, with 5 cm decalcified sandstone bed	c.1
Small gap?		
H	Mudstone, weathered brown and greenish grey, silty, with 7.5 cm lens of very fossiliferous limestone	c.1
Small gap?		
G	Mudstone, weathered, with fossiliferous limestone lens	c.1
Gap 6 m		
F	Mudstone, brown, silty, with calcareous siltstone beds	c.2
Gap c.3 m		
E	Mudstone, maroon	c.2
D	Mudstone, maroon	c.3
Gap. c.0.5 m		
C	Mudstone, maroon with calcareous siltstone lenses and beds	c.2
B	Mudstone, maroon, with silty, calcareous limestone bed near top (probably in part equivalent to subsections A and C)	c.3.5
A	Mudstone, maroon, with minor green lenses and beds of calcareous siltstone	c.3.5

Collections were also made at a temporary trench [6383 0513] (exposing strata lower in the sequence than the lowermost beds of the main section), along a back-cut [6403 0562], and at a trench [6403 0512], in strata probably slightly above those in the main section. The following fossils were well represented throughout the entire sequence seen at the excavations: *Amphistrophia* (*A.*) *whittardi, Clorinda* sp., *E.* cf. *penkillensis,* and *Pholidostrophia* (*Mesopholidostrophia*) *salopiensis salopiensis.* The following were common in the lower part but were not recorded from the upper part: *A. grayi, Coolinia applanata, Gotatrypa?* sp., *E. curtisi, Skenidioides lewisii, Encrinurus* sp., cf. *Craspedobolbina* sp. and *Kodonophyllum* sp.

Wenlock Shale: Buildwas Beds

At an exposure in the River Severn [6400 0455], the basal strata of the Buildwas Beds overlying the Hughley Shales comprise grey mudstones interbedded with thin, argillaceous limestones and hard calcareous siltstones. They contain a prolific fauna including cf. *Resserella sabrinae, Archaeoconularia microscopica, Monotrypa crenulata, Eospirifer radiatus, Leptaena* aff. *oligistis, Streptis grayii, Striispirifer plicatellus, Ecculiomphalus?* *laevis, Acaste downingiae, Dalmanites caudatus, Otarion* cf. *megalops, Dendrograptus?* sp. and *?Monograptus priodon.*

Approximately 7 m of greenish, blocky mudstones, with persistent layers of hard calcareous siltstone nodules in the lower part of the sequence are exposed in Sheinton Brook [6010 0116]. The fauna collected includes *Dicoelosia biloba, Eoplectodonta duvalii, Glassia* cf. *obovata, Lingula* cf. *symondsii* and *Daw-*

sonoceras annulatum. In a tributary of Sheinton Brook, several exposures [e.g. 6101 0203] of pale greenish grey mudstone contain large, oval nodules of calcareous siltstone up to 0.2 m thick and 0.5 m across. In the higher parts of the sequence the nodules form bands 0.1 m to 0.15 m thick.

Wenlock Shale: Coalbrookdale Beds

An exposure in Whitwell Coppice [6194 0204] has been designated the standard section for the base of the Homerian Stage (Bassett et al., 1975, p.14). At a nearby section [6193 0205] in the middle part of the sequence, *Cyrtograptus ellesae*, *Monograptus flemingii* and *Pristiograptus dubius* have been recorded, indicative of the *C. ellesae* Zone. The fauna from a stream section [6196 0275] in Flat Coppice includes *Syringaxon siluriense*, *Leangella segmentum*, *Resserella* sp., *Bellerophon* sp., *Acastoides constrictus*, *D. caudatus*, *Deltacoleus?* sp., *Arabellites* sp., *M. flemingii* and *M. priodon*. At a locality in Bannister's Coppice [6198 0291], *Eoplectodonta* sp., *G. obovata* and *L.* cf. *symondsii* have been recorded. To the east, at a brook source [6230 0281], *E. duvalii*, *R.* cf. *sabrinae*, 'Orthoceras' cf. *subundulatum*, *Cyrtograptus* sp., *M. flemingii*, *M. flemingii compactus* and *P. dubius* were collected.

North of the River Severn, the largest exposure in Loamhole Dingle [6641 0555] reveals 15 m of blue-grey mudstone with beds of bentonitic clay (Walker's Earth) up to 50 mm thick. The fauna collected includes 'Orthoceras' *recticinctum*, *C. exporrecta*, *Cyrtograptus lundgreni* and *M. flemingii*.

Tickwood Beds

The Tickwood Beds are seldom well exposed; the best section occurs just below the bend of the road [6100 0035] over Harley Hill. Bassett et al. (1975, p.4) designate this as the standard section for the base of their Farley Member (Table 2). The lower part of the exposure has few nodules and the beds are transitional to the underlying Coalbrookdale Beds but, ascending the sequence, nodules of slightly calcareous siltstone become numerous and begin to form distinct layers, grading into silty limestones. The thickness of Tickwood Beds is of the order of 24 m, and their junction with the overlying Wenlock Limestone Reef Facies is taken at a horizon which is at road level, a few metres up the hill from the bend in the road.

An exposure [6197 0132] in the wood alongside the footpath from Homer to Much Wenlock yielded *Gothograptus nassa* and *Pristiograptus dubius*, as well as *Atrypa reticularis*, *Eospirifer radiatus*, *Howellella elegans* and *Pholidostrophia* sp.

Wenlock Limestone Reef Facies

South-west of the Much Wenlock to Harley road, massive to flaggy limestones with many ballstones can be examined in small disused quarries, from one of which [6085 0003] a colony of *Arachnophyllum diffluens* has been collected. Immediately overlying the Tickwood Beds in Harley Hill road cutting, the Reef Facies includes two thin beds of waxy bentonitic clay, exposed in the lower part of an old quarry face. A disused quarry [6196 0050] at Limekiln Bank exposes 2 m of massive ballstones at the top of the Reef Facies, overlain by flaggy, sparry, crinoidal Wenlock Limestone.

Sections in Shadwell Rock Quarry [6260 0085] contain many large ballstones. Fossils recorded include *Stromatopora typica*, *Catenipora* sp., cf. *Entelophyllum articulatum*, *Favosites* sp. (*F. cristatus* pars of authors), *Heliolites megastoma*, *H. murchisoni*, *Ketophyllum* sp., *Paleofavosites alveolaris*, *Pycnactis mitrata*, *Tryplasma* sp., *Atrypa reticularis*, *Coolinia pecten*, *Crytia?* sp., *Dolerorthis* cf. *rigida*, *Ferganella borealis*, *Leptaena* cf. *depressa*, *Meristina obtusa*, *Ptychopleurella bouchardi*, *Resserella canalis*, *Rhynchospirina salterii*,

Sphaerirhynchia wilsoni, *Bellerophon* sp., *Poleumita discors* and *P. globosa*. A soft weathered clay bed, 0.1 m thick, may be equivalent to the bentonites in the Harley Hill section. At the Gleedon Hill quarries [6290 0170], this same bed forms a continuous, nearly horizontal seam, 3 m to 4 m above the (1973) quarry floor and is overlain by about 8 m of flaggy limestone with ballstones. The latter are structureless, usually 2 m to 3 m high and 7 m to 8 m across, with a convex upper surface and a flat base. Strata dip steeply away from their lateral margins and sagging locally affects underlying beds. The presence of mudstones overlying the ballstones suggests that an influx of clastics terminated reef growth. A large ballstone on the eastern face [6295 0165] of the quarry exceeded 10 m in height. Fossils from these quarries include *Acervularia ananas* and *Platyceras? prototypum*.

An old collection from the disused Bradley Quarry [634 018] includes *Coenites* sp., *Favosites gothlandicus forbesi*, *Ketophyllum turbinatum*, *Kodonophyllum truncatum*, *Phaulactis* cf. *angusta*, *Propora tubulata*, *Propora?* sp., *Stelliporella* sp., *Syringopora fascicularis*, *Thecia expatiata*, *Craniops implicatus*, *?Dalejina hybrida*, *Homoeospira baylei*, *Howellella elevata*, *Strophonella euglypha*, *P. discors rugosa*, *Encrinurus?* sp., cf. *Beyrichia kloedeni*, crinoid debris and *Arabellites* sp. From an old quarry nearby [6303 0124], the fauna includes *Spongophylloides grayi*, *Gypidula galeata* and *M. obtusa*.

Along the crest of Benthall Edge, the ballstones become smaller and less common as the Reef Facies passes laterally into the Benthall Beds.

Benthall Beds

The best exposure of Benthall Beds, selected here as the standard section, is in Bowers Brook on Benthall Edge [6665 0337]. Almost the entire sequence is exposed and consists of about 6 m of thickly bedded to massive, sparry limestone separating similar thicknesses of flaggy limestones with very thin, impersistent siltstone beds. The limestones contain an abundant fauna of brachiopods and corals including *A. reticularis*, *D. rigida*, *Catenipora* sp., *Coenites* spp., *Cystihalysites* spp., *Favosites* spp. and *H. murchisoni*.

At Lincoln Hill [6700 0380], the Benthall Beds have been extensively worked underground and in deep quarries (Pocock et al., 1938, p.116). A central 12 m to 15 m of relatively pure thickly bedded limestone separates upper and lower series of flaggy and concretionary beds. In the roof of the mined middle beds a waxy, pale grey, silty clay up to 0.1 m thick is present. Analyses of this suggest that it is probably not the same horizon as that present in the Gleedon Hill quarries. A similar clay bed reportedly worked on the brow of the hill leading down to Coalbrookdale was not found during the present survey, but this may correlate with the Gleedon Hill occurrences.

Wenlock Limestone

Flaggy, crinoidal, detrital limestones are exposed in a disused quarry [6196 0050] at Limekiln Bank, at the Gleedon Hill quarries [6285 0185], and at a small exposure [6490 0247] north of Wyke.

Lower Ludlow Shales

The base of the Lower Ludlow Shales is exposed in the north-eastern face [6266 0081] of Shadwell Quarry. Up to 2.5 m of greenish grey mudstone, weathering brown, with diffuse calcareous siltstone nodules up to 0.1 m thick, common in the lower part, pass down into nodular, rubbly layered Wenlock Limestone.

An abandoned railway cutting [6207 0000] on the margin of the area exposes 3 m of greenish grey, blocky to slightly shaly, silty mudstones, dipping at 15° south-east. A low Gorstian fauna includes *Glassia* sp., *Howellella elegans*, *Lingula* cf. *symondsii*, *Meristina obtusa*, *Nucleospira pisum*, *Bellerophon* cf. *wenlockensis*, *Ecculiomphalus? laevis*, *Loxonema* sp., *Temnodiscus* sp., '*Ctenodonta*' *anglica*, *Grammysia? impressa*, *Hyolithes forbesi*, *Arabellites* sp. and *Saetograptus* (*Colonograptus*) *varians pumilus*. Pale greenish grey, shaly sandstone in a stream bank [6238 0016] near Much Wenlock Priory yielded *Atrypa reticularis*, *Dalejina?* sp., *Gypidula galeata*, *Protochonetes minimus*, *Skenidioides lewisii* and *Primitia* cf. *punctata*. This low Gorstian assemblage suggests a correlation with Lower or Middle Elton Formation of the Ludlow type area (Table 3).

In a stream bank [6294 0053] 0.8 km north-east of Much Wenlock, 0.75 m of grey-brown, sandy mudstone, also correlated either with the Lower or the Middle Elton Formation, contains a shelly fauna which includes: *Ainia?* sp., bryozoa (decalcified), *Anastrophia deflexa*, *Craniops implicatus*, *?Isorthis* (*I.*) *clivosa*, *I.* (*Tyersella*) *amplificata*, *Leptostrophia filosa*, *Mesopholidostrophia lepisma*, *Resserella sabrinae*, *Colpomya?* sp., '*Orthonota*' *rigida*, *Cheirurus?* sp., *Encrinurus* cf. *variolaris*, *Hemiarges* cf. *bucklandi*, *Aechmina cuspidata*, *Beyrichia* s.l., *Cytherellina siliqua*, *Thlipsura* cf. *plicata uniplicata*, *T.* cf. *tuberosa* and crinoid columnals.

Downstream from the previous locality [6302 0069], 1km north-east of Much Wenlock, a single example of *Monograptus uncinatus orbatus* was found (p.14, and White, 1974) in mudstones estimated to lie only 3 m to 5 m above the Wenlock Limestone. A diverse shelly fauna was also collected, indicating a correlation with the Lower Elton Formation; it includes *Dicoelosia biloba* (common), *Leangella segmentum*, *?Salopina conservatrix*, *Cypricardinia subplanulata*, '*Orthoceras*' sp., *Eophacops musheni*, *Otarion* cf. *megalops*, *Phacops?* sp. and *Hemsiella maccoyiana*.

A small exposure [6420 0158] near Newhouse Farm shows silty mudstone with a diverse fauna indicating a probable correlation with the Middle Elton Formation. Important fossils are *Aegiria grayi* and *S. lewisii* (both common), *Pristiograptus dubius* and *Saetograptus colonus*. The fauna also includes *Leptaena* cf. *depressa*, *Orbiculoidea rugata*, *Pholidostrophia?* sp., *?Protochonetes ludloviensis*, *Loxonema* cf. *planatum*, *Kionoceras angulatum*, *Leurocycloceras* cf. *nobile*, *Tentaculites* sp. and *Dalmanites myops* (common).

North of the River Severn, between the Limestone and Warrensway faults, an excavation [6779 0446] exposed basal Hadley Formation (Upper Coal Measures) overlying 2 m of deeply weathered, mustard-coloured mudstone. The fauna collected from the mudstone may belong to the Wenlock Series or the basal part of the Lower Ludlow Shales: *?Dalejina hybrida*, *H. elegans*, *L. segmentum* and *Dalmanites* cf. *caudatus*.

In 1973, the BGS Dean Borehole [6799 0006] proved 44.27 m of Lower Ludlow Shales to the base of the borehole, comprising medium grey, argillaceous, calcareous, flaggy siltstones with shelly limestone beds and nodules, which gradually become less calcareous and more silty down the succession. The top 25 m of these strata are correlated with the Lower Bringewood Formation(Table 3), containing a few examples of *Saetograptus chimaera chimaera* and a prolific shelly fauna in which large strophomenids are conspicuous. The following brachiopods are common: *Amphistrophia funiculata*, *A. reticularis*, *Eospirifer radiatus*, *L. depressa*, *L. filosa*, *M. lepisma*, *P. minimus*, *Sphaerirhynchia wilsoni* and *Strophonella euglypha*. The solitary coral *Phaulactis?* sp. is common and *Rhabdocyclus porpitoides* also occurs. The remainder of the Lower Ludlow Shales proved to the bottom of the borehole are probably equivalent to the Upper Elton Formation; brachiopods are less numerous than in the Lower Bringewood Formation, while bivalves are well represented and include examples of *C. subplanulata*, *Modiomorpha gradata*, *Mytilarca mytilimeris*, '*O.*' *rigida* and *Paracyclas insueta*.

Aymestry Group

Brash in fields [6440 0020] 600 m south-east of Ash Coppice includes specimens of *Dayia navicula*, *Howellella elegans*, *Hyattidina canalis* and *Sphaerirhynchia wilsoni*, together with specimens of bored limestone and an intraformational conglomerate possibly indicating the Gorstian–Ludfordian junction (see Table 3). This brash is estimated to be from approximately 10 m below the base of the Upper Ludlow Shales.

About 6 m of calcareous beds within the upper part of the group, about 5 m below the Upper Ludlow Shales, are exposed in a roadside section [6793 0045] 500 m north-west of The Dean. The fauna includes *Leioclema* cf. *explanatum*, *Orbignyella fibrosa* (encrusting gastropods), *Atrypa reticularis*, '*Camarotoechia*' *nucula* (common), *D. navicula* (common near top of section), *Isorthis* (*I.*) *clivosa*, *I.* (*Protocortezorthis*) *orbicularis*, *Orbiculoidea rugata*, *Protochonetes ludloviensis*, *Salopina lunata*, *S. wilsoni* (common), *Bembexia? lloydii*, *Cyclonema corallii*, *Fuchsella amygdalina*, *Goniophora cymbaeformis* and *Paracyclas perovalis*. This is a characteristic Ludfordian assemblage and the strata can be correlated with the Lower Leintwardine Formation (Table 3).

Forming a small waterfall [6836 0025] in a tributary of the Dean Brook, 0.7 m of coarsely crystalline limestone is taken as the top bed of the Aymestry Group. Underlying silty, calcareous mudstones contain numerous examples of *Shaleria ornatella*, also *Leptaena depressa*, *Shagamella minor*, *Cornulites serpularius*, *Calymene* cf. *puellaris*, proetid, *Amphitoxotis* cf. *curvata*, *Cytherellina siliqua*, *Neobeyrichia torosa* and crinoid columnals. About 30 m downstream, 2 m of interbedded limestones and grey-green, blocky, silty mudstones, 4 m or 5 m below the top of the group, have yielded the following further species: *Leptostrophia filosa*, *Lingula* sp., *S.* cf. *ornatella*, *Euomphalopterus alatus*, *Poleumita globosa*, *Actinopteria?* sp., and *Tentaculites* sp. These two faunas from the upper part of the group indicate a Ludfordian age, and the presence of *S. ornatella* and *C.* cf. *puellaris* suggests a possible correlation with the Upper Leintwardine Formation.

The Dean Borehole proved Aymestry Group strata from a depth of 17.5 m to 55.5 m. Unfortunately, the beds are disturbed, being vertical at several levels, and the true thickness is estimated as 25 m. In the upper part of the sequence, many beds of coarse, shelly limestone up to 0.5 m thick, some nodular or concretionary, are interbedded with pale khaki, very calcareous siltstone.

At a depth of 31 m, a conspicuous bored conglomerate marks the boundary between the Gorstian and Ludfordian stages. This is interpreted as a penecontemporaneously eroded or disrupted hardground. From just above the conglomerate to the base of the group, the beds consist almost entirely of limestone nodules in a very calcareous siltstone matrix, at some levels forming beds up to 0.1 m thick. The Gorstian fauna below the conglomerate includes *A. reticularis* (common), *Coolinia pecten*, *Gypidula lata*, *H. elegans* (common), *S. wilsoni*, *Strophonella euglypha*, *E. alatus subundulatus* and *P. globosa*. This contrasts with the Ludfordian in which '*C.* *nucula*, *D. navicula*, *H. elegans* and *S. wilsoni* are common.

Upper Ludlow Shales

An exposure in Dean Brook [6752 0056] shows 2 m of silty mudstone in the middle part of the Upper Ludlow Shales, containing a typical fauna including bryozoa (decalcified), '*Camarotoechia*' *nucula* (common), *Howellella elegans*, *Protochonetes ludloviensis* (common), *Salopina lunata* (common), '*Ctenodonta*' *anglica*, *Nuculites antiquus*, *Pteronitella?* cf. *rectangularis*, *Ptychopteria* (*Actinopteria*) *tenuistriata*, *Leurocycloceras whitcliffense*, '*Orthoceras*' *recticinctum*, *Cornulites serpularius*, *Cytherellina siliqua, Neobeyrichia torosa*, crinoid columnals, *Serpuloides?* sp. and fish scales.

Temporary sections dug in the bank of a tributary of Dean Brook [6836 0025] at the base of the Upper Ludlow Shales revealed 4.9 m of green silty mudstone with siltstone beds and purple staining. A low Ludfordian fauna collected 3.4 m above the base includes '*C*. *nucula* (common), *Isorthis clivosa* (common), *Lingula* cf. *lata*, *P. ludloviensis* (common), *Shaleria ornatella*, *P.* (*A.*) *tenuistriata* and *Serpuloides? longissimus*.

The Dean Borehole proved Upper Ludlow Shales to a depth of 17.52 m. Below 11.38 m, a diverse fauna is present, including: *Atrypa reticularis*, '*C*. *nucula*, *Dayia navicula*, *Isorthis orbicularis*, *Leptaena* cf. *depressa*, *P. ludloviensis*, *S. lunata*, *Shagamella minor*, *S. ornatella* and *Sphaerirhynchia wilsoni*. The strata are correlated with the Upper Leintwardine Formation. Of these fossils only '*C*. *nucula*, *P. ludloviensis* and *S. lunata* persist into the beds above 11.38 m, which are considered to equate with the Lower Whitcliffe Formation (Table 3).

Upper Ludlow Shales in the bank of a sunken lane [6809 0001] at The Dean, Willey, representing part of the Whitcliffe Formation, yielded numerous fossils, but of characteristically restricted variety, including: bryozoa (decalcified), '*C*. *nucula* (abundant), *H. elegans*, *Orbiculoidea rugata*, *P. ludloviensis* (common), *S. lunata*, *N. antiquus*, *Ptychopteria* (*Actinopteria*) sp., *Cornulites?* sp., *Calymene* sp. and *Homalonotus* sp.

Downton Castle Sandstone and Temesides Shales

Blocks of orange Downton Castle Sandstone containing small *Lingula* sp. are common in the fields west of Barrow [6550 0015] and south-east of Dean Corner [6700 0005]. The outcrop of the lower part of the Temeside Shales was also detected by augering.

In a tributary of Dean Brook [6755 0037], flaggy sandstone can be seen separated by a gap of 60 cm from a thin rottenstone bed. Ostracods are common in the sandstone, including cf. *Cytherellina siliqua*, *Frostiella groenvalliana* and *Londinia fissurata*. The rottenstone contains numerous examples of *Modiolopsis complananta* and *F. groenvalliana*; also *Lingula minima*, *Cymbularia carinata*, scales of the fish *Climatius?* sp. and an acanthodian fish spine.

LOWER CARBONIFEROUS (DINANTIAN) ROCKS

Strata of Dinantian age crop out along the western and southern margins of the Coalbrookdale Coalfield, in a sinuous strip from around Steeraway, south of Wellington, through Little Wenlock to Horsehay (Figure 2). The rocks rest unconformably on Lower Palaeozoic strata and are overlain unconformably by the Coal Measures, the base of which cuts down to rest on progressively lower horizons to the south and east. Dinantian rocks are believed to underlie the productive measures beneath the whole of the northern half of the coalfield (Figure 2), and they reappear as a fault-bounded inlier at Lilleshall, just beyond the north-eastern corner of the district.

The Dinantian rocks are now not well exposed, but the limestones in particular have been extensively quarried and mined in the past, and the writings of Murchison (1839, pp.105–109) and Prestwich (1840, pp.424–428), which date from a time when the workings were active, are still reliable sources of detailed information. The suc-

cessions have been described in the Wolverhampton and Shrewsbury memoirs by Whitehead et al. (1928) and Pocock et al. (1938) respectively. Although the Lilleshall inlier is outside the area resurveyed, the sequence is summarised here because the same succession is almost certainly present beneath the north-eastern part of the district. The major differences between the sequences at Lilleshall and Little Wenlock are the presence of early Tournaisian strata at Lilleshall and the absence there of the Little Wenlock Basalt (Table 4 and Figure 4). Table 4 attempts to relate the lithological sequences known in the two areas to the chronostratigraphic stages of George et al. (1976), using the biostratigraphical information published by Whitehead et al. (1928) and Pocock et al. (1938).

The coral-brachiopod zones S_2, D_1 and D_2 used by these authors correspond roughly with the stages Holkerian, Asbian and Brigantian, respectively. Note also that the terms Upper and Lower Limestones used by the same authors are not used on the Telford map, where both are labelled Carboniferous Limestone.

The Lilleshall district has been described at some length by Whitehead et al. (1928), who gave fossil lists, but little palaeontological work has been done along the sinuous western and southern outcrop. The White Limestone of Lilleshall was correlated by these authors with the Lower Limestone to the south-west on lithological grounds, because both comprise the only creamy, nodular limestones in their respective successions. However, the available faunal evidence suggested that the Lower Limestone is somewhat younger than the White Limestone, as indicated in Table 4. The underlying sandstone, likewise, was considered to be somewhat older at Lilleshall than at Little Wenlock. The Tournaisian age of the lowest strata at Lilleshall (Table 4) has been confirmed by Mitchell and Reynolds (1981), implying a major non-sequence above the lowest two units there.

Lydebrook Sandstone

The succession commences with a sequence of fine- to coarse-grained, gritty to pebbly, yellow to orange-brown sandstones. Fossils are not common but those collected by previous workers indicate an Asbian age (Lower Dibunophyllum (D_1) Zone). The sequence evidently maintains a uniform thickness of about 30 m (Figure 5), except in the south-east (Jiggers Bank), where it is overstepped unconformably by the Coal Measures, and at an outlier at Saplins Farm [6330 0573] where it is probably no more than 10 m thick.

Lower Limestone

The Lydebrook Sandstone is overlain by the Lower Limestone, a bed of nodular or rubbly, creamy white or yellow, crystalline limestone with dark grey to black shale bands. A characteristic gritty texture results from contact metamorphism by the overlying basalt. Although only 6 m to 8 m thick, the bed is persistent across most of the area (Figure 5). It is overstepped by the Coal Measures at

Table 4   Classification of Dinantian strata.

CHRONOSTRATIGRAPHY			LITHOSTRATIGRAPHY, TELFORD DISTRICT	
Series	Stage		Western outcrop	Lilleshall
Viséan	Brigantian		Upper Limestone	limestones and shales
			Little Wenlock Basalt	
				sandstone
	Asbian		Lower Limestone	White Limestone
			Lydebrook Sandstone	sandstone
	Holkerian		no deposits preserved	no deposits preserved
	Arundian			
	Chadian			
Tournaisian	Courceyan			
				shales with limestones
				sandstones

Lydebrook Dingle [6630 0594] and south-east of the Moors [6557 0543] and is absent at Doseley Quarry. To the north, its outcrop is much obscured by quarrying and mining of the overlying strata, but around Little Wenlock it produces a feature traceable beneath the thin glacial drift. The best exposures occur in the bank of Lydebrook Dingle. The age was given by Pocock et al. (1938, p.125) as late D_1 (late Asbian) to early D_2 (early Brigantian).

Little Wenlock Basalt

The Little Wenlock Basalt was described by Pocock et al. (1938, p.126) as a 'microporphyritic olivine-basalt of Dalmeny type in which small well-formed phenocrysts of olivine occur in a matrix of slender labradorite laths,

small granules and prisms of augite and some finely divided magnetite'. The flow is thickest and freshest in the south-east at Doseley Quarry (Figure 5) and in the disused Horsehay Quarry, where it is still visible. It is thinner in the west at Little Wenlock and Lydebrook Dingle, where it has a highly vesicular and somewhat slaggy texture and where, consequently, quarry ventures have been less extensive.

Pocock et al. (1938) concluded that the basalt was extrusive, noting the highly vesicular and slaggy lavas and pillow lavas, the presence of a bole between the basalt and the apparently unaltered overlying sediment, and the constant horizon of the basalt throughout the district. Two boreholes drilled in 1972 near Little Wenlock showed the basalt to be overlain by sandstone at the base of the Upper Limestone; the base of the sandstone was

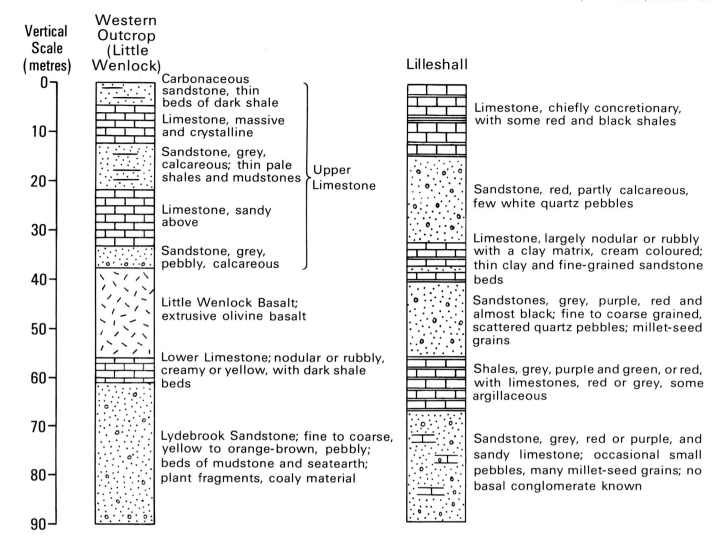

Figure 4   Generalised Dinantian successions in the western outcrop (Little Wenlock) and Lilleshall Inlier.

sharp and well defined with no signs of contact metamorphism, and basalt pebbles occurred within the sandstone. Similar pebbles were noted by Pocock et al. (1938) in the base of the Coal Measures.

Since the Upper Limestone is of Brigantian age and the Lower Limestone is early Brigantian or latest Asbian, the basalt must also be of Brigantian age.

Upper Limestone

The Upper Limestone overlies the Little Wenlock Basalt (Figure 5) and is confined to areas north-west of the Little Wenlock Fault. The sequence comprises about 40 m of yellow-brown, friable, calcareous sandstones, grey rubbly or massive limestones, micaceous shales and mudstones, yielding a D_2 Zone (Brigantian) fauna (Pocock et al., 1938, p.126). The following lithological sequence was recognised during the resurvey:

	Thickness m
Sandstone, carbonaceous, with thin beds of dark shale, passing downwards and probably in part laterally into sandy limestone	3–6
Limestone, generally massive and crystalline, characterised by large productids	6–10
Sandstone, grey, calcareous, fossiliferous, with thin beds of pale shale and mudstone	about 10
Limestone, impure, generally sandy in upper parts, characterised by corals	7–15
Sandstone, grey, calcareous, with pebbles at base, resting on Little Wenlock Basalt	3–6

Concealed Dinantian strata

At the eastern extremity of the district, Lilleshall No. 5 Borehole [7688 1095] penetrated the base of the Coal

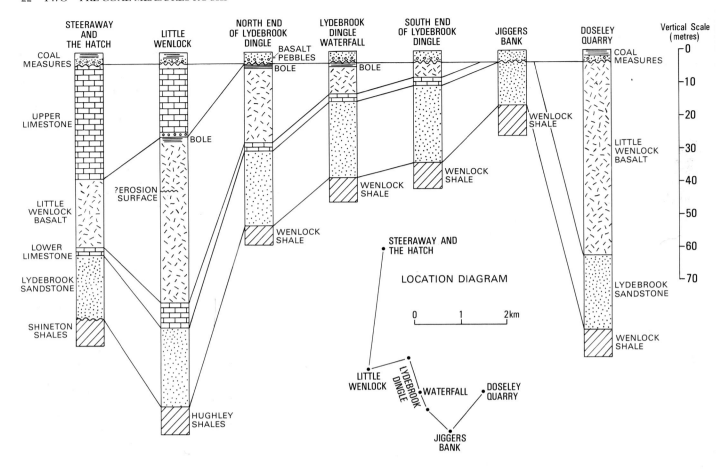

Figure 5 Comparative vertical sections showing the thickness variations within the Dinantian sequence beneath the unconformity at the base of the Lower Coal Measures.

Measures at a depth of 646.8 m and proved 8.5 m of greenish, vesicular, brecciated, calcareous, basaltic tuff. Samples from the core contained bowlingite replacing olivine, chlorite, possibly palagonite, and pyrite; calcite occurred as vesicles and as coarse-grained veins cementing the volcanic fragments. The age of the rock is not known, but it may be contemporaneous with the Little Wenlock Basalt.

Shaft deepening at Granville Colliery in 1957 proved 19.66 m of Dinantian strata:

	Thickness m
Limestone, cream and grey	4.87
Sandstone and bind, pale to dark grey	6.71
Limestone, dark grey	0.53
Sandstone and bind, pale to dark grey	2.06
Limestone, dark grey, with some grey-green mudstone in lowest 0.7 m	2.75
Bind, grey-green and brick red	1.21
Limestone, pale grey, sandy above	0.56
Bind, brick red, grey and yellow-green	0.97

These strata are best equated with the 15 m-thick unit of limestones and shales at the top of the succession at

Lilleshall (Figure 4), although they are rather thicker and may thus include limestone younger than any known at Lilleshall.

Many shafts in the north-east of the coalfield, around Wombridge and Hadley, are known to have struck limestone below the Coal Measures, and it has undoubtedly been mined from at least one. It is assumed that this limestone is of Dinantian age, but there is insufficient detail to place it accurately in the succession. Wombridge Water Engine Pit [6920 1212] proved limestone at 180.7 m depth, while Prestwich (1840, p.426) records level-bedded limestone at only 24.4 m depth in a sinking half a mile south of Watling Street. He also records limestone 'striking parallel to the fault' met in digging 'the pool'; presumably this refers to limestone caught up in the crush zone of the Boundary Fault at the southern corner of Trench Pool [688 123]. Strata of Dinantian age are not known north-west of the Boundary Fault, where all known boreholes (Figure 2) proved younger beds resting unconformably on Precambrian. The Boundary Fault may therefore form the north-western limit of a wide strip of Dinantian strata which is continuous beneath the Coal Measures from the Little Wenlock outcrop to Lilleshall.

DETAILS

Lydebrook Sandstone

The outcrop of the Lydebrook Sandstone extends from just south of the Club House [6512 1050] of Wellington Golf Course, towards Limekiln Wood. Its top is readily fixed by features, but the disposition of orange sandstone blocks through the wood suggests a complex faulted contact with the underlying Comley Sandstone. Two exposures [6502 0936; 6504 0933] south-west of Steeraway show dips of 14° and 26° to the north-east respectively. Along the eastern flanks of Maddocks Hill [645 088] the contact with the underlying Shineton Shales is marked by an abrupt change in soils. This contact forms a strong feature with an associated seepage line through Wenlocks Wood [636 079].

South of Spout Lane [6340 0697], the outcrop is obscured by drift, but its width suggests some thickening. Conversely, around Saplins Farm [6330 0573], the Lydebrook Sandstone is probably more than 10 m thick. Coarse-grained yellow sandstone is exposed in Harris's Coppice [644 059] and can be seen dipping north in an overgrown lane [6443 0595]; farther east [6475 0585], it forms conspicuous crags 10 m high. Pebbly sandstones are exposed as detached blocks or small crags along the upper slopes of Holbeach Coppice [650 055] and of Timber Wood [655 053], associated with small-scale landslipping. Farther east, a prominent feature with seepages at its base marks the contact of these pebbly sandstones with the underlying Wenlock Shale.

The best exposures of Lydebrook Sandstone are to be found in Lydebrook Dingle [662 060], in disused building stone quarries and natural waterfalls. At Stoneyhill [6650 0575], much of the 20 m sandstone/shale sequence is inaccessible, but the lowest 12 m are blocky or massive pebbly sandstones, commonly cross-bedded and slightly micaceous. In Loamhole Dingle [6630 0575], no more than 12 m to 15 m of Lydebrook Sandstone remains, unconformably overlain by Coal Measures.

Pocock et al. (1938) noted 4.5 m of yellow sandstone in an old overgrown quarry [6735 0625] near Woodlands Farm, dipping gently to the north-north-east. Very pebbly sandstones can be seen in small disused quarries [6750 0645], 250 m west-south-west of Doseley Church.

Lower Limestone

Pocock et al. (1938, p.125) noted an exposure of Lower Limestone in old surface workings [6537 0993] between two faults north-west of Steeraway. Farther south, the outcrop narrows as a result of an increase in dip. Surface fragments can be found east of Maddocks Hill [6480 0880] and in the northern part of Marmers Covert [6347 0694]. Prominent features indicate the outcrop to the east of Wenlocks Wood [636 079] and from near Little Wenlock [6455 0675] south-eastwards to the Little Wenlock Fault. Boreholes near Little Wenlock prove the limestone to be about 8 m thick, the uppermost 1 m subjected to contact thermal metamorphism by the overlying basalt.

On the northern slopes of Harris's Coppice [6440 0595], blocks of creamy coloured crystalline limestone contain fragments of large productids. Small exposures of rubbly limestone can be traced along both sides of Lydebrook Dingle and its western tributary [655 066].

Little Wenlock Basalt

This is probably no more than 20 m in thickness north-west of Steeraway and in Limekiln Wood, where surface fragments comprise very weathered amygdaloidal basalt. South-west of The Hatch [6460 0853], the outcrop forms a prominent feature and a rich reddish soil. A lane south-south-west of Wil-

lowmoor Farm [6408 0805] reveals deeply weathered basalt or 'rottenstone', which has been worked in a nearby field [6410 0808]. The soil colour clearly indicates the outcrop west of Little Wenlock, where the basalt thickens to more than 30 m. The boreholes near Little Wenlock record over 51 m of basalt (Figure 5). Attempts have been made to work the basalt in quarries adjacent to the Little Wenlock Fault [6465 0650; 6515 0725]. During opencast coal operations on the downthrow side of this fault, the fault plane and the basalt were widely exposed.

About 5 m to 6 m of 'bedded' basalt can be seen above the waterline in flooded disused quarries [6340 0563; 6355 0562] south-east of Saplins Farm. The basalt is overstepped quite rapidly by the Coal Measures south-east of The Moors [6563 0544]. The quality of the basalt was sufficient to sustain limited quarrying alongside Lydebrook Dingle. In a disused quarry [657 070] north of the Horsehay–Little Wenlock road, basalt was recorded as being overlain by a Coal Measures conglomerate containing basalt pebbles. Up to 60 m of basalt exposed in the disused Doseley Quarry [6750 0680] show columnar jointing and sphaeroidal weathering. No exposures are known in the inlier of basalt at Newdale [676 094], which was postulated by Pocock et al. (1938, p.127).

Upper Limestone

North of the Reservoir [6533 1015], the mapped outcrop is conjectural. West of Steeraway [6547 0962], the presence of limestone is shown by shafts, levels and crop workings. The limestone worked was the lower of the two beds in the Upper Limestone (Figure 4). Mining extended south-westwards to The Hatch [6462 0854] and along Hatch Bank [644 082] to Old Quarry Plantation [642 074]. A report in 1840 describes a 15 m bed of limestone worked from a shaft 36.6 m deep at Steeraway. Exposures [6488 0870; 6495 0876] 300 m and 400 m north-east of The Hatch reveal 3 m of massive to blocky or nodular hard limestones, with abundant crinoid ossicles and large productids, dipping at 30° to 35°. The limestone was mined from levels and overlies 2 m of dark bluish shale. In Old Quarry Plantation a section [6425 0742] reveals strata in the upper part of the Upper Limestone: concretionary ferruginous bed, 0.3 m; dark paper shales crowded with ostracods, 0.6 m; grey carbonaceous and calcareous sandstones, passing laterally into limestones, 1.2 m. Shallow excavations in Little Wenlock show that the greater part of the village is underlain by a thin, grey, coarse-grained, calcareous sandstone near the bottom of the Upper Limestone. Boreholes sunk in the vicinity of Little Wenlock prove at least 14.7 m of strata overlying the Little Wenlock Basalt, which may be summarised as follows:

	Thickness m
Sandstone, grey, medium- to fine-grained, with ironstone nodules; wispy bedded, with thin beds and nodules of sandy limestone	c.26
Limestone, central and lower parts massive and crystalline, with finely comminuted shell debris; sporadic compound corals towards base; calcareous shale and mudstone beds in upper 2 m	c.8.2
Sandstone, greenish grey, gritty to pebbly, including pebbles of basalt; sandy mudstone and shale beds in upper part	c.3.9

There is evidence of shallow workings for limestone adjacent to the road [6505 0735] leading from Little Wenlock to Huntington. The Huntington quarries [6515 0800] were formerly worked for the upper parts of the limestone, but these are no longer exposed.

THREE

Coal Measures: general stratigraphy

CLASSIFICATION AND NOMENCLATURE

The Coal Measures of the Coalbrookdale Coalfield have been variously subdivided and named on the basis of litho-, chrono- and biostratigraphy. The relationships between the lithostratigraphical classification, the stages and the bivalve zones, are shown in Figure 6.

The informal term 'productive measures' refers to all the dominantly grey strata between the basal Silesian unconformity and the first significant appearance of primary red measures. In terms of the classification introduced by Stubblefield and Trotter (1957), and shown on the Telford map, it comprises the Lower Coal Measures, of Langsettian (Westphalian A) age, and the Middle Coal Measures, of Duckmantian (Westphalian B) and early Bolsovian (Westphalian C) age. A small thickness of late Namurian strata may be included at the base of the Lower Coal Measures.

The boundary between Middle and Upper Coal Measures is defined by these authors at the top of the Cambriense Marine Band, but this horizon has not been identified in the district, so the boundary is drawn on lithostratigraphical grounds at the base of the primary red beds.

As thus defined, the Upper Coal Measures (referred to also as barren measures) comprise great thicknesses of red and grey strata in which coal seams are rare. They are of Bolsovian and Westphalian D age, and may extend up into the Stephanian and Autunian. They are divided into four lithostratigraphical units: the Hadley Formation, Coalport Formation, Keele Beds and Enville Beds, in ascending sequence. The Enville Beds are included, in this description, in the Upper Coal Measures, although they may straddle the Carboniferous (Stephanian) to Permian (Autunian) boundary, or may be entirely of Early Permian age (Besly, 1988).

North-west of the Boundary Fault, where the productive measures are absent, the lowest three formations of the Upper Coal Measures are present, and the terminology established around Shrewsbury (Pocock et al., 1938) has been retained for the lower two of these. Thus, the Ruabon Marl is the local equivalent of the Hadley Formation, and the Coed-yr-Allt Beds correspond to the Coalport Formation. The term Keele Beds has been applied to both parts of the area, however (Figure 6).

Within the Lower and Middle Coal Measures, six marine bands are known. Of these, the Pennystone Marine Band has the richest fauna and is the most widespread. It is equivalent to the Vanderbeckei Marine Band and forms the boundary between the Lower and Middle Coal Measures, as well as between the Langsettian and Duckmantian. The Duckmantian/Bolsovian boundary lies at the base of the Chance Pennystone

(Aegiranum) Marine Band. The lowest three marine bands in the local Lower Coal Measures sequence (Figure 6) are tentatively equated with the Subcrenatum, Listeri and Amaliae marine bands (Ramsbottom et al., 1978). The Subcrenatum Marine Band is conventionally taken as the base of the Westphalian series (Stubblefield and Trotter, 1957), implying that measures below the Bottom Marine Band, proved only in Lilleshall No. 2 Borehole, are Namurian in age. However, only *Lingula* is recorded from the Bottom Marine Band and, for convenience, these lowest beds are here included in the Lower Coal Measures.

The Cambriense Marine Band (Ramsbottom et al., 1978), which is taken as the boundary between the Middle and Upper Coal Measures (Stubblefield and Trotter, 1957), is not known in the Coalbrookdale Coalfield. In the Hadley area, primary red-bed sedimentation commenced at about the level of the Chance Pennystone Marine Band, well below the level of the Cambriense Marine Band. In the north-east of the coalfield, however, deep boreholes prove about 40 m of grey measures overlying the Chance Pennystone, but with no record of a marine fauna. In the absence of this marine band, the base of the Upper Coal Measures is taken at the first major incoming of primary red beds, and thus at the base of the Hadley Formation.

The onset of red-bed sedimentation at about the level of the Chance Pennystone Marine Band in Coalbrookdale is comparable to the situation in South Staffordshire (Poole, 1970) and the Forest of Wyre (Poole and Calver, 1966). By contrast, the facies change occurs considerably later in North Staffordshire, where some 300 m of the normal grey facies lie between the Cambriense Marine Band and the first red-bed (Etruria) formation (Wilson et al., 1992, fig. 3).

In the north-east of the Coalbrookdale Coalfield there is a conformable, though diachronous, contact between the Hadley Formation red beds and the underlying productive measures. In the south and west, however, the red beds rest unconformably on productive measures or on older strata.

North-west of the Wrekin and Boundary faults, the equivalent of the Hadley Formation in the Shrewsbury and Denbighshire coalfields is named the Ruabon Marl. Pocock et al. (1938) attributed the meagre development of these 'marls' around Shrewsbury to an unconformable overstep across Lower Palaeozoic rocks. This is also the case west of Wellington, where thin 'marls' rest unconformably on the Precambrian. Although equivalent to the Hadley Formation, the name Ruabon Marl is used here for these strata, because the area north of the Boundary Fault forms the edge of the Shrewsbury Coalfield.

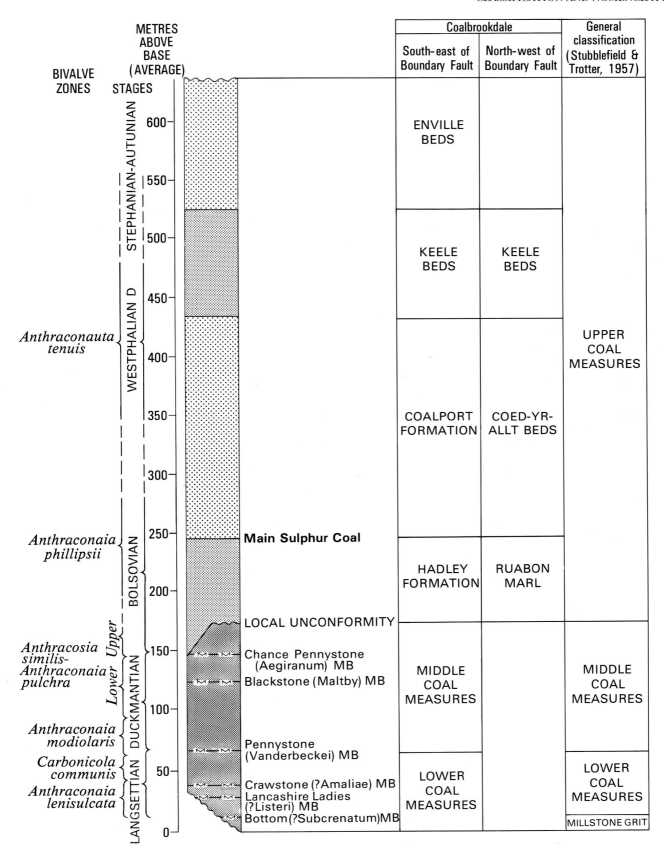

Figure 6   Generalised vertical section of the Coal Measures of the Coalbrookdale Coalfield.

The Hadley Formation is succeeded by the Coalport Formation, which records a partial return to grey measures, with subordinate development of red beds. It is the local equivalent of the Halesowen Formation of South Staffordshire and of the Newcastle Formation of North Staffordshire. Its base is marked by the development of the Main Sulphur Coal. Palynological study of this coal and the succeeding Little Sulphur Coal, by Dr B Owens, indicates a late Bolsovian age, thus implying that the bulk of the formation is of Westphalian D age. The lowest part of the Coalport Formation is, however, somewhat older than the lowest part of the Newcastle Formation, from near the bottom of which an *Anthraconauta tenuis* fauna indicates a wholely Westphalian D age (Trueman, 1948; Myers, 1954).

The equivalent of the Coalport Formation in the Shrewsbury and Denbighshire coalfields are the Coed-yr-Allt Beds, which succeed the Ruabon Marl with apparent conformity; the term Coed-yr-Allt Beds is used for these strata north-west of the Boundary Fault in the Coalbrookdale area. The one coal known in these beds, in the Wrekin Buildings Borehole, is probably equivalent to the Main Sulphur Coal.

In the Coalbrookdale Coalfield, south-east of the Boundary Fault, the Coalport Formation is succeeded conformably by red measures referred to the Keele Beds, because of a general resemblence to the Keele Formation of the type area in North Staffordshire. The age of the Keele Formation is generally referred to Westphalian D (Smith et al., 1974, p.9) or Stephanian (Wagner, 1983), but there is no evidence in the Telford area to confirm either dating. The base of the Keele Beds in the area south-east of the Boundary Fault is taken at the first reappearance of primary red beds, and is notably diachronous. Along the outcrop on the eastern side of the Coalbrookdale Coalfield, the base of the Keele Beds corresponds to the base of a prominent sandstone, the Brookside Rock. Boreholes demonstrate that, to the east, the red measures commence lower in the succession, so that individual sandstones as far down the sequence as the Thick Rock, can be traced from the Coalport Formation into the Keele Beds (see Figure 16). An analogous facies change is recorded in North Staffordshire (Wilson et al., 1992, fig. 3).

A different situation is envisaged for the area north-west of the Boundary Fault. Here, some of the red strata assigned to the Keele Beds are believed to represent secondarily reddened Coed-yr-Allt Beds and Ruabon Marl, as discussed below and illustrated in Figure 17. Two other interpretations of the relationship shown in this figure cannot be ruled out, however. One is that the base of the red facies is primary, but strongly diachronous, as in Figure 16; the other is that unconformable Keele Beds overlap the two older formations on to the Uriconian.

In the Coalbrookdale Coalfield, the Enville Beds which succeed the Keele Beds conformably, are characterised by conglomerates containing Carboniferous limestone and chert, as well as by a higher proportion of sandstone than occurs in the Keele Beds. The base of the Enville Beds is taken at the base of the lowest group of thick sandstones. The term 'Enville Series' was introduced by Arber (1916, 1917) to include all the strata between the Keele and the Bridgnorth Sandstone (Permian) in the South Staffordshire Coalfield and surrounding areas. In the Coalbrookdale region only the lower part of this sequence is present and was referred to as Enville Beds or Enville Group by Whitehead et al. (1928).

The age of the Enville Beds is not known with certainty; no fossil evidence is available from the Coalbrookdale Coalfield and that from other coalfields is equivocal, but they are normally regarded regarded either as Westphalian D (Ramsbottom et al., 1978, pl. 3), or Stephanian to Autunian (Wagner, 1983). The pebbles contained in the conglomeratic sandstones of the Enville sequence in the Coalbrookdale area are derived from the west or north-west; in contrast those of the Enville type area (South Staffordshire) are derived from the south.

LITHOLOGY

The Lower and Middle Coal Measures form a grey clastic coal-bearing sequence similar to that present in other parts of the Pennine basin of deposition, and accumulated in a poorly drained delta-plain environment (Guion and Fielding, 1988). Occasional flooding of the delta plain by the sea produced thin beds of marine mudstone ('marine bands') but the majority of the sediments were deposited by alluvial processes, either in river channels and levees or in overbank floodplains and lakes. Soils were formed on emergent areas, with widespread coal-forming peat-swamps.

The Upper Coal Measures are predominantly red beds, formed on better-drained alluvial plains situated closer to the upland areas from which the clastic sediment was derived (Besly, 1988). Periodic lowering of the water table allowed oxidation of recently deposited sediment, with resultant reddening. A pattern of fining-upward cycles of fluvial deposition can be recognised. Thus, in the Hadley Formation simple fining-upwards cycles from sandstone to mudstone can be detected. The Coalport Formation, though grey in colour, also contains clearly marked upward-fining cycles; these start with a massive erosive-based sandstone, which grades up into flaggy sandstone, siltstone and mudstone, with a seatearth, thin coal or limestone (calcrete) commonly present near the top.

Fining-upward cycles can also be distinguished in the Keele Beds, with erosive sandstones fining upwards into flaggy sandstone, siltstone, silty mudstone and finally 'smooth' mudstone. The sandstones represent river channel sands, and the fine sediments are interpreted as overbank floodplain deposits. The concretionary limestones represent calcreted palaeosols, which may have been ripped up and incorporated as intraclasts in the channel deposit of the next cycle. Similar rhythms occur in the Enville Beds, with the sandstone member of each cycle generally being thicker than in the Keele Beds.

Coals

Few coal seams in the productive measures of the Coalbrookdale Coalfield exceed 1.2 m in thickness. They are mostly bituminous and dull, with a high incombustible content. Dirt partings are common, and the New Mine Coal in the Lower Coal Measures is pyritic. Only a few poor thin coals are known in the Hadley Formation. The coals of the Coalport Formation are mostly thin, dirty and pyritic, and pass locally into cannel and black carbonaceous shale. No coals are known in the Keele Beds at outcrop, but one was found above the Brookside Rock in Brickkiln Plantation Borehole, and two in Childpit Lane Borehole. None occurs in the Enville Beds.

Seatearths

Coal seams commonly rest upon seatearths (fossil soils) of crumbly, unbedded clay with rootlets, which may be smooth to silty, or sandy, and pale to dark grey or brown, depending on the amount of carbonaceous material and degree of leaching that has affected the former soil profile. Fireclays are high-alumina seatearths and are economically important in the upper part of the Lower Coal Measures. Less often, the coal seams rest directly upon a coarser, hard, siliceous sandstone or 'ganister', such as the Big Flint, which underlies the coal of the same name. Similar ganisters occur locally below the Lancashire Ladies, Crawstone and Three-Quarter coals. The ganisters were also formed in soil profiles, by silica enrichment, and are suitable for use in the production of siliceous refractory materials.

Limestones

Thin, fine-grained or clayey limestones occur commonly in the Coalport Formation and rarely in the Hadley and Keele formations. They are pale grey to brown in colour, nodular, porcellaneous with a conchoidal fracture, and are often brecciated, with limestone fragments set in a matrix of calcite, sand and clay. They commonly contain the freshwater worm, *Spirorbis pusillus* (Etheridge, 1880; Cox, 1926; Trueman, 1946, p.lxii) and are hence considered to be lacustrine in origin.

Mudstones

Marine mudstones are few and generally thin. They are dark grey to black, and pyritic. An exception is the Pennystone Marine Band, which is thicker and includes fossiliferous ironstone nodules. Non-marine mudstones in the productive measures are pale grey to dark grey, generally becoming paler upwards. Several of the dark grey mudstones overlying coals include thick 'mussel' bands, such as those above the Big Flint and Top coals. The mudstones may be smooth or silty and are typically bedded but not particularly fissile. Ironstone nodules containing siderite occur at many levels and are generally pale brown, though some are dark brown or grey due to the presence of carbonaceous material. The nodules are generally small and of various shapes, but where sufficiently numerous they fuse to form flat sheets. Their colours and shapes are reflected in the names of the seams formerly worked: Pennystone, White and Blue Flats, Yellowstone, Brickmeasure, Ballstone and Blackstone.

The mudstones of the Hadley Formation, traditionally known as marls, are insufficiently calcareous to merit that term. They are generally unbedded, blocky, and veined and mottled in shades of purple, red, chocolate brown, green, yellow, grey and lavender. They commonly include oxidised rootlet beds in which the root traces have been replaced by iron minerals. They may be silty or sandy, and commonly contain very coarse angular detrital grains. Rare black carbonaceous shales, some with pyrite, also occur. Grey mudstones are more common higher in the Hadley Formation, the top of which is marked by the grey clayey seatearth beneath the Main Sulphur Coal.

The finer sediments of the Coalport Formation are siltstones and smooth to silty mudstones, which are bedded to blocky and commonly micaceous. They are dominantly grey, paler than those of the productive measures, with brown and black staining caused by iron and manganese. Red and purple mottling and banding occur throughout the formation, but more so towards the top; yellow and olive tinges are weathering effects. Siderite and pyrite are common, the latter both as large crystals and finely disseminated, but there are no ironstones of economic importance.

The dominant lithology of the Keele Beds is marl or calcareous mudstone, most commonly brick red, deep purple or brown, but sometimes yellow, orange, khaki or blue, and commonly mottled with pale green or grey reduction patches. The marls are smooth or silty and micaceous, and they may be well bedded or unbedded and blocky; the latter commonly contain small scattered ferruginous or calcareous concretions ('race'). Pyrite and carbonaceous material are rare, and plants only survive as impressions. The mudstones of the Keele Beds north of the Boundary Fault are dominantly silty and are mottled purple, red, blue and green. Chocolate-brown, smooth mudstones are also common, and ironstones and a seatearth are recorded.

The marls (calcareous mudstones) of the Enville Beds are on the whole redder than those of the Keele Beds, although purple, lilac or yellow hues also occur, and green reduction spots are common. These marls too may be smooth or silty and micaceous, and either bedded or blocky. They are less calcareous than the associated sandstones, with a little calcareous 'race' and intergranular calcite.

Sandstones, breccias and conglomerates

Sandstones in the productive measures are generally white to pale grey or pale brown, and weather to a deeper brown. Most are fine to medium grained, but some are coarse grained, especially those low in the sequence. Many contain a siliceous cement and show a flinty fracture. Cross-bedding and convolute structures are widespread, as are siderite nodules, which weather to limonite. Conglomerates are common in the lower sandstones, particularly in the west and south, and contain angular to rounded fragments of Carboniferous and Precambrian rocks.

The characteristic coarse-grained sandstones and fine breccias of the Hadley Formation are called 'espleys', a term which originated in the Coalbrookdale Coalfield (Arber, 1914). They display graded bedding and, locally, cross-bedding. They contain angular fragments of red and green Uriconian igneous rocks, feldspar fragments, pebbles of limestone and Coal Measures sandstones, and tabular, pale grey and green shale clasts, in a matrix of angular quartz sand, clay and rock fragments or iron oxide. The resultant rock is pale green or pinkish grey, usually friable at outcrop, with a soft matrix and highly weathered clasts. Espleys commonly have sharp erosive bases and channel into the underlying mudstone; they grade upwards into mudstone. They are interpreted as river channel deposits which, in exposures, are usually seen to be only a few metres in width; the length of these espley channels is unknown. Their coarse, angular and crudely bedded debris indicates that they represent the deposits of flood waters flowing from a relatively close upland source. The espleys are concentrated in the southern and western parts of the area, where debris from nearby sources is associated with the overstep of the Hadley Formation and Ruabon Marl on to Lower Carboniferous, Silurian and Precambrian rocks.

The sandstones of the Coalport Formation are more sheet-like in form with individual units persisting for several kilometres. They are usually coarse grained, dominantly with subrounded to angular quartz grains; however, they also include feldspar and carbonaceous debris, as well as coal and small rock fragments, largely derived from the productive measures and the Precambrian rocks to the west. Wisps and layers of espley material are also present. The sandstones are pale to medium grey or olive-green, depending on their content of carbonaceous material. They may be stained brown or black, although red and purple staining is evident in the higher sandstones. Cross-bedding is common and the sandstones are more micaceous than those of the productive measures, often containing large flakes of muscovite and biotite. Typically, they have erosive bases. The lower parts of individual beds are massive and hard, but they become more flaggy and softer upwards. Similar sheet-like sandstones are known in the Hadley Formation, particularly near the top, but they are subordinate to the espleys and do not cover such large areas as do those in the Coalport Formation.

The Keele Beds north of the Boundary Fault include about 60 per cent of red and purple sandstones, which are generally coarse grained and fairly calcareous. They form beds up to 15 m thick, the lower parts of which are cross-bedded; they become more evenly laminated or wispy bedded, and hence more flaggy, upwards. In contrast, sandstones make up only 30 per cent of the Keele Beds south of the Boundary Fault; they lie predominantly in the lower part of this formation and are rarely more than 5 m thick. They vary from red and deep purple to lavender, although shades of grey, buff and green also occur. They are cross-bedded and may include feldspar and mica. Breccias of mudstone intraclasts are common, particularly near the base of the thicker sandstones; they contain angular, tabular flakes of purple, green or khaki calcareous mudstone, generally 0.5 cm to 5 cm across, in a sandstone or, more rarely, a mudstone matrix.

Calcareous sandstones are the dominant lithology in the Enville Beds, and are uniformly distributed through the sequence. They are typically dull reddish brown, but locally greenish brown, and are more subdued and uniform in colour than the sandstones of the Keele Beds. Sandstones up to 20 m or more in thickness are recorded; they are coarse to fine grained, micaceous and feldspathic, cross-bedded in the lower part, but becoming flaggy above. Mudstone breccias are less common than in the Keele Beds and are typically found towards the base of the lower sandstone members.

Conglomerates are widespread in the Enville Beds, typically at the base; they pass up into pebbly sandstone. The conglomerates contain more calcite cement than do the sandstones. The larger clasts, subrounded and up to about 12 cm across, are dominantly yellow, red, grey and black Lower Carboniferous chert. Other constituents include well rounded, pale grey and red Carboniferous limestone pebbles, chiefly crinoidal and often silicified, rounded pebbles of quartzite and jasper, and subangular clasts of white quartz, sandstone and grit, with some *Spirorbis* limestone. The source of the pebbles, which are mostly of Lower Carboniferous types, is uncertain (Hull, 1896; Cockin, 1906, p.529; King, 1921; King and Lewis, 1913). King (1899) and Wills (1935, 1948) considered the material in the type Enville area to be derived from the 'Mercian Highlands' to the south and east. However, in Coalbrookdale, the conglomerates fine and die out southwards, suggesting a derivation from the Lower Carboniferous outcrops of the Welsh Borders, to the west or north-west.

Red beds

The original assumption that primary red beds in the Coal Measures always indicate a desert or semi-arid environment (e.g. Arber, 1917; Wills, 1929) is not sustainable. It is invalidated by the quantity of oxidised rootlet beds and plant debris in the Hadley Formation, and by the existence of contemporaneous red and grey strata. Red beds in the Coal Measures are now ascribed to weathering and erosion in a warm, humid climate, with subsequent deposition on well-drained alluvial plains at the landward margins of coal basins, where the groundwater was free-draining and high in oxygen. The diachronous upward change from grey productive measures to red beds in Coalbrookdale was probably caused by a northward migration of the marginal facies belt, but in detail the depositional history of the Hadley Formation red beds was complex, involving an interplay of pedogenic processes and water-table fluctuations (Besly, 1988). Similar red beds occur locally low in the Lower Coal Measures; they probably mark a brief migration of the basin margin in Langsettian times.

Beneath the unconformity at the base of the Hadley Formation in the south of the coalfield, originally grey strata have been reddened by secondary weathering and erosional processes associated with the unconformity. For example, the Madeley Wood boreholes in the Shifnal area have revealed Middle and Lower Coal Measures stained red, purple, lilac, brown and yellow. Coals were destroyed by oxidation, causing the overlying measures to collapse and form breccias in which extensive replacement, particularly of coals, by hematite and siderite occurred. Boreholes in the Old Park area have demonstrated reddening of Middle Coal Measures and substitution of hematite for coal; at the Woodside Housing Estate reddened Lower Ludlow Shales were observed below the Hadley Formation. In Madeley Wood No. 5 and 6 boreholes, only the highest coal is replaced by ironstone, lower coals being represented by collapse breccia. This suggests that the substitution is a two-stage process, the coal first undergoing oxidation, with hematite then infilling the resultant breccia.

The Keele Beds north of the Boundary Fault are also believed to be secondary red beds, reddened beneath the Permian unconformity at the base of the Bridgnorth Sandstone (see p.95). However, the Keele and Enville red beds in the Coalbrookdale Coalfield are of primary origin. Evidence for this conclusion includes the thickness of the red-bed sequence (as it is unlikely that secondary reddening below the base of the Bridgnorth Sandstone would account for the red colour of more than 370 m of Keele and Enville strata) and the fact that the base of the red Keele facies becomes stratigraphically lower eastwards (Figure 16), whereas the base of the Bridgnorth Sandstone cuts down farther in the west. However, compared to the marginal and coal basin environment of the Hadley and Coalport formations, the Keele and Enville strata formed in increasingly drier conditions. Wills (1956, p.82) described the environment as semi-arid, but this may exaggerate the degree of climatic change, as it is evident that, for a time, the Coalport and Keele facies were deposited contemporaneously.

STRATIGRAPHY

The distribution of Coal Measures strata in the Coalbrookdale Coalfield, and the localities described here, are shown in Figure 7. The principal data sources, comprising shaft sections, boreholes and opencast sites, are detailed in Appendices 2, 3 and 4. Additional data for the concealed coalfield come from deep coal boreholes in the east, between Kemberton and Lilleshall.

Macrofossils collected during the resurvey, and earlier collections from opencast sites by Dr G H Mitchell and Mr R H Hoare, have been identified by Dr M A Calver. Micropalaeontological identifications are the work of Dr B Owens. No attempt has been made to reclassify the collections of the previous survey (Whitehead et al., 1928), of Prestwick (1840) or of other early workers.

Lower Coal Measures

Lower Coal Measures crop out widely in the centre and west of the coalfield from Lawley to Little Wenlock and Ironbridge; throughout this area they have been extensively mined by opencast methods. In the south-west of the coalfield, they are exposed south of the Broseley Fault. These two areas represent the south-western limits of the Donnington and Madeley synclines, which plunge north-eastwards, so that Lower Coal Measures rocks are preserved at depth beneath younger strata, at least as far as Lilleshall, Sheriff Hales and Shifnal. A third, more southerly syncline, the Coalport Syncline, includes Lower Coal Measures which crop out at Caughley, but the north-eastward extent of these measures at depth is poorly known.

The variation of the Lower Coal Measures across the coalfield is summarised in Figure 8. The thickest recorded section is 120.7 m, not bottomed, in Lilleshall No. 6 Borehole in the north-east. South-westwards the Lower Coal Measures thin to 37.5 m at Madeley Meadow Pit. This thinning takes place almost entirely within the lower, arenaceous part of the sequence (Figure 8) and is caused partly by basin-margin onlap to the south-west and partly by thinning of individual beds in the condensed sequence. In the exposed coalfield, the Lower Coal Measures below the Little Flint Coal range from 59 m at Lawley, to only 7 m at Madeley Meadow Pit; however, in the concealed coalfield they thicken to at least 95 m (in Lilleshall Borehole No. 6). The upper part of the Lower Coal Measures slightly increases in thickness from west-north-west to east-south-east, though with much local variation (Figure 9).

The strata in the north-east contain a high proportion of mudstone and siltstone, especially in the upper part, whereas in the thinner sequence to the west, sandstones form a higher proportion of the measures and continue to be important higher in the sequence (Figure 8). At Limekiln Lane in the north-west, the coals split and become associated with primary red beds; the latter could suggest an approach to the basin margin, and it is possible that the Boundary Fault and the ridge of Precambrian rocks of the Wrekin were active and, for a time, formed a western limit of deposition.

Below the Little Flint Coal, sandstones with conglomerates and mudstones predominate. There area few thin coals and at least three marine bands; the only mineral extracted has been the Crawstone ironstone. These strata crop out over a large area of the south and west of the coalfield, but are poorly documented owing to the lack of workings below the Crawstone. The measures are better known in boreholes farther east; indeed, because the Lower Coal Measures transgressed the area from the north-east, the oldest strata are known only from these boreholes.

The lowest strata are conglomerates and sandstones succeeded by fireclays, shales and mudstones, which include a *Lingula* band. The latter is the Bottom Marine Band of Wills (1948, p.49), which is a possible local equivalent of the Subcrenatum Marine Band. These measures are succeeded by a massive sandstone known as the Farewell Rock, which ranges up to 29 m in thickness (Lilleshall Borehole No. 6) in the north-east, but dies out to the south-west. It contains beds of conglomerate in the west, and is overlain locally by a sandy fireclay. The Lancashire Ladies Coal follows, resting generally on the fireclay or the Farewell Rock, but directly overlying Silurian strata at Madeley Meadow Pit in the south-west. This coal is 0.6 m or less in thickness, and is locally overlain by the Lancashire Ladies Marine Band, which is believed to cor-

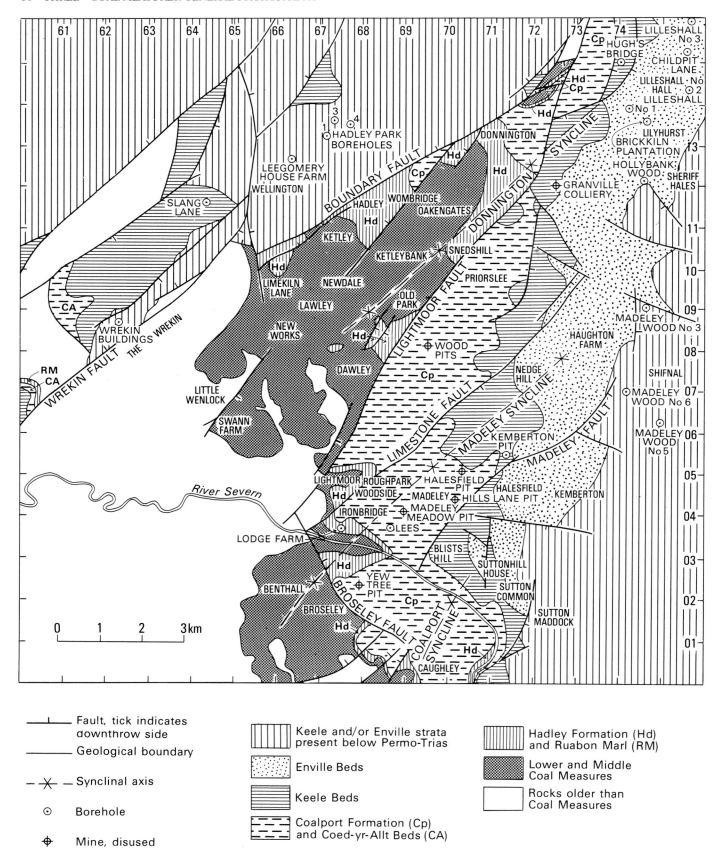

Figure 7   Distribution of Coal Measures in the Coalbrookdale Coalfield, showing localities mentioned in Chapter 3.

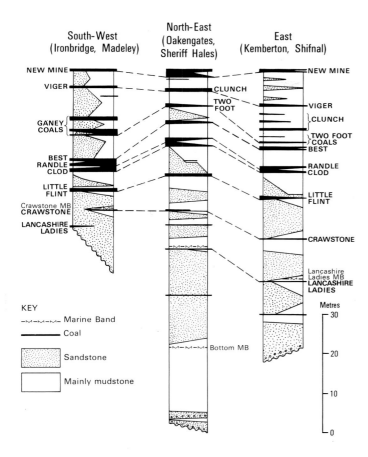

South-West
(Ironbridge, Madeley)

North-East
(Oakengates,
Sheriff Hales)

East
(Kemberton, Shifnal)

NEW MINE

VIGER

GANEY
COALS

BEST
RANDLE
CLOD

LITTLE
FLINT

Crawstone MB
CRAWSTONE

LANCASHIRE
LADIES

NEW MINE

CLUNCH

TWO
FOOT

NEW MINE

VIGER

CLUNCH

TWO FOOT
COALS
BEST

RANDLE
CLOD

LITTLE
FLINT

CRAWSTONE

Lancashire
Ladies MB
LANCASHIRE
LADIES

Bottom MB

Metres
— 30

— 20

— 10

— 0

KEY

—ᴹ—ᴹ—ᴹ— Marine Band

——————— Coal

Sandstone

Mainly mudstone

Figure 8 Comparative sections of the Lower Coal Measures of the Coalbrookdale Coalfield.

relate with the Listeri Marine Band. In the Lilleshall boreholes, another coal occurs above that marine band. The succeeding measures include the Crawstone Flint Rock, a ganister 1.7 m to 7.6 m thick. This is overlain successively by the Crawstone Coal (up to 0.3 m thick) and the Crawstone ironstone. A marine fauna recorded at this level at Lodge Farm, Ironbridge, is tentatively correlated with the Amaliae Marine Band. Above the ironstone lies the Little Flint Rock, a ganister similar to the Crawstone Flint Rock.

Above the Little Flint Rock, sandstones become less dominant and the remainder of the Lower Coal Measures are characterised by fireclays, with numerous workable coals. The Little Flint Coal is typically only 0.3 m to 0.8 m thick, but was widely mined as a blast furnace coal, despite the presence of a thin dirt parting in a few places. The separation between the Little Flint Coal and the succeeding Clod Coal thickens from 1 m in the west to 14 m in Lilleshall Borehole No. 5. Generally, the Little Flint Coal is directly overlain by 1.5 m to 5.5 m of sandstone, the Little Flint Coal Rock, which is locally followed by a thin unnamed coal. The Clod Coal rests on the Little Flint Coal Rock between New Works and New Dale, but elsewhere mudstone and fireclay intervene. The Clod, Randle and Best coals form a group normally falling within 3 m of measures, except in the east where

the parting between the Randle and Best locally thickens markedly (Figure 8). The Clod Coal is typically 0.4 m to 0.8 m thick and is overlain either directly by the Randle or by a parting of up to 0.9 m of fireclay. The Randle Coal ranges between 0.4 m and 1.0 m, and the Best Coal 0.3 m to 0.7 m; except in the east and northeast, they are commonly united or at most only 0.5 m apart. The parting is usually black shale, rarely pale grey fireclay.

The measures between the Best Coal and New Mine Coal, which lies at the top of the Lower Coal Measures, just below the Pennystone Marine Band, comprise fireclays with subordinate coals and sandstones. The fireclays are the most valuable in the coalfield, and have been widely worked at several levels in the west and south. The number of coals varies from two, in areas north and west of Dawley, to six in the north-east of the Madeley Syncline, with resultant confusion of nomenclature. The sandstones are lenticular and overlie the coals at various levels; lenses of coarse-grained sandstone occur within the developments of sandy shales and flaggy siltstones, which pass upwards and laterally into the fireclays. These arenaceous strata predominate to the south-west of the Madeley Syncline and in the north-west of the coalfield, particularly in the lower part of this interval. The measures are thickest (23.8 m, mainly sandstone) at Yew Tree Pit, Broseley. Rapid variations in the number of coals and the thickness of the measures, and the presence of lenticular coarse-grained sandstones, imply conditions of depositional instability unparalleled elsewhere in the productive measures of this coalfield.

The parting between the Best and Two Foot coals is composed mostly of dark fireclay, locally named 'Linseed Earth', but includes patchy developments of sandstone and siltstone, the Best Coal Rock. In the north, Two Foot Coal is a single seam of almost constant thickness (0.5 m to 0.9 m), but southward and eastward it splits into as many as five seams, referred to as the Ganey Coals (Figure 8). Above the Two Foot Coal lie about 5 m of fireclay (Lower Clunch Clay), which thickens south-eastwards into 9.6 m of mudstones and sandstones, locally referred to as the Two Foot Rock. The succeeding Clunch (or Viger or Sill) Coal varies between only 0.15 m at Benthall and 1.2 m at Ketley Bank; it develops a parting up to 5 m thick in the north-west. Between the Clunch (or Viger) Coal and the New Mine Coal lie the richest fireclays in the succession; they are up to 13.5 m thick and are known as the Upper Clunch, New Mine or Nine Feet Clays. However, to the south-east these become arenaceous, and between Blists Hill and Rough Park the parting is wholly sandstone, the Viger Coal Rock (Figure 8). The New Mine Coal is dirty and pyritic; it varies from a single seam 0.3 m to 0.6 m thick in the Madeley Sycline to a 2.1 m seam, including a central parting, in the north-west.

Middle Coal Measures

The dominant lithology of the Middle Coal Measures is grey, bedded, nonmarine mudstone. Compared to the Lower Coal Measures sandstones are of less significance,

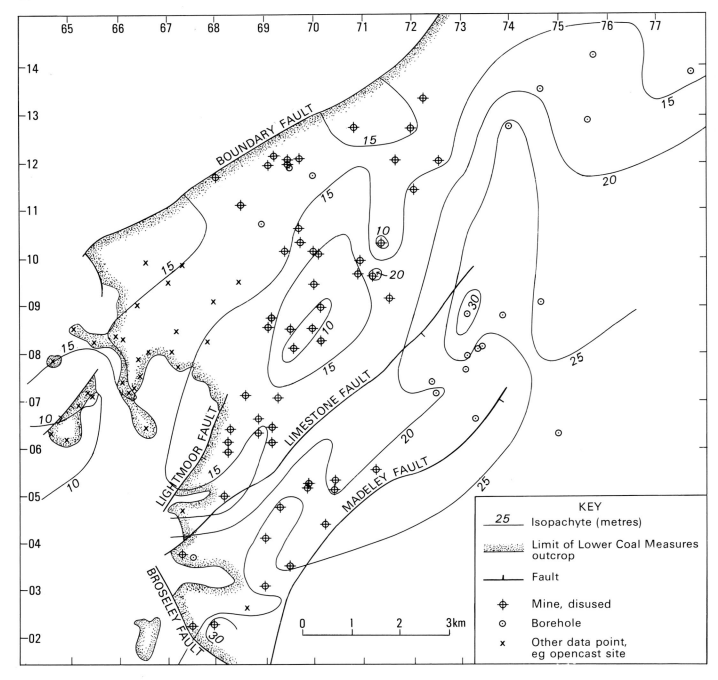

Figure 9   Isopachytes for the upper part of the Lower Coal Measures, from the base of the Clod Coal to the top of the New Mine Coal.

and workable fireclays are absent. Apart from the Big Flint, the thick valuable coals of the Middle Coal Measures lie in two well-defined groups referred to as the Top and the Fungous Coal groups after the highest coal in each (Figure 10). Ironstones in the mudstones have been worked at ten horizons, and three marine bands are known.

The strata between the Pennystone (Vanderbeckei) Marine Band and the Top Coal thicken north-eastwards from less than 25 m to more than 50 m (Figure 11). Measures higher in the sequence evidently thicken in the same direction, although their variation also reflects the diachronous base of the Hadley Formation. At Hollybank Wood Borehole (west of Sheriff Hales) this facies change occurs below the level of the Chance Pennystone Marine Band, whereas at Hadley and Ketley it lies conformably just above that marine band. To the north-east there are up to 40 m of grey measures,

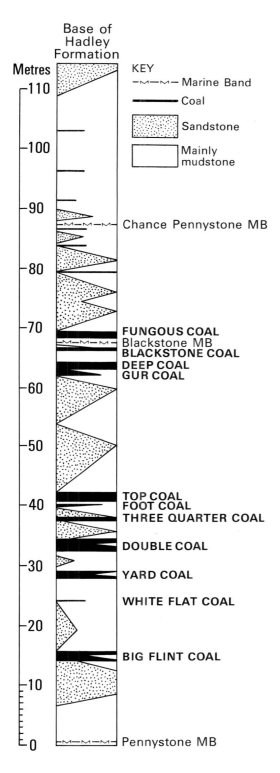

Figure 10 Generalised vertical section of the Middle Coal Measures.

The base of the Middle Coal Measures is taken at the base of the Pennystone, the most renowned ironstone in the coalfield and so named for its small, flat, round, brown nodules. The Pennystone Marine Band generally occupies the lower 1 m to 2 m of the Pennystone ironstone, but thickens locally to a recorded maximum of about 6 m at Swann Farm [648 065], in the extreme west of the coalfield. It is thus the thickest marine band in the coalfield and the only one to contain a significant fauna apart from *Lingula*. The fauna is richest in the south (Smith, 1862, p.242), but the iron ore potential increases northwards. The Pennystone lies at the base of the most complete cyclothem in the productive measures of Coalbrookdale, being succeeded by nonmarine mudstone, sandstone (Big Flint Rock), seatearth and the Big Flint Coal. In the western half of the coalfield the Big Flint Rock is a well-defined unit, generally 4 m to 9 m thick, but varying from 1.8 m to 11.0 m. However, towards the western and southern limits of the coalfield, and also generally in the concealed coalfield to the east, it passes into more argillaceous measures.

The Big Flint Coal is widely worked throughout most of the coalfield as a single 1.1 m to 1.6 m seam, but it splits north-eastwards. The resultant parting ranges up to 6.2 m thick. The Big Flint Coal has a roof of black shale with mussels (Flint Coal Bass). The succeeding measures comprise: Flint Coal Roof (mudstone); Flint Coal Rock (sandstone); White Flat ironstone; Pitcher (or Pitchy) Bass (black mudstone), with the thin White Flat Coal; Blue Flat ironstone; 'quoiceneck' (seatearth) and Yard Coal. This succession is constant, except towards Little Wenlock in the south-west, where the measures thin and both ironstones are wanting; also in the north-west, where the Pitcher Bass fails and the two ironstones unite. In the Madeley Sycline, the sequence thickens north-eastward from 3.7 m at Madeley Meadow Pit to 8.1 m in the Madeley Wood Colliery boreholes, with concomitant thickening of the two ironstones and the seatearth. Similar thickening occurs between the Lightmoor and Limestone faults; north of the Lightmoor Fault, the thickening is even more pronounced due to the local importance of the Flint Coal Rock.

The Yard Coal is consistently 0.8 m to 1.1 m thick and locally includes a single parting in the north-east. It is overlain by black shale with an *Anthraconaia* fauna typical of the uppermost *Modiolaris* Zone, followed by the Yellowstone ironstone (with yellowish brown nodules) and then by 0.9 m of seatearth clay beneath the Double Coal. The separation between Yard and Double coals, normally about 1 m to 3 m, increases north-eastward. South of the River Severn, and in Madeley, this sequence is replaced by washout sandstones, siltstones and mudstones, which are orientated north-eastwards along the Madeley Syncline. In Broseley, thin coarse-grained sandstones, apparently part of this washout, rest on beds as low as the Pennystone Marine Band. The greatest recorded thickness of these measures is 30 m at Halesfield, where their base rests on the Big Flint Rock.

The Double Coal is the thickest seam in the coalfield, generally 1.5 m to 1.9 m, with a maximum of 3.13 m (including partings) in Madeley Wood Borehole No. 3.

including five thin coals, above the Chance Pennystone Marine Band. The greatest overall thickness of Middle Coal Measures thus occurs in the north-east, in Childpit Lane Borehole (154.2 m).

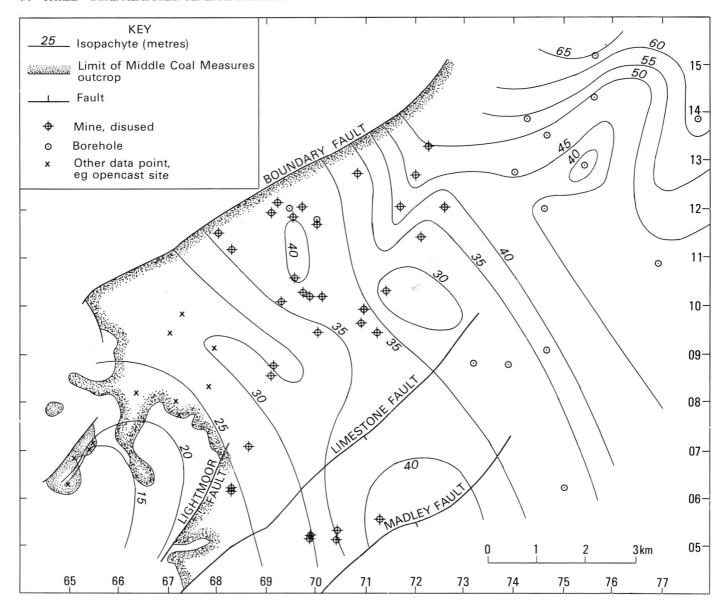

Figure 11 Isopachytes for the lower part of the Middle Coal Measures, from the top of the New Mine Coal to the base of the Top Coal.

The parting between the Double and Three-Quarter coals is generally wholly occupied by the Double Coal Rock, a sandstone up to 3.8 m thick, but north-east of Granville Colliery this is replaced by a thicker argillaceous sequence. The Three-Quarter, or Half-Yard Coal, is generally only 0.4 m to 0.7 m thick and has thus rarely been worked. It is locally overlain by a ganister called the Three-Quarter Coal Rock, but normally by argillaceous measures, which in places include the Foot (or Tow) Coal, possibly a lower leaf of the Top Coal. The Top Coal is 1.1 m to 1.9 m thick and contains a parting at Limekiln Lane opencast site.

The Top Coal roof comprises up to 1.0 m of black shale with a mussel fauna typical of mid Lower Similis-Pulchra Zone. This is succeeded by: the Ballstone (ironstone with large rounded or oval nodules); the Bind Rock or Ballstone Roof (sandstone and siltstone); the Bind Bass (dark grey to black, silty, fissile shales); and the Brickmeasure (ironstone with brick-shaped nodules). The Brickmeasure ironstone is overlain by a sandstone that locally develops into a major washout aligned north-eastwards between Dawley and Sheriff Hales, and thus paralleling the Yard Coal washout on the opposite side of the Limestone Fault. The washout cuts down to the Yellowstone ironstone in the southwest; in the north-east it does not cut down into lower strata but attains a thickness of 30.3 m at Hollybank Wood Borehole.

The Fungous group of coals is a clearly defined sequence of strata comprising, in ascending order (Figure 10): the Gur Coal; argillaceous measures; Deep or Stone Coal (including a lower leaf again named the Tow Coal); measures including the Blackstone ironstone; Blackstone or Foot Coal; measures including the Ragged Robins ironstone and Blackstone Marine Band; Fungous (or Marquis or Donnington Wood) Coal. The Fungous Coal has been widely worked, the Deep Coal and the two ironstones less extensively. The Gur Coal is thin, shaly and commonly absent, either dying out or joining the Deep Coal. The Blackstone Marine Band forms the lower part of the parting between Blackstone and Fungous coals and comprises dark, silty, micaceous fissile mudstone with abundant well preserved *Lingula* and fish remains. It is generally identified as the Maltby Marine Band and is thus correlated with the Sub-Brooch of South Staffordshire (Mitchell et al., 1945) and the Moss Cannel of North Staffordshire, although Calver (1966) suggests an alternative correlation with the higher Haughton Marine Band.

The measures between the Fungous Coal and the Chance Pennystone Marine Band vary between 8.3 m and 24.6 m in thickness and include up to three thin coals. The Fungous Coal Rock directly overlies the Fungous Coal in Wombridge and Hadley, and splits at Donnington into the Fungous Rock and Seven Yard Rock. This sandstone is followed successively by: a coal; the Chance Pennystone ironstone; the Chance Pennystone Rock; and the Chance Pennystone Marine Band, which is identified as the Aegiranum Marine Band, forming the boundary between Duckmantian and Bolsovian. It is equivalent to the Charles Marine Band of South Staffordshire and the Gin Mine Marine Band of North Staffordshire (Wills, 1948), and to the Eymore Farm Marine Band of the Wyre Forest (Poole and Calver, 1966). At Old Park, the measures above the Fungous Coal comprise washout sandstones, siltstones and silty mudstones, cutting down gently to below the Gur Coal.

The measures above the Chance Pennystone Marine Band (of Bolsovian age) are thickest and best known in the boreholes in the north-east of the coalfield, reaching 40 m at Childpit Lane in the extreme north-east. The sequence comprises mudstones with some sandstones, seatearths and up to five coals; here it passes conformably up into the red measures of the Hadley Formation.

Hadley Formation

The Hadley Formation is the local equivalent of the Etruria Formation (formerly Etruria Marl) of North Staffordshire and comprises reddish mudstones and lenticular 'espley' sandstones in proportions that vary considerably throughout the coalfield. Poor coals, slickensided seatearths and *Spirorbis* limestone are recorded, but no reliable marker horizon is known with which to subdivide the formation. The thickness of the formation also varies greatly, from 10 m over 90 m (Figure 12), and over large areas the red beds are unconformable on the grey productive measures or on older rocks. The Hadley Formation is Bolsovian in age, although at Lilleshall No. 5

Borehole the lowest strata may possibly be Duckmantian, the Chance Pennystone Marine Band being absent there.

The Hadley Formation is thickest in the north around Donnington, where it is conformable on the Middle Coal Measures. The lithology there largely comprises mudstones, which crop out from Donnington to Snedshill and Hadley. In the north-east of the coalfield, the formation also remains relatively thick and conformable on the Middle Coal Measures, but the proportion of sandstone increases. However, over most of coalfield the Hadley Formation rests unconformably on Middle and Lower Coal Measures strata (Figure 13; see also Figure 22 on p.56), and in the south-east on rocks as old as Silurian (see section 2 on published Telford map). These unconformable measures include a higher proportion of sandstone than do the thick marls of Donnington. In general, as the Hadley Formation thins the proportion of sandstone increases, despite the fewer individual sandstones, which evidently split and then die out as they are traced across the basin from areas of thin to thick argillaceous sedimentation. Where the overstep of the sub-Hadley unconformity is pronounced, the formation is generally thinner (Figure 13).

The unconformity at the base of the Hadley Formation was well known to miners as early as the 18th century, and originally named the Symon Fault. Scott (1861) first appreciated that the break represented an unconformity and Clarke (1901) showed that it was caused by intra-Coal Measures folding. Unfortunately, the term 'Symon Fault' has also subsequently been used where coal seams disappear against features other than the sub-Hadley unconformity, notably the bases of the washouts which develop above the Yard, Top and Fungous coals; consequently, it is considered best to avoid the use of the term. The alternative term 'Symon Unconformity' has also been used, but this is tautologous, symon in old mining parlance meaning unconformity.

Hoare (1959) first recognised secondary reddening below the unconformable base of the Hadley Formation, which was then still included in the Coalport Group as defined by Whitehead et al. (1928). Hoare noted such effects in the Madeley Wood boreholes in the south-east of the coalfield, but it probably occurs wherever the Hadley Formation has an unconformable base. During the resurvey it was seen to affect Middle Coal Measures strata at Old Park, and Silurian strata at Woodside.

Hoare suggested (1959, p.189) that 'calaminker', a multi-coloured red, blue and yellow gritty clay, commonly recorded at the unconformable base of the Hadley Formation in old mine records, represents secondarily reddened productive measures, and in general terms this is undoubtedly true. Prestwich (1840), Scott (1861), Jones (1871) and Arber (1914) all comment on its presence in association with the Symon Fault; Scott records 0.3 m to 4.7 m of such material in most cases, but a maximum of 14.6 m at Wood Pits. However, these authors give the impression that the calaminker is above the unconformity, and in some shaft sections (such as Kemberton Pit) the term is also used for strata of similar lithology at levels above the base of the Hadley Formation. In reality, the calaminker recorded in old mining

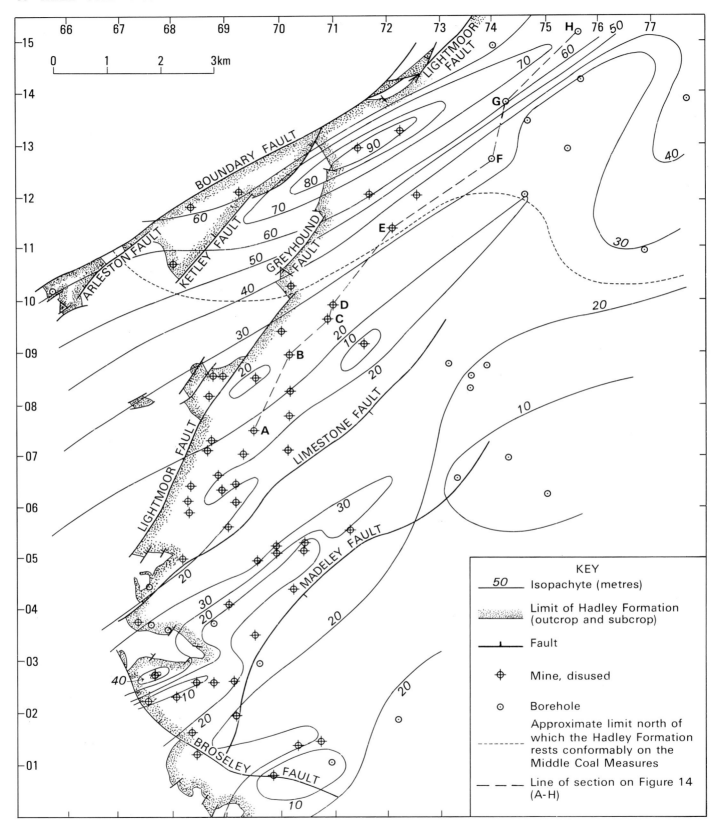

Figure 12   Isopachytes for the Hadley Formation.

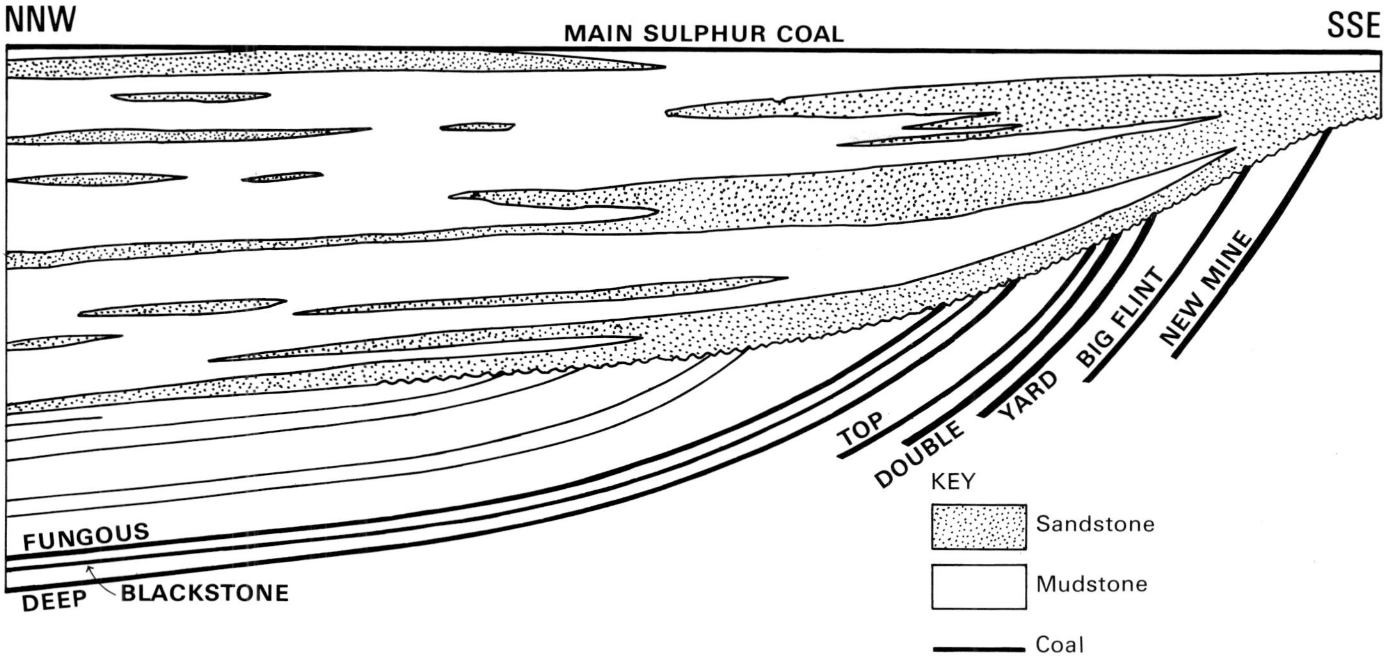

Figure 13 Diagrammatic cross-section through the Hadley Formation and underlying Coal Measures, approximately between Shifnal Manor and Donnington, showing the Symon Fault unconformity and the splitting of espley sandstones within the Hadley Formation.

records, usually at the base of the formation, probably includes both material reddened below the unconformity and the material resting upon it since, in practice, these are not easy to distinguish in the field. Indeed, even in boreholes such as Lees Farm Borehole 1A, the unconformity, which must have been present, proved impossible to define precisely, because the degree of reddening and bioturbation of the Middle Coal Measures below the unconformity rendered them quite indistinguishable from the overlying primary red beds. Thus, in this account, all references to calaminker are included in the Hadley Formation, although in many cases these will include some secondary reddened strata below the unconformity.

In the north-east of the coalfield, specifically in the Lilleshall boreholes, Stonehouse (1950) and Hoare (1959) considered the Symon Fault unconformity to persist, but placed it within the strata here defined as Hadley Formation. They considered the lower part of the Hadley Formation in that area to be an Etruria Marl facies conformable on the grey measures, but equated the upper part with traditional 'Coalport Group' resting unconformably on the Etruria Marl. However, during the resurvey, a review of shaft records in the centre of the coalfield, and of the more recent deep boreholes sunk in the north-east and south-east (Figure 14), shows that, as the Hadley Formation thickens northwards into the basin, the basal unconformity becomes steadily less marked, until it dies out.

The basal unconformity was exposed in the opencast site at Limekiln Lane, where it is overlain by 60 m of typical red mudstone with espleys, and there is now no doubt that in this coalfield the Hadley Formation, of Etruria facies, is conformable on the productive measures in the north and is unconformable on them farther south. The northern limit of the unconformity is therefore ill-defined (Figure 12). The possibility remains that there may be a further unconformity within or near the top of the Hadley Formation, equivalent to that widely present below the Halesowen Formation of South Staffordshire. However, this is unlikely since no evidence for it has been found. At Blockleys Brick Pit, Hadley, Etruria-type mudstones, with espleys similar to those recorded low in the Hadley Formation of the Lilleshall boreholes, were seen to be overlain almost directly by the Main Sulphur Coal of the Coalport Formation, with no sign of an unconformity. Most espley sandstones have a downcutting relationship with the measures below, but there is no reason to postulate a major regional break beneath any one of them.

Ruabon Marl

The equivalent of the Hadley Formation in the area north-west of the Boundary Fault is referred to as Ruabon Marl. The outcrop is confined to the south-west of this area, between the Wrekin and Burcot faults. No exposures are recorded, but the formation was proved in the WrekinBuildings Borehole to be 12.9 m thick and to rest on Precambrian rocks; it passes up without a break into the Coed-yr-Allt Beds. The strata are sandy to gritty, structureless, mottled mudstones with nodules and beds of impure silty *Spirorbis* limestone.

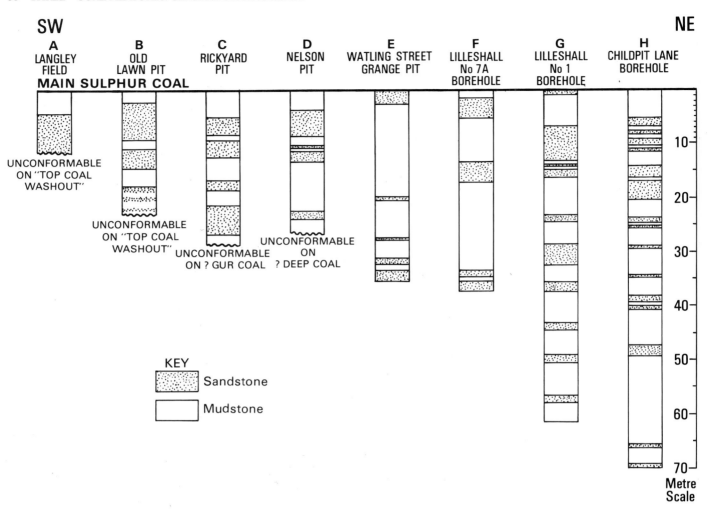

Figure 14 Shaft and borehole sections through the Hadley Formation, along the line indicated on Figure 12.

Coalport Formation

The Coalport Formation comprises roughly equal proportions of sandstones and argillaceous sediments. It includes 11 coals, all thin and pyritic, and several beds of *Spirorbis* limestone; the formation represents a return to coal-swamp conditions rather similar to those of the productive measures. The Coalport Formation shows little thickness variation, in contrast to the Lower and Middle Coal Measures and Hadley Formation; such variations as occur do not follow the clear patterns seen in the lower formations. The boundary with the overlying Keele Beds is conformable, although in the east of the coalfield it is diachronous.

The Main Sulphur Coal, at the base of the formation, is the only seam to have been widely mined. Although thin (normally 0.3 m to 0.7 m) and comprising up to four leaves, it is the most widespread seam in the Coalbrookdale Coalfield and probably equates with the Main Sulphur Coal of the Wyre Forest (Cantrill, 1895, p.19) and with the Thin, Deep or Best Coal of the Shrewsbury Coalfields. Palynological samples from boreholes at Limekiln Lane and Lees Farm have been dated by Dr B Owens as late Bolsovian, as has a sample of the lowest coal in the Halesowen Formation of the South Staffordshire Coalfield. The measures between the Main and Little Sulphur coals vary between 6.1 m at Lees Farm and 38 m at Madeley Meadow Pit; they include a basal ostracod bed with *Carbonita agnes* and *C. humilis* and a variable proportion of sandstone (Figure 15). Where a thick sandstone is present it is locally known as the White Rock (or Main Sulphur Coal Rock), but up to five separate sandstones are present in some areas. The Little Sulphur Coal (a name introduced here for the first time) is thinner than the Main Sulphur Coal, but it is almost as widespread and similarly forms a good marker. It may occur as one, two or three leaves, locally including cannel or black shale; miospores from a sample from Lees Farm have been dated by Dr B Owens as late Bolsovian in age also. Strata higher in the formation may therefore be of Westphalian D age.

The overlying Sulphur Rock and argillaceous measures below the Thick Rock together total between

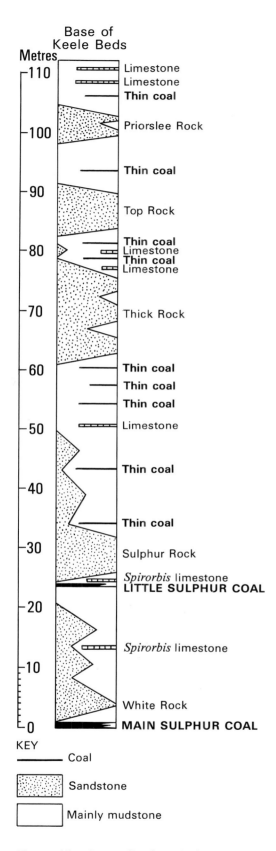

Base of Keele Beds

Metres

- 110 — Limestone / Limestone / **Thin coal**
- 100 — Priorslee Rock
- 90 — **Thin coal** / Top Rock
- 80 — **Thin coal** / Limestone / **Thin coal** / Limestone
- 70 — Thick Rock
- 60 — **Thin coal** / **Thin coal** / **Thin coal**
- 50 — Limestone
- 40 — **Thin coal**
- 30 — **Thin coal** / Sulphur Rock
- 20 — *Spirorbis* limestone / **LITTLE SULPHUR COAL** / *Spirorbis* limestone
- 10 —
- 0 — White Rock / **MAIN SULPHUR COAL**

KEY

— Coal

▒ Sandstone

☐ Mainly mudstone

Figure 15 Generalised vertical section of the Coalport Formation.

18.3 m (Brickkiln Plantation Borehole) and 45.2 m (Hills Lane Pit). The Sulphur Rock (less commonly called the Stinking Rock) is best developed in the south-west of the coalfield and may include one, two or three individual sandstones. Two coals are locally developed within the Rock, and up to three thin coals and a limestone in the measures above (Figure 15). The Thick Rock is the most persistent sandstone in the Coalport Formation, reaching a thickness of 38.1 m at Kemberton Pit, but locally it splits into two or three sandstones. It is overlain by a monotonous sequence of mudstones, which usually include a single coal, although two were intersected in Childpit Lane Borehole. *Spirorbis* limestone is recorded in three boreholes in the north-east.

The Top Rock is typically 5 m to 10 m thick and contains no partings thicker than 2 m. The overlying argillaceous measures vary in thickness and include a single coal seam, which in places splits into two or three leaves. Despite variation in the thickness of strata between the Top Rock and the highest sandstone, named here the Priorslee Rock, the latter appears to persist throughout the coalfield, usually as a single bed, but locally splitting into two or three thinner sandstones. It is overlain by mudstone with subordinate siltstones and sandstones. Limestones are better developed in these measures than lower in the formation, and *Spirorbis* is recorded; a single thin coal is present.

Coed-yr-Allt Beds

Strata equivalent to the lower part of the Coalport Formation north of the Boundary Fault, and also of Bolsovian age, are equated with the Coed-yr-Allt Beds of the Shrewsbury Coalfield. They are confined to the south-western part of the area between the Wrekin and Burcot faults. There are no surface exposures, but an 18 m sequence is recorded in the Wrekin Buildings Borehole, lying conformably between the Ruabon Marl and the Keele Beds. The sequence includes one coal, which is believed to be the lower of two seams recorded by Murchison (1839, p.39) in the Dryton Coalfield (Figure 1). This coal correlates with the Thin Coal (also known as the Deep or Best Coal) of the Shrewsbury Coalfield, and with the Main Sulphur Coal of Coalbrookdale. It is possible (see below) that the overlying Keele Beds in this area may partly represent secondarily reddened Coed-yr-Allt strata; on this hypothesis, it could be postulated that, before oxidation, all three coals of the Coed-yr-Allt Beds of Shrewsbury were present.

Keele Beds — south of the Boundary Fault

The Keele Beds, which comprise red mudstones, marls and subordinate sandstones, with sporadic *Spirorbis* limestones, lie conformably between the Coalport Formation and the Enville Beds. Their outcrop forms a north–south belt of low ground from Hugh's Bridge near Lilleshall, to the Severn Gorge west of Sutton Maddock; the variable width of this outcrop is due to faulting rather than thickness variation. The Keele Beds are poorly exposed, owing to their low relief and an extensive cover of drift, but much information has been acquired from excavations and drilling by the Telford Development Corporation and from boreholes sunk for Madeley Wood and Granville collieries.

The base of the Keele red-bed facies is diachronous and not easy to define, because subordinate red beds also occur within the Coalport Formation. Along its outcrop, from Priorslee to the Severn Gorge, the base is clearly at the base of the Brookside Rock. However, to the east and north the red-bed facies transgresses diachronously down the sequence, so that in places strata equivalent to the upper half of the Coalport Formation are assignable to the Keele Beds (Figure 16). It is thought that, in these eastern areas, primary red Keele strata were deposited at the same time as the upper Coal-port strata to the west. The hypothesis that Coalport Formation strata were secondarily reddened to this extent below the Bridgnorth Sandstone unconformity is discounted, because of the great thickness of red beds and because secondary Permian reddening would be expected to deepen westwards rather than eastwards.

The Keele Beds can be divided into the Brookside Rock and strata below and above it; further subdivision is not practicable. Keele red beds below the Brookside Rock range in thickness from zero in Madeley Wood No. 7 Borehole, and at outcrop, to 97.5 m in Lilleshall Borehole No. 6. The strata are mostly red mudstones and marls. However, in five boreholes, they include a red-brown sandstone believed to be a Keele facies equivalent of the Priorslee Rock (Coalport Formation); an even

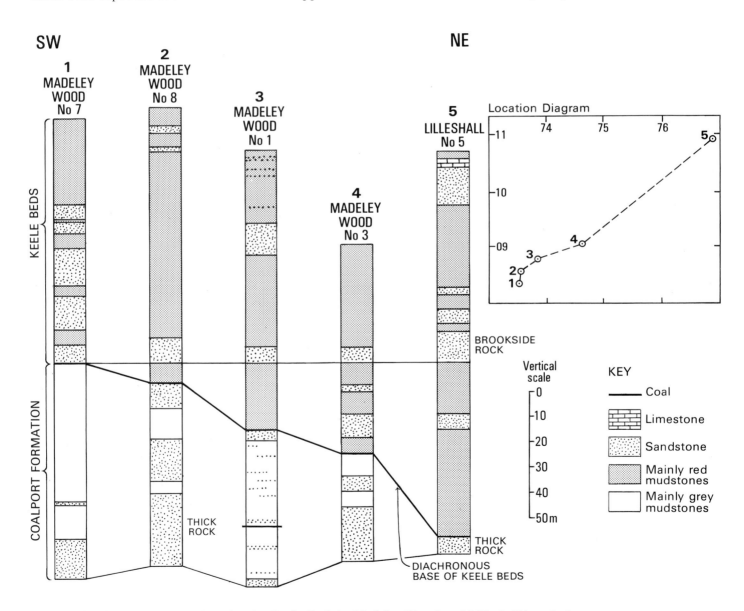

Figure 16 Comparative sections for the Keele Beds in Madeley Wood and Lilleshall boreholes, demonstrating the diachronous base of the Keele facies and the consistent interval between the Brookside Rock and the Thick Rock.

lower red-brown sandstone, believed to correlate with the Top Rock, is recorded in Madeley Wood Borehole No. 3. The stratigraphical interval between the Brookside Rock and reliable marker-beds low in the Coalport Formation (such as the Thick Rock) is quite constant, and little affected by the diachronous Coalport–Keele facies change. The Brookside Rock is thickest in Lilleshall No. 1 Borehole (18.3 m) and Madeley Wood No. 5 Borehole (19.8 m including a mudstone parting).

The Brookside Rock is succeeded by a substantial sequence of red mudstones with lenticular sandstones up to about 7 m thick; three sandstones can commonly be mapped. The greatest thickness of strata recorded above the Brookside Rock is 158.5 m in Lilleshall No. 6 Borehole but, generally, thicknesses are around half that figure.

The total thickness of strata assigned to the Keele Formation increases northwards and eastwards, from 85.3 m (Madeley Wood No. 3) to 259.1 m (Lilleshall No. 6). This wide variation is partly due to a thickening of the measures above the Brookside Rock, and partly to the inclusion of up to 97.5 m of diachronous red measures below it.

Keele Beds — north of the Boundary Fault

Strata mapped as Keele Beds in the Wellington area, north of the Boundary Fault, dominantly comprise massive purple sandstones, with subordinate mudstones and siltstones. In contrast to the Keele Beds south of the fault, seatearths, beds with plant and root remains, and ironstone beds occur. The Keele Beds rest conformably on the Coed-yr-Allt Beds (at Wrekin Buildings) or on the Ruabon Marl (at Slang Lane), or unconformably on the Uriconian; they are overlain unconformably by the Bridgnorth Sandstone. They are present in most of the area north of the Boundary Fault, but are concealed by the Bridgnorth Sandstone or covered by Drift, except for a small area east of Donnington where a few exposures are recorded. A maximum thickness of 93.75 m is known at Leegomery House Farm Borehole.

The stratigraphy of these Keele Beds can be deduced from a study of the boreholes drilled by BGS during the resurvey, which supplement those sunk by the Shropshire Coal Company in the 1860's around Hadley Park (Figure 17). The basal 7 m to 19 m are principally sandstones, with conglomerates containing pebbles of Uriconian rocks. These are followed by mudstones and siltstones, ranging from less than 1 m thick in Hadley Park No. 2 Borehole to about 14.5 m at Leegomery House Farm; a well-developed seatearth occurs at the top of the latter sequence. Succeeding sandstones range up to about 20 m in thickness and appear to cut down strongly into the mudstones below. They pass up into 4 m to 11 m of mudstones. A plant-rich bed nearly 1 m thick occurs in the Leegomery House Farm and Wrekin Buildings boreholes. *Alethopteris serli* and *A*. cf. *lesquereuxi* were collected from this bed in the Wrekin Buildings Borehole core (identified by Prof. W G Chaloner); their ranges are respectively Bolsovian to Westphalian D and Westphalian D to Stephanian A, dating this part of the sequence as Westphalian D. The overlying sandstones are 8 m to

12 m thick and are succeeded by 5 m to 13 m of dark mudstones. Finally, a further thick sandstone is found in Wrekin Buildings and Leegomery House Farm boreholes; in the latter, 33 m are preserved, including beds of mudstone and siltstone (Figure 17).

Fossils other than plant impressions are rare in these strata, but a blattoid insect *Archimylacris pringlei* from the Slang Lane Borehole in Wellington was compared by Bolton (1921) with those of the late Westphalian of northern France.

The stratigraphy of the Keele Beds here described is not consistent with that of the Keele Beds only 5 km away on the south side of the Boundary Fault; the proportion of sandstones is far greater, and the strata are, on the whole, much darker coloured. The relationships with the underlying strata are also different: in most of the boreholes north of the Boundary Fault the Keele Beds are unconformable on Uriconian rocks; and at Wrekin Buildings they rest conformably on Coed-yr-Allt Beds only 14 m above a coal believed to equate with the Main Sulphur Coal of the Coalport Formation. However, south of the Boundary Fault, the Keele Beds rest conformably on up to 185 m of Coalport Formation, with up to eleven more thin coals intervening between the Main Sulphur Coal and the base of the Keele. Thus, the Keele Beds north of the Boundary Fault may be a secondarily reddened equivalent of the Coalport and Hadley formations to the south because, in general, the stratigraphy of the lower strata can be matched with that of those formations (Figure 17). The well-developed seatearth in the Leegomery House Farm Borehole may equate with that beneath the coal in the Wrekin Buildings Borehole, which in turn is believed to be equivalent to the Main Sulphur Coal at the base of the Coalport Formation.

On this hypothesis, strata below that seatearth would then correlate with the Ruabon Marl, despite being classified as Keele Beds (Figure 17). The plant-rich horizon which occurs in both the Wrekin Buildings and the Leegomery House Farm boreholes can possibly be correlated with the ironstone in Hadley Park No. 3 Borehole, and with the Little Sulphur Coal of the Coalbrookdale Coalfield. The overlying two main sandstones at Wrekin Buildings and Leegomery House Farm would then respectively be the Sulphur Rock and the Thick Rock of the Coalport Formation.

If the Keele Beds in the north are partly equivalent to the Coalport and Hadley formations in the south, it is possible that their characteristic colour developed as a result of secondary reddening below the Bridgnorth Sandstone unconformity. The proportions of sandstone and mudstone in the Keele Beds in the north could be interpreted as matching those in the Coalport Formation in the south and it is not unreasonable to postulate reddening of around 95 m of measures below that major Permian unconformity.

Enville Beds

Strata conformably overlying the Keele Beds on the east of the Coalbrookdale Coalfield are assigned to the Enville Beds and dominantly comprise brownish sand-

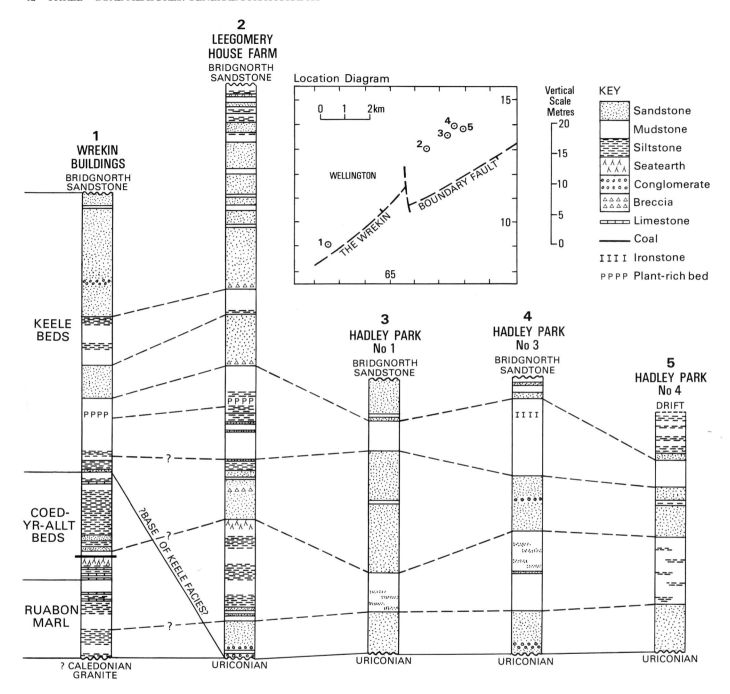

Figure 17 Comparative borehole sections through the Keele Beds in the Wellington area, north-west of the Boundary Fault.

stones and calcareous conglomerates with subordinate mudstones. The lower sandstones in the Enville sequence form a west-facing scarp which runs southwards from Lilleshall Hall to Halesfield; higher sandstones form scarp features farther to the east. South-west of Kemberton, the lowest two sandstones form discontinuous features around Suttonhill House and Sutton Common, but to the south-east Enville strata are cut out

where the unconformable Bridgnorth Sandstone oversteps on to the Keele Beds. Formal subdivision of the Enville Beds is impracticable in this area, because there are many very similar sandstones, which tend to split and wedge out laterally; furthermore, the strata are much faulted, making detailed correlation impossible. The greatest thickness preserved below the Bridgnorth unconformity is 112.8 m in Lilleshall No. 6 Borehole.

However, in the centre of the outcrop, west of Shifnal, six persistent major sandstones can be distinguished. The two principal topographical features here are formed by the second and fifth sandstones; these include the most common conglomeratic beds and those which persist farthest to the south. At least six sandstones are also present north of Lilyhurst, but there is no evidence for a direct correlation between the six sandstones in the two areas, particularly as the highest two near Shifnal disappear beneath the Bridgnorth Sandstone unconformity north of the A5 road (Watling Street). However, the upper leaf of the third sandstone in the north, which is conglomeratic and makes a strong feature at Lilleshall Hall, may correlate with the distinctive fifth sandstone of the Shifnal area. Conglomerates are not known in the Enville sequence south of Madeley Wood Borehole No. 5 [7500 0628]; they are not recorded at outcrop south of Nedge Hill [718 071], where they appear only in the second sandstone. South of Haughton Farm [733 081] they appear in the fifth sandstone, but become steadily more important northwards.

FOUR
Lower and Middle Coal Measures: details of stratigraphy

The Lower and Middle Coal Measures (or productive measures) are largely of Langsettian and Duckmantian age, with some Bolsovian at the top. They may include some Namurian strata at the base. The stratigraphy is described for two geographical areas, which are separated by the Limestone Fault (Figure 18). The **Dawley area** equates with the Donnington Syncline, to the north-west of the fault, and the **Madeley area** includes the Madeley and Coalport synclines, to the south-east. There are distinct differences between the sequences on each side of the Limestone Fault, and there is a belt along that fault [from 685 050 to 719 080] within which the productive measures were wholly removed from beneath the unconformity at the base of the Hadley Formation. Abbreviated data from many more shafts, borehole logs and opencast sections than are included in the text are given in Appendices 2, 3 and 4.

DAWLEY AREA

Lower Coal Measures

Comparative vertical sections for the Lower Coal Measures of the Dawley area are shown in Figure 19.

The lowest strata, below the Lancashire Ladies Coal, are largely arenaceous and thicken markedly in the north-east. In the south-west, from Steeraway [654 097] to Lincoln Hill [671 039], these hard arenaceous measures crop out widely. Sandstones are exposed at several points on the path to Lincoln Hill from Castle Green [6724 0447] and Dale Coppice [6706 0475], resting on Wenlock Shale and Wenlock Limestone. Whitehead et al. (1928, p.59) recorded these strata on the south-east side of the main limestone quarry at Lincoln Hill [6721 0407] (now infilled):

	Thickness m
Coal smut (?Lancashire Ladies)	—
Grey shale	1.22
Flaggy sandstone with interbedded sandy shale; tar in cracks at top	1.83
Sandstone, conglomeratic towards the base; base dips SE at 30°	2.44
Grey shale with 0.15 m ironstone bed	0.76
Wenlock Limestone	—

At the roadside section at Jiggers Bank [6650 0577] the measures rest on Lydebrook Sandstone, with virtually no angular discordance. The Lydebrook Sandstone is irregularly reddened and weathered up to 0.5 m below the unconformity, above which the basal Coal Measures comprise up to 2 m of shale and mudstone with pockets of rotten conglomerate near the base. An estimated 8 m of beds between these and the Lancashire Ladies Coal are flaggy, ferruginous pebbly sandstones, with sandy mudstone partings. The following section was recorded in 1945 on the eastern bank of Lydebrook Dingle [6580 0708]: white pebbly sandstones, 0.9m +; rusty shales with ironstone nodules, 0.6 m; rotten conglomerate, 0 m to 0.3 m; basalt (Dinantian). A rather thicker sequence can be seen in the disused and flooded basalt quarry at Horsehay [6688 0741]:

	Thickness m
Dark brown sandstone with many rounded quartzite pebbles	c.1.5
Grey sandy mudstone	c.0.4
Light grey to greyish brown shales with ironstone	c.1.5
Weathered top of basalt	—

Around Steeraway [6560 0960], the beds are obscured by debris from former workings in Carboniferous Limestone, but exposures in old overgrown levels 300 m south-south-west of Steeraway show coarse-grained, yellow to red-brown, gritty to pebbly sandstone. The pebbles include quartzite, dark rocks resembling weathered basalt or basic Precambrian rocks, pale greenish shale, similar to Shineton Shale, and pale grey sandstone pebbles. A compound section for 'Lawley and Steeraway' recorded by Williams (1846) notes 44 m of strata below the Lancashire Ladies Coal:

	Thickness m
Coal (Lancashire Ladies) and shale	—
Underclay	1.5
Arenaceous shale and Poor Robin ironstone	7.1
Farewell Rock	25.2
Argillaceous shales, sandstones, limestone, coal and underclay	8.0
Sandstone, hard and compact	2.2
Limestone, containing productids and corals	—

Some shaft sections also record the strata below the Lancashire Ladies Coal. At Deepfield Pits, Dawley (Figure 19), 36 m of strata overlie Wenlock Shale. The basal 8 m are sandstones and shales including a thin coal, probably equivalent to that at Lawley and Steeraway. These beds are overlain by 16 m of Farewell Rock and a further 12 m mostly of mudstone but including a 1.8 m sandstone and a 'Poor Robin' ironstone.

By contrast, farther north at Wombridge Water Engine Pit, only 13.7 m of 'Little Flint Rock' lies between the Little Flint Coal and a 'limestone' which is presumably of Dinantian age (Figure 19). At Granville Colliery, where the Little Flint Coal was not proved, the equivalent strata are 13.8 m thick; 1.1 m of fireclay, believed to underlie the Crawstone Coal horizon, are underlain by 6.2 m of sandstone, ganister and a basal conglomerate, resting on Dinantian limestone (Figure 19).

North of Granville, the Lower Coal Measures sandstones crop out in the heavily faulted area south of Lilleshall, but the long sandstone outcrop shown on earlier maps between Lilleshall Old Hall [728 149] and Muxton is more limited than previously thought; BGS Honnington Borehole A1 [7240 1448] on the top of the feature revealed grey mudstone. BGS Borehole Lilleshall A1 [7286 1495], adjacent to the Upper Cambrian 'Dolgelly Beds' of the Lilleshall inlier, records 14.0 m of grey mudstone. An exposure of sandstone recorded by Whitehead et al. (1928) in a ditch [7299 1494] may well be a continuation of the outcrop that extends northwards to the east of the Lilleshall inlier, but its proximity to the Comley Sandstone does not prove overstep (Whitehead et al., 1928) since the Cambrian and Carboniferous outcrops are separated by faults.

Figure 18
Localities of
shafts, adits,
boreholes and
opencast sites in
Lower and
Middle Coal
Measures
(except
Lilleshall 5
[7688 1095] and
6 [7770 1395]
boreholes,
which lie to the
east).

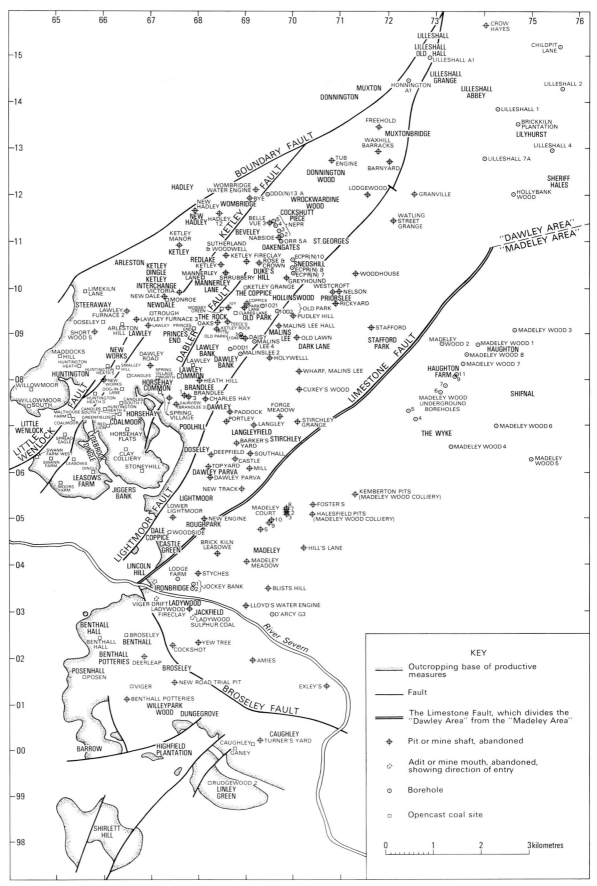

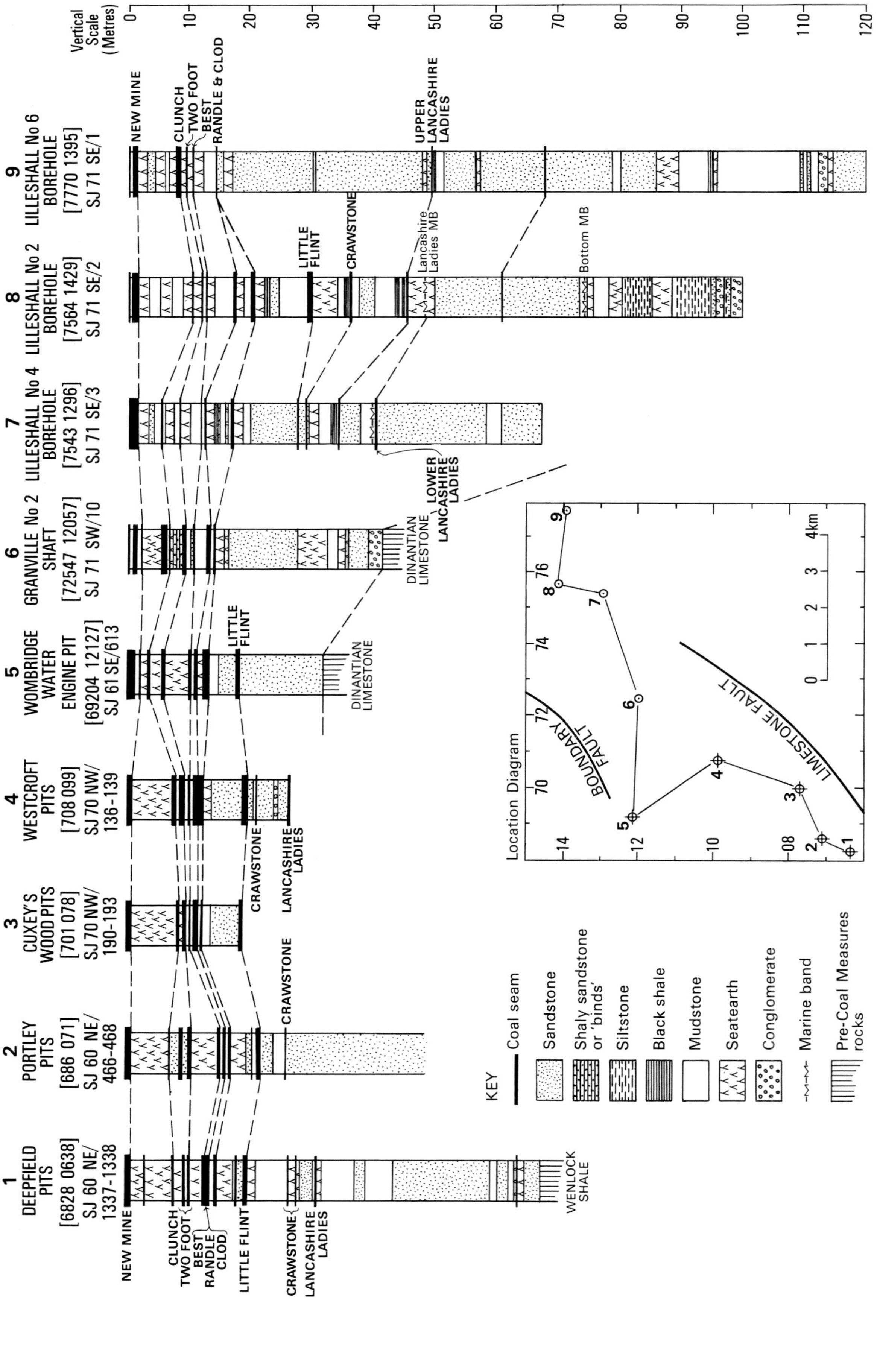

Figure 19   Comparative vertical sections for the Lower Coal Measures in the Dawley area, between the Limestone Fault and the Boundary Fault.

North-east of Granville, thicker sequences are recorded in four coal boreholes. Lilleshall No. 7A [7400 1273] and No. 4 [7543 1296] record 25 m and 27 m of sandstone respectively below the Lower Lancashire Ladies Coal, and in both cases the base of the Coal Measures was not reached (Figure 19). In No. 2 Borehole [7564 1429], the **Lancashire Ladies Marine Band** (level of the Lower Lancashire Ladies Coal) was underlain by 3.0 m of seatearth, then 22 m of sandstones and grits (Farewell Rock), including a thin coal. Below the Farewell Rock came the **Bottom Marine Band**, consisting of buff shale with *Lingula*; then 19.5 m of shales, seatearths and siltstones with ironstones, and 5.2 m of basal sandstones, ironstones and conglomerates (Figure 19). Thus the measures below the Lower Lancashire Ladies total 50 m, without the base being reached. More sandstone was recorded in No. 6 Borehole [7770 1395], which can be correlated with No. 2. The Farewell Rock was 29.3 m thick, including a 0.13 m coal, as in Borehole 2, and was underlain by 3.7 m of seatearth, 19.8 m of shales including a 0.15 m coal, and finally 11.0 m of shale with sandstone, conglomerate, and seatclay; the base of the productive measures was not reached. The Bottom Marine Band was not recorded in this borehole, although it was drilled to well below the appropriate stratigraphical level; possibly the marine band had been washed out beneath the thickened Farewell Rock.

The Lancashire Ladies Coal is rarely recorded in shafts or boreholes, but it is evidently present as a single seam throughout most of the coalfield, although it was never worked. Its thickness varies between 0.1 m and 0.5 m. It occurred at Jiggers Bank, Brandlee No. 3, New Track and Westcroft pits, but is unrecorded at Wombridge (Water Engine Pit), Granville Colliery and Crow Hayes shaft. North-east of Granville, two coals are recorded, the lower being 0.38 m thick in Lilleshall No. 4 Borehole (Figure 19) though absent in Nos. 2, 6 and 7A, while the upper is 0.08 m to 0.58 m thick and occurs in all four boreholes. The **Lancashire Ladies Marine Band** occurs above the lower of these coals; *Orbiculoidea* and *Lingula* were found in grey silty mudstone in Lilleshall No. 7A, and *Lingula* in black shale in No. 2. Only fish remains were found at this level in No. 6.

The Crawstone Flint, a pale grey to brown, fine-grained, massive ganister, with rootlets and tree trunks, overlies the single Lancashire Ladies Coal in the area bounded by Brandlee, Wombridge, Priorslee and the Limestone Fault. Thicknesses recorded include 4.5 m at Nelson Pit, 4.7 m at Westcroft Pit and 2.74 m at Brandlee No. 3 Pit, in the last two of which the sandstone is dark and pebbly in its lower part. The Lancashire Ladies Coal is overlain by 7.8 m of 'arenaceous shale and poor ironstone,' at Lawley and Steeraway (Williams, 1846). On the south-east of the main Lincoln Hill limestone quarry [6721 0407] (now overgrown) Whitehead et al. (1928) recorded the following: dark fireclay with roots (?Crawstone Coal seatearth), 0.91 m; grey shales and ferruginous yellow sandstones, 2.44 m; very hard ironstone, 0.15 m; grey shales with ferruginous sandstone at base, 1.07 m; coal smut, ?Lancashire Ladies. Boreholes in the north-east show a rather variable interval between the Crawstone and Lancashire Ladies coals, mostly sandstone and up to 19 m thick.

The Crawstone Coal is locally present within the area bounded by Brandlee, Princes End, Sheriff Hales and the Limestone Fault. It is up to 0.23 m thick, and two leaves are present at Deepfield Pit (Figure 19). It is overlain by the **Crawstone ironstone** which is generally a single layer of large brown irregular ovate nodules, locally coalescing into a seam, in a matrix of fine white sandstone or, less commonly, of black shale with mussels. Its thickness ranges up to a recorded maximum of 2.2 m of shale and ironstone at Portley Pit (Figure 19). It is recorded in an area bounded by Huntington, Lawley, Ketley, Hadley, Lille-

shall, Sheriff Hales and the Limestone Fault, but it has been worked only at Ketley. Throughout that area it is locally absent, because of downcutting by the Little Flint Rock. Although the ironstone is more commonly present than the Crawstone Coal, there are instances where the ironstone is absent and the Little Flint Rock rests on the coal.

The Little Flint Rock normally separates the Crawstone ironstone and the Little Flint Coal. Lithologically, it resembles the Crawstone Flint, but is less pebbly. Purton (1865, p.514) records petroleum in the rock in a quarry in Lightmoor Wood. Thicknesses recorded vary from 0.91 m at Westcroft and Brandlee No. 3 pits to 4.6 m at Cuxey's Wood. In the north-west, from Little Wenlock to Wombridge, up to 1.1 m of fireclay locally overlie the rock; in some localities between Lawley, Lilleshall and Sheriff Hales, the sandstone is absent, the Crawstone ironstone either directly underlying the Little Flint Coal (as at Crow Hayes Shaft) or separated from it by fireclay (as at Lilleshall No. 2 Borehole and Nelson Pit). In the west of the coalfield, between Leasows Farm (near Little Wenlock) and Newdale, a single 4 m to 7 m sandstone, presumably the Little Flint Rock, is all that separates the Little Flint Coal and the Lancashire Ladies Coal. In places, both the Lancashire Ladies Coal and the Crawstone Coal are absent, and all the measures below the Little Flint Coal are described as sandstone and named 'Little Flint Rock'. The thickness of these strata is greater than is the undoubted Little Flint Rock, so possibly the Little Flint, the Crawstone Flint and the Farewell Rock have run together, for example at Wombridge Water Engine Pit (13.7 m) and Lightmoor Whimsey Pit (14.6 m).

The Little Flint Coal is the lowest worked coal; despite its depth and thinness, it has been widely mined because it proved an excellent blast-furnace coal (Scott, 1861, p.458). It is generally a single coal and has a sandstone roof and a firm sandstone or sandy fireclay floor. However, it was rarely worked by opencast methods because of its depth and the presence of the Little Flint Coal Rock in its roof. It is typically 0.3 m to 0.8 m thick, but locally it varies considerably; thus in Dawley it varies between 0.18 m at Castle Pit and 1.12 m (including a thin parting) at Top Yard Pit. From Dawley Parva to Lawley Common (Dawley Road Pits) it is commonly 0.9 m to 1.3 m thick. It is absent in the extreme west of the coalfield, between Willowmoor South Opencast [6445 0745] and the Ketley Interchange [6710 1015], and also at Granville Colliery and Lilleshall No. 6 Borehole (Figure 19) in the extreme northeast. Tar is recorded in the coal at the Woodside Opencast [674 046].

The Little Flint Coal Rock overlies the Little Flint Coal; at Huntington Heath Opencast [655 083] 0.10 m of black shale separates the two. The Little Flint Coal Rock is usually white or grey, fine-grained and massive, locally cross-bedded, and has coaly films and rootlets in its upper part. Over most of the exposed coalfield, it varies between 1.5 m and 5.5 m thick, but in the west it is thinner in an area bounded by Lightmoor, Portley Pit and the Coalmoor [654 072] and Moors Farm [651 058] opencast sites; it is locally absent in an area bounded by Castle Pit and the Woodside [674 046], Leasows A [654 063] and Huntington Heath E [660 073] opencast sites. In Greenfields Opencast [662 072], 'large lenses of sandstone' recorded in clays between the Little Flint and Clod coals may represent the Little Flint Coal Rock. At Limekiln Lane Opencast [656 099], both the Little Flint and Clod coals die out; the measures in this interval are red conglomerates, sandstones and bastard fireclays. In the north-east of the coalfield, the Little Flint Coal Rock thickens to 7.3 m near Donnington, and up to 12.0 m of ganister and sandstone are recorded at Granville Colliery and in Lilleshall Nos. 4 and 6 boreholes (Figure 19). However, Lilleshall Nos. 2 (Figure 19) and 7A and Brickkiln Plantation boreholes record 5.5 m to 8.2 m of seatearths, smooth and silty mudstones and siltstones, with sandy wisps, thin sandstones and ironstone nodules between the Little Flint and Clod coals.

A 0.06 m coal with clayey streaks rests on the Little Flint Coal Rock at the Moors Farm Opencast [651 058]. A thicker (0.2 m) seam rests upon the rock at Heath Hill Pit, and just below its top at Portley and Deepfield pits nearby (Figure 19). At Stafford and Watling Street Grange pits a 0.25 m seam is recorded, separated from the rock by 1.17 m of brown clunch at Watling Street Grange.

The Clod Coal rests on the Little Flint Coal Rock between New Works and Newdale, but elsewhere pale bluish grey mudstone and fireclay separate the Clod Coal from the Little Flint Coal Rock or the thin coal which overlies it. This mudstone and fireclay are normally 1.0 m to 3.0 m thick and, in places, include ironstone nodules in their lower part; these ironstones are recorded as New Mine Stone and Black Flatt at Watling Street Grange and Greyhound pits respectively, so possibly they have been worked.

Prestwich (1840, p.436) noted that the Clod Coal was an excellent smelting coal and it was therefore one of the most widely worked seams in spite of its relative thinness. On the north-west side of the Lightmoor Fault it is generally 0.7 m to 1.2 m thick; it is more uniformly thick in the area between Dawley and Wombridge, where it reaches 1.4 m at Shrubbery Colliery. In the west of the coalfield it becomes more variable; thus at Willowmoor Opencast [645 078] it varies between 0.2 m and 0.6 m but at the nearby Huntington Heath D site [6585 0770] it reaches 1.37 m. The greatest recorded thickness, 1.55 m including six dirt partings, is at Maddocks Hill (Figure 20). Elsewhere, a parting 0.3 m to 0.4 m thick is recorded only to the north-east of Arleston Hill [665 097]. West of there, the seam thins to 0.36 m at Steeraway and 0.4 m in boreholes at Limekiln Lane [656 099]. On the south-east side of the Lightmoor Fault the seam thins northwards from 0.66 m at Roughpark to 0.36 m at Dawley Parva and Stirchley Grange Pit, then thickens steadily to 0.9 m at Stafford and Watling Street Grange pits. It has been extensively mined as far north-east as Granville Colliery, where it thinned to 0.30 m; similar thicknesses are recorded in boreholes farther to the north-east (Figure 19).

The measures between the Clod Coal and Randle Coal usually comprise up to a metre of fireclay (Figure 20, Section B). Soft brown fireclay 0.69 m thick was worked at this level at Mossey Green Opencast [685 095]. Records of black shale are scattered throughout the coalfield from Short Wood and Spring Village pits to Granville Colliery. The beds are thickest in the west, generally more than 2 m between New Hadley and Maddocks Hill. At Willowmoor Opencast [645 078] the parting varies from only 0.3 m to more than 9 m, being thickest at a point where the Clod Coal is thinnest (0.2 m). In the Maddocks Hill Opencast [651 085], the parting was sandy and varied from 0.9 m to 5.0 m in a lenticular manner within a horizontal distance of 18 m.

Thick sequences are rare in the eastern part of the coalfield, although 3.66 m are recorded at Lilleshall No. 4 Borehole (Figure 19). Up to 4 m of pale grey, fine- to medium-grained, massive sandstone are recorded between Lawley Bank, the Ketley Interchange [6710 1015] and south of Short Wood.

The Clod and Randle coals join to become a single seam along a north-east-trending line from Horsehay Flats [665 069] and Clay Colliery [665 065] opencast sites to Lilleshall Nos. 6 and 7A boreholes, passing through Heath Hill Pit, Ketley Grange Opencast [690 100] and Malins Lee, Priorslee and Stafford pits. The thickest record for this single seam is 2.08 m at Greyhound Pit. The Randle and Best coals join to form a single seam locally within an area bounded by Swann Farm Opencast [649 063], Limekiln Lane [656 099] and Tub Engine

Pit [7081 1274]. The combined seam is generally 0.9 m to 1.2 m thick, with maximum values of 1.52 m at Wombridge Water Engine Pit (Figure 19), 1.47 m at Willowmoor South Opencast [6445 0745] and 1.45 m at Dingle Opencast [658 060]. In the north-west it thins considerably to 0.15 m at New Hadley Pits and 0 m to 0.4 m at Limekiln Lane. There are some places where the Best, Randle and Clod combine to form a single thick seam, as at Heath Hill Pits (2.13 m thick) and Ketley Grange Opencast [690 100] (2.30 m). At Short Wood, the Randle, Best and Two Foot coals form a singleseam up to 2.44 m thick.

Where it is a separate seam the **Randle Coal** is generally 0.5 m to 0.9 m thick, thinning in the north-west and north-east to 0.3 m near Arleston Hill and at Brickkiln Plantation Borehole. The thickest records known are 1.67 m at Shrubbery Colliery and 1.22 m at Brandlee No. 3 Pit. Three black dirt partings are recorded in this seam at Maddocks Hill Opencast [651 085]; elsewhere there is no parting. The Randle has been extensively worked near Donnington as a smith's coal, and was taken with the Clod in the Dark Lane, Malins Lee and Langley Field estates.

The parting between the Randle and Best coals, south-west of Donnington, rarely exceeds 0.5 m and is usually black shale, sometimes canneloid, as at Woodside Opencast [674 046]; in places it is a pale grey fireclay. However, north and east of Priorslee and Snedshill, the parting thickens; near Donnington the Randle and Best are separated by 2.4 m to 3.1 m of 'Linseed Earth' (dark grey fireclay) and the parting reaches a maximum of 6.7 m in Lilleshall No. 7A Borehole; a fish bed overlies the lower coal in this borehole.

The Best Coal is usually 0.3 m to 0.7 m thick, and has not been widely worked except where it coalesces with the Randle. In boreholes north-east of Granville Colliery it thins even further, to 0.1 m in Brickkiln Plantation and Lilleshall Nos. 4 and 6 boreholes (Figure 19) and only 0.02 m in No. 7A.

The measures between the Best Coal and Two Foot Coal are most commonly dark grey sandy fireclay, often siliceous and indurated and locally resting on black shale containing megaspores. The measures are typically up to 2 m thick, but are thinner in places, particularly in the area between Priorslee, Stirchley and Old Park; they are completely absent at Pudley Hill, Rickyard Pits and in parts of Short Wood. Locally they become much thicker, for example 3.1 m at Barnyard Pits (Donnington), 4.5 m at Portley Pits (Dawley), 3.7 m at Wombridge Water Engine Pit (Figure 19) and up to 6.0 m north of Coalmoor. In the roof of the Best Coal at Horsehay Flats Opencast, a rich *Communis* zone fauna has been collected: *Lepidophlois laricinus*, *Carbonicola* cf. *browni* (figured by Trueman & Weir, 1946, pl.II, fig. 11), *C.* cf. *bipennis* (Trueman & Weir, 1947, pl. VI, fig. 17), *C. martini*, *C. pseudorobusta* and *C.* aff. *rhomboidalis*. In a trial pit [6614 0838] in Huntington Heath No. 5 Opencast, 4.0 m of fireclay were recorded overlying 0.03 m of black and brown streaky shaly clay. These clays are referred to as 'Linseed Earth' at New Hadley, Wombridge and Crow Hayes, and between Priorslee, Dawley and Lightmoor; they have been partly worked as 'Two Foot Clay' north and north-west of Horsehay. Ironstone nodules are noted between Coalmoor and Princes End; they are abundant in 0.71 m of fireclay at Greenfields Opencast [662 072] and towards the base of 0.94 m of fireclay at Princes End Opencast [679 091].

The Best Coal Rock is a lenticular development of flaggy fine-grained sandstones and siltstones, locally with coarse brown massive sandstone or hard ganister, the facies coming and going rapidly in the area between Dawley (Castle Pit), Smalleyhill [663 083], Arleston Hill [664 097] and Ketley Grange [690 100]. It also occurs at Granville and Watling Street Grange pits and in Brickkiln Plantation. In Lilleshall No. 7A Borehole

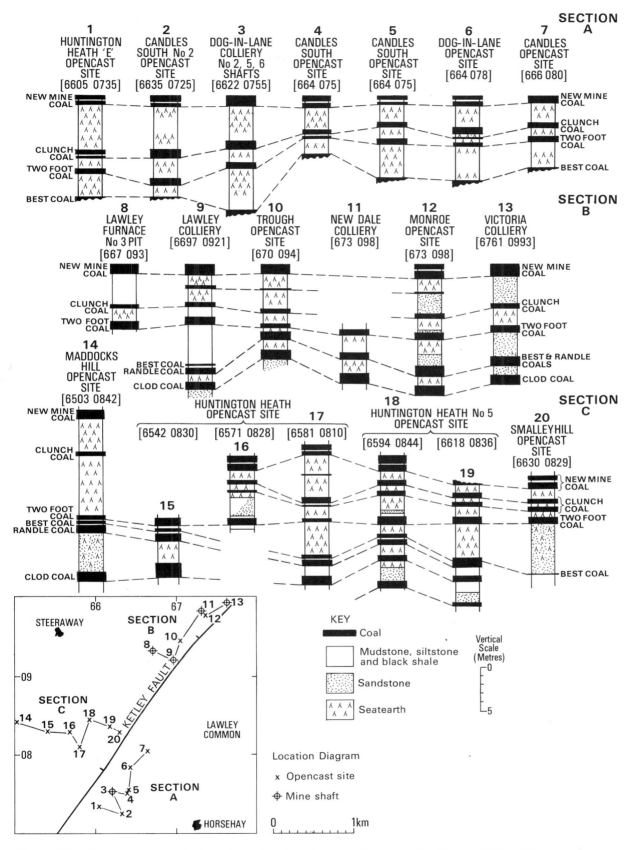

Figure 20 Comparative vertical sections showing the strata between the Best and New Mine coals in opencast sites and shafts west of Dawley.

0.56 m of pale fine-grained sandstone lies 0.7 m above the Best Coal; elsewhere, the Best Coal Rock forms either the lower part of the parting (underlying fireclay) or the whole parting, where it is thicker, reaching 3.25 m at Watling Street Grange, 4.0 m at Barker's Yard and 5.5 m at Sutherland Colliery. At Smalleyhill Opencast [663 083], it comprises 6.0 m of pale grey, fine-grained and argillaceous sandstone, which is more massive in the lower part and a ganister above. It is cross-bedded and contains irregular inconsistent sandy mudstone partings, carbonaceous films, and *Calamites* fragments a metre long, preserved as coaly films. In faces adjacent to the fault which passes to the north-west of the Moors Farm Opencast [651 058], the Best Coal was overlain by 1.2 m of yellow sandy shales, then by 1.8 m to 3.0 m of massive sandstones, which wedged out northwards and passed laterally into the underlying sandy shales; above were about 1.8 m of fireclays, pale grey in the upper part but ferruginous and yellow in the lower part, with some small ironstone nodules. In the Dog-in-Lane Opencast [664 078], the workable fireclays below the Two Foot Coal were 1.5 m thick, underlain by 3 m to 4 m of very sandy fireclays which passed locally into sandy ferruginous shales (Figure 20). The name 'Coffin Lid', which reflects the tendency of rectangular joint-sheets of sandstone to fall from the mine roofs, is applied to the rock immediately overlying the Best Coal at The Rock and Mannerley Lane, where it is a thin, hard ganister with rootlets. At Mannerley Lane Opencast [681 102], the Best Coal is overlain by up to 0.3 m of 'Coffin Lid', 0.1 m of grey shale, 2.44 m of sandstone and 0.91 m of pale grey fireclay. The thick central sandstone often cuts out the 'Coffin Lid'.

The Two Foot Coal is one of the most constant in the succession over the greater part of the area north-west of the Limestone Fault, and as far north-east as Granville Colliery. It is a good quality coking coal, normally 0.5 m to 0.9 m thick, and was widely worked except around Donnington. However, there are exceptions in the western, southern and north-eastern extremities of the area. In Willowmoor Opencast [645 078], the Two Foot Coal is 1.1 m thick and contains three partings totalling 0.27 m, but in Willowmoor South [6445 0745] it is represented by about a metre of fireclay with thin coaly bands. At Huntington Heath Opencast [655 083] it is 0.94 m including two partings and at Ketley Interchange [6710 1015] it varies between 0.3 m of dirty coal and 0.75 m of coal with many partings. At the northern end of Short Wood [6599 0938], the Two Foot is split into two leaves, 0.30 m of Upper Two Foot and 0.46 m of Lower Two Foot Coal. To the south, along the Two Foot Coal outcrop, adits [6588 0921, 6584 0913] in the southern part of Short Wood show 2.44 m and 2.28 m of coal respectively, overlain by sandstones; thus the Two Foot Coal there forms a continuous seam with the Randle and the Best. The drift entrance [6585 0903] for Short Wood No. 5 Mine showed (in 1923) 1.14 m of Two Foot Coal, overlying 0.25 m of shale on the Best Coal.

From Portley Pit, Dawley, through Dawley Parva to Castle Green, the Two Foot Coal is split into an upper leaf 0.18 m to 0.46 m thick and a lower leaf 0.61 m to 0.87 m thick, separated by up to 0.46 m of black shale, sandstone or clay. At the New Engine Pit in Roughpark, three widely separated leaves of coal were recorded: coal, 0.10 m; 'Lower Clunch' 3.05 m; coal, 0.46 m; rock, 7.32 m; coal, 0.10 m. The thickest record of the Two Foot Coal is 1.22 m at Stafford Pits near Priorslee, but to the north-east the seam becomes thin (Figure 19). In Lilleshall Nos. 1, 2 and 6 boreholes it is 0.3 m to 0.5 m thick; in No. 4 it is only 0.15 m; and in No. 7A and at a trial pit between Muxton and Lilleshall Grange it was absent.

Fireclays between the Two Foot Coal and Clunch Coal have been widely worked in the exposed coalfield as the Clunch or Lower Clunch Clay. They are typically 1.0 m to 3.0 m thick, locally more in the western part of the coalfield; 5.0 m were recorded at Dawley Parva and at Lightmoor, and 5.1 m (all workable) at Red Lion Opencast [661 070]. This clay was more valuable than the overlying Clunch Coal and was often mined in preference, as at Stoneyhill Opencast [668 060], and Clay Colliery Opencast [665 065], where the Clunch Coal had been left as roof support and the succession is: Clunch Coal; fireclay, 1.5 m; dark grey mudstones with coaly films, 1.0 m; fireclay, 0.3 m; black shaly mudstones, 0.4 m; Two Foot Coal. Coaly beds within the workable fireclay are elsewhere known only at Greenfields Opencast [662 072], where a 0.03 m coal occurs 1.3 m above the base of 2.3 m of Clunch Clay. Black shale at the base of the Clunch Clay is, however, much more common, at least over the area encompassed by Woodside Opencast [674 046], Huntington Heath Opencast [655 083] and Belle Vue Colliery No. 3 Shaft [6951 1141]; it reaches a maximum of 1.37 m at Ivy No. 2 Pit [6865 0956] near the middle of this area. Dark fireclay or bass is also locally recorded at the top of the Clunch Clay in the north of the coalfield, e.g. 0.1 m thick at Lodgewood Pit. A fish band is recorded in Lilleshall No. 7A Borehole just above a seatearth believed to represent the Two Foot Coal. *Carbonicola oslancis* was collected from the roof of the Two Foot Coal in a temporary exposure 340 m east-south-east of Coalmoor Farm.

Often, only the upper part of the measures between the Two Foot and Clunch coals was workable, the fireclay passing downwards or laterally into flaggy or massive sandstones. For example, at Brandlee Colliery No. 1 Pit [6772 0765], the whole of the 2.76 m of strata between the coals was workable fireclay (called here the Best Fireclay), but at nearby Fairview Colliery (No. 2 Brandlee) [6753 0746], 1.22 m of 'Best Fireclay' overlies 1.83 m of 'hard bind'. The lenticular sandstones are not known east of Dawley and are better developed in the far west, replacing the fireclays completely around Limekiln Lane [656 099], where they are 2.5 m to 3.0 m thick; at Nabbside Pit 5.49 m of 'hard bind' separate the Two Foot and Clunch coals. At Doseley Opencast [6600 0925], layers of 'pebbly rock' are recorded in the basal 1.5 m of a 3.2 m sequence of hard grey clays. At Huntington, Swann Farm and Spread Eagles opencast sites, a thin (0.15 m to 0.28 m) hard 'Coffin Lid' sandstone is recorded below the Clunch Clay, similar to that which locally overlies the Best Coal; this rests directly on the Two Foot Coal in the Swann Farm and Spread Eagles sites, but is separated from the Two Foot by 0.15 m of black clay with coaly streaks at Huntington. In all three cases, it is overlain by pale fireclay with ironstone nodules.

The Clunch Coal is a single seam throughout the area between the Limestone Fault and a line through Wombridge, The Rock, Lawley Common and Swann Farm. It is referred to as the Sill Coal at some places, such as Langleyfield, Holywell Pit, Castle Green and New Works. It varies widely in thickness and has been worked extensively only where it is relatively thick. Elsewhere in the exposed coalfield, fireclays above and below it were often mined in preference. It is about 0.9 m thick at Coalmoor, Brandlee, Lawley Bank and near Donnington, thickening to 1.22 m at Snedshill and Ketley Fireclay Mine, where it has been extensively worked. Conversely, it thins to around 0.5 m at Old Park and 0 m around Redlake. Southeast of the Lightmoor Fault it is only 0.15 m thick at New Engine Pit, Roughpark, and 0.3 m to 0.5 m from Woodside to Langleyfield, thickening north-eastward to 1.22 m at Nelson Pit, Priorslee. It has not been worked between Langleyfield and Priorslee, but a small area has been taken east of Granville and Watling Street Grange pits. North-east of Priorslee its thickness varies between 1.02 m at Crow Hayes and 0.15 m at Lilleshall No. 4 Borehole (Figure 19). Thin bass partings are recorded at Holywell, Granville and Crow Hayes pits.

In the north-western part of the coalfield, the Clunch Coal splits into two seams, the Lower and Upper Clunch Coals; each is generally around 0.5 m but varies between 0 m and 0.9 m. They have rarely been worked underground, but they have been taken along with fireclays in opencast sites. The parting between them generally comprises up to a metre of black shale or fireclay, but thicker partings occur in the area between the Ketley Interchange [6710 1015], the Trough Opencast [670 094] and the Limekiln Lane site [656 099]. At the Ketley Interchange and Monroe Opencast Site [673 098], the parting comprises 2.3 m to 3.0 m of sandstone and siltstone (Figure 20). However, at Trough [670 094] and Doseley [660 092] opencast sites and at Lawley Colliery, 1.8 m to 2.4 m of fireclays lie between 0.41 m to 0.86 m of Lower Clunch Coal and a very thin Upper Clunch Coal. Finally, at Limekiln Lane, the Lower Clunch Coal has died out and the Upper Clunch Coal is underlain by 3.0 m to 6.0 m of grey shale and sandstone, locally conglomeratic.

The measures between the Clunch Coal and New Mine Coal are largely pale grey fireclays, weathering yellow, with black layers. They are known as the Upper Clunch or New Mine Clays, but as Nine Feet Clays around Brandlee and the Dog-in-Lane [664 078] and Stoneyhill [668 060] opencast sites, because of their thickness. In general, they are thicker than the fireclays below the Clunch Coal, with a higher proportion of valuable pale fireclays. The thickness is very variable, most commonly 1 m to 6 m, but thickening to 10.2 m at Stafford Pit in the east and 13.5 m at Castle Green in the south. Megaspores were noted 0.6 m above the Clunch Coal at Smalleyhill Opencast. The basal part of the sequence is commonly black and shaly; for example, 0.76 m of bass underlies 5.5 m of fireclay at Park Lane Pits. In the south-west, from Coalmoor to Moors Farm Opencast [651 058], a central layer of sandy ironstone nodules occurs; the following section was recorded in a trench about 150m north-west of the Moors:

	Thickness m
New Mine Coal	—
Yellow-grey, greasy fireclay	0.61
Black and yellow clays	0.56
Yellow-grey hard clay with grey sphaerosiderite nodules	1.45
Black shale	0.05
Grey clay	0.05
Black shaly clay	0.51
Dark grey and yellow-grey clay	0.44
Hard black clay	0.04

Thin coals are recorded within the Upper Clunch Clay at scattered localities. In the Huntington area, a 0.23 m coal occurs in the centre of 4.0 m to 6.4 m of clays, and at Barker's Yard, Castle Mill and Deepfield pits, Dawley, a 0.14 m to 0.51 m coal separates 2.5 m to 4.9 m lower and 1.8 m to 2.4 m upper units of clay. At Stafford Pits, a 0.1 m coal lies between a 9.47 m lower and a 0.66 m upper clay, and at Watling Street Grange a thin coal similarly occurs in the upper part of the sequence.

Lenticular sandstones are less common in the Upper Clunch Clay than in the lower fireclays, and are restricted to the area between Willowmoor, Lawley, Ketley Dingle and Limekiln Lane. The thickest is 5.5 m at Lawley Furnace No. 2 Pit, filling the gap between the Clunch and New Mine coals; pebbly sandstones are recorded in this interval at Victoria Colliery (Figure 20) and at the Ketley Interchange [6710 1015].

The New Mine Coal is dirty and pyritic, usually parted, but widely worked because its slow-burning properties were ideal for brickmaking (Scott, 1861, p.458). Often, all or part of the seam was worked with the overlying Pennystone ironstone or the underlying New Mine Clay. It is thinnest (typically 0.5 m to 0.9 m) in the south-west, in an area bounded by Dawley, Coalmoor, Jiggers Bank, Roughpark, Swann Farm, Maddocks Hill and Limekiln Lane. An unparted seam, 0.45 m to 0.75 m thick, was recorded in the Stoney Hill Opencast [668 060], and 0.75 m of pyritic coal in the Swann Farm Opencast [6493 0667]. However, within this area, the seam is often thicker and parted; the Coalmoor–Malthouse opencast complex [654 072] worked 1.2 m to 1.5 m of coal with an 0.15 m parting in its upper part. Boreholes for the opencast site at Limekiln Lane [656 099] show the seam varying rapidly in thickness from 0.5 m to 1.5 m; it is poor and shaly, and commonly includes a parting in its lower part.

North-eastwards from Doseley, Dawley and New Works, the seam is generally 1.2 m to 1.6 m thick and typically includes a 0.04 m to 0.20 m parting of black bass roughly in the centre. The parting is locally 0.6 m thick, and reaches 1.5 m (between two 0.6 m leaves of coal) at Lawley Furnace No. 2 Pit, Arleston Hill. Multiple partings are rare; two are recorded in 1.93 m of coal at Rickyard Pits. A relatively thick unparted seam is more common; it is 1.25 m thick in Old Park Borehole 1002 [6965 0950]. The seam has been worked in patches around Priorslee and widely around Stafford Park and in the Dark Lane, Malins Lee, Langleyfield, Dawley and Old Park estates; also between Deepfield Pits and Lightmoor in the Coalbrookdale Company's estate. At The Rock, it has been extensively mined because dips as low as 1° allowed shallow workings below the Big Flint Rock outcrop.

The New Mine Coal is thickest in the north-west near the Boundary Fault, reaching 2.13 m at New Hadley, Lodgewood (Donnington) and near Muxton. At Wombridge, Prestwich (1840, p.479) recorded 0.30 m of 'foot coal' 0.30 m below the main 1.83 m seam (Figure 19). It has also been widely worked in Ketley, New Hadley, Wombridge and Oakengates; however, in Snedshill and Donnington it was not worked (despite its thickness) because of its poor quality. The bottom 1.22 m of a single seam was worked from Granville Colliery. In Lilleshall No. 7A Borehole, 1.04 m of New Mine Coal, with no parting, was recorded but most of the boreholes north-east of Granville Colliery recorded upper (0.30 m to 0.60 m) and lower (0.58 m to 0.92 m) leaves, separated by up to 0.23 m of seatearth or ganister.

Middle Coal Measures

The Middle Coal Measures commence with the ***Pennystone Marine Band and ironstone***, which rest on the New Mine Coal; comparative sections of the sequence are shown in Figure 21. The Pennystone is the most renowned ironstone in the coalfield and is named from its layers of small, flat, round, septarian ironstone nodules. The nodules are cracked irregularly, the fractures being filled with calcite or baryte. The matrix comprises pale to dark grey, sometimes bluish mudstone, which may be pyritic at lower levels, but is more commonly smooth than silty. The marine band is the thickest in the coalfield; generally the marine fauna is restricted to the lowest metre or two of the mudstone, but in places extends considerably higher.

In the north-west of the coalfield, bounded by Lightmoor, Priorslee, Wombridge, Ketley and Little Wenlock, the Pennystone, 4.5 m to 8.0 m thick, may be subdivided into an Upper Pennystone with thin ironstone layers, and a Lower Pennystone with flat rounded ironstone 'pennies'; the former has been extensively worked, but the latter is only locally exploited. In the Candles South Opencast [664 075], the Pennystone is 4.57 m thick and comprises grey to pale blue-grey, blocky mudstones with ironstone nodules, and contains abundant *Lingula*

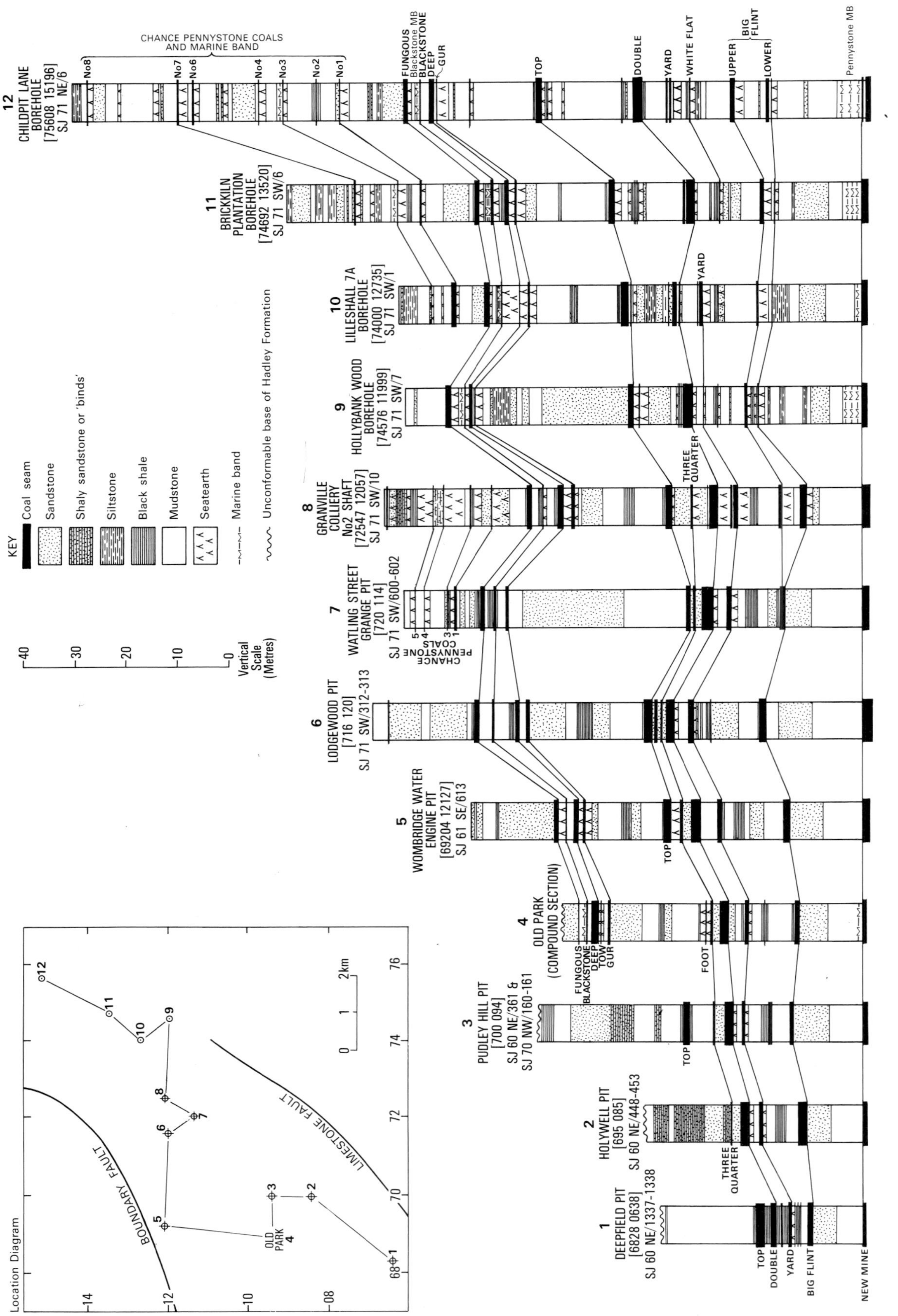

Figure 21   Comparative vertical sections of the Middle Coal Measures in the Dawley area, between the Limestone and Boundary faults.

in the lowest 2 m. The Swann Farm Opencast [6495 0665] yielded *L. mytilloides* throughout a 6 m section overlying the New Mine Coal; layers of ironstone nodules 1 m to 3 m above the coal yielded a spectacular fauna, consisting of *Levipustula piscariae, Lingula mytilloides, Orbiculoidea* cf. *nitida, Productus carbonarius, Spirifer pennystonensis, Edmondia* cf. *transversa, Anthraconeilo* cf. *laevirostris,* cf. *Tomaculum* sp. (faecal pellets) and infilled burrows or coprolite trails 6 mm wide. *Pseudocatastroboceras prestwicki* recorded from a loose block was clearly from this horizon. At Dog-in-Lane Opencast, *L. mytilloides* was recorded 0 m to 1.27 m above the New Mine, with megaspores, *Serpuloides* sp., *Paraconularia* sp., *Hindeodella* sp., and *Orbiculoidea* in the lowest 0.6 m. A more diverse fauna typical of a nearshore environment was found in a 0.05 m to 0.08 m ironstone bed 1.5 m above the coal; it included *Bucaniopsis navicula, L. mytilloides, Levipustula piscariae, O. nitida, P. carbonarius, S. pennystonensis,* cf. *Nuculopsis aequalis.* Dr Calver comments that *Anthracoceras vanderbeckei,* originally recorded here, has not been confirmed. A subsidence hole near New Works Colliery yielded *L. mytilloides* (5.5 mm), *Edmondia* sp. and *Geisina*? from 0 m to 8 m above the New Mine Coal, and a coal trial borehole on Huntington Heath yielded *L. mytilloides* from less than 0.3 m to 3.1 m above the coal.

At Smalleyhill Opencast [663 083] the Pennystone comprised 6.0 m of medium grey mudstone with banded ironstones above and nodular ironstones below; *L. mytilloides,* up to 3 mm across, was abundant in the basal metre. At Ketley Colliery the term Top Pennystone was used to distinguish the extensively worked 1.8 m-thick upper part of the Pennystone, from the 6.4 m-thick lower part. In the Old Park area the Pennystone thins north-eastwards, from 7.47 m at Oaks Colliery [684 092] to 4.57 m at Coppice Pits. In Old Park Borehole 1002 [6965 0950], *Lingula* occurred in the lowest 0.45 m above the New Mine Coal, in grey pyritic mudstone. Around Old Park the upper measures have been widely worked, and the lower measures were also taken over the northern half of the Old Park Company estate around The Coppice.

South-east of the Lightmoor Fault and south of Priorslee, the Pennystone varies between 7.9 m at Old Lawn Pit and 3.7 m at Mill Pit, Dawley. The Upper Pennystone has been worked throughout the Malins Lee, Dark Lane, Langleyfield, Dawley and Lightmoor colliery estates, but the lower beds only in small patches between Forge Meadow, Paddock, Dawley Parva and Lightmoor pits. At the Woodside Opencast [674 046] 4.57 m of grey shales with ironstones contain *Lingula* near the base, and are overlain by 0.6 m of yellow clay.

To the north-east of a line from Priorslee to Redlake the Pennystone tends to be thicker, generally 5.0 m to 10.0 m, but the ironstone beds become poor and sporadic, so that ironstones higher in the Middle Coal Measures tended to be worked instead. At Shrubbery Colliery 2.82 m of grey bind are recorded beneath 5.49 m of Pennystone; presumably the former is barren, sandy Lower Pennystone. However, at nearby Woodwell Pits 9.14 m of Pennystone are overlain by 1.52 m of clod, suggesting that here the Upper Pennystone is barren. Oakengates Ring Road Borehole 5A recorded ironstone beds throughout the Pennystone, with *Lingula* sp. (*juv*) and *L. mytilloides* (up to 4 mm across), respectively 1.1 m and 5.5 m above the base. Between St Georges and Donnington the Pennystone was worked only in patches, due to sporadic ironstone development. At the Tub Engine Pits, 0.91 m of poor ironstone was worked at the top of the interval. However, other shaft sections (such as Westcroft, Stafford and Watling Street Grange) record 'Pennystone' overlain by an assortment of measures, suggesting that here the normally rich Upper Pennystone has failed and that the limited workings in these collieries are in the usually poorer Lower Pennystone. At Watling Street Grange Pit the

'Pennystone Measure' is 6.27 m thick, overlain by 3.78 m of 'Pennystone Roof' (brown mudstone). Near Granville Colliery shaft [at 7265 1193], there is a record of the New Mine Coal overlain by at least 0.91 m of yellow oily seatclay, but 50 m away the normal Pennystone is present, with *L. mytilloides* (up to 2 mm across) up to 0.3 m above the New Mine Coal. Eight boreholes north-east of Granville record a similar total thickness for the Pennystone, divisible into three units:

	Thickness m
Grey slightly silty mudstone with ironstone	0.6–5.5
Grey slightly silty mudstone with ironstones and mussels	up to 2.4
Dark grey mudstone and black shale, with ironstone and Lingula	1.5–4.6

The Big Flint Rock normally occupies the whole interval between the Pennystone and the Big Flint Coal, and stands out as the thickest, widest-ranging sandstone in the middle part of the productive measures. South-west of a line from Priorslee to Wombridge it is a well-defined sandstone, generally 4 m to 9 m thick, but varying rapidly and apparently randomly between extremes of 1.8 m (Spring Village North Opencast) and 11.0 m (Teece's Pit, north of Dawley Bank). The sandstone is typically pale to medium grey, sometimes stained greenish, brownish or orange, massive below and flaggy above, with medium to coarse, moderately sorted, subrounded to subangular grains; it is often cross-bedded and has an erosive base. The heavily faulted outcrop of the Big Flint Rock can be traced discontinuously from the Lightmoor Fault at Poolhill [682 068] to the Ketley Fault near Beveley [688 112]. Sandstone about 6.5 m thick makes a prominent feature in Doseley Road [680 070], and forms the base of many shallow shafts at Brandlee and Horsehay Common. Only glimpses of the rock can now be seen in the disused railway cutting [6765 0808] west of Brandlee, where Whitehead et al. (1928, p.72) record 3.05 m of hard grey sandstone dipping eastwards at 3°. Between the Dabler and Ketley faults, bare rock platforms occur at Beveley, Redlake and at the aptly named hamlet of The Rock.

To the west of its discontinuous outcrop, many outliers of Big Flint Rock occur. In the far west at Swann Farm Opencast [6495 0665] near Little Wenlock, 3.4 m of Big Flint Rock were exposed; there it was a coarse-grained gritty sandstone (rather like the espleys of the Hadley Formation), cross-bedded, ferruginous and with occasional carbonaceous wisps. Similar coarse friable ferruginous sandstones, with espley-type grains up to 10 mm across, were found in boreholes for the Ketley Interchange [670 103]. In the extreme north-west at Limekiln Lane, boreholes [656 099] show a rather ill-defined sequence of sandstones, grey sandy shales and coarse conglomerates.

South-east of the Lightmoor Fault and south of Priorslee, the Big Flint Rock is thickest (10.1 m) at Langley Field, 'Langley' and Southall pits, thinning north and south to 4.57 m at Holywell and Wharf Pit, Malins Lee, and 4.9 m at Deepfield, Dawley. Farther north, sandy clay intervenes between the Big Flint Rock and the Big Flint Coal. At Bye Pit, Wombridge, 0.5 m of seatearth clay rests upon 5.3 m of sandstone, while boreholes (NEPR 2 to 5) record 4.5 m to 6.5 m of sandy grey mudstone, including a 1.25 m to 2.0 m bed of hard sandstone. At Westcroft Pits the succession is: Flint Coal Pricking, 0.38 m; Flint Rock, 4.25 m; Glasson stone (more-massive sandstone), 1.02 m. North-eastwards the proportion of argillaceous strata increases: at Granville Pits 1.47 m of fireclay overlie 1.37 m of fine-grained grey sandstone (Figure 21). Boreholes farther north-east record an expanded sequence; Lilleshall No. 7A (Figure 21) may be taken as typical:

	Thickness m
Big Flint Coal	—
Grey siltstone with rootlets; sandy layers	3.48
Grey silty mudstone with ironstone nodules	2.03
Big Flint Rock: pale grey to cream, banded and massive, fine-grained sandstone	5.05
Pennystone Measures	—

In the extreme case, at Childpit Lane (Figure 21), the sandstone is reduced to a 0.76 m bed, overlain by 6.3 m of silty and sandy mudstone with ironstone nodules and two beds of seatearth.

The Big Flint Coal, throughout the area north-west of Watling Street Grange Pit, is a single seam of good quality coal and has been widely worked. It is generally 1.1 m to 1.6 m thick, the thinnest record being 0.76 m in the Coalmoor–Malthouse opencast complex [653 071]. It is thickest south-east of Little Wenlock; Prestwich (1840, p.477) records 1.83 m at Little Wenlock Colliery and a measured section [6495 0665] in Swann Farm Opencast revealed 2.1 m of coal, apparently unparted. The only records of partings in the exposed coalfield are in the far west at Limekiln Lane and the Coalmoor Opencast where a 1.36 m section showed: old workings, c.0.6 m; coal, 0.23 m; dirt, 0.05 m; coal, 0.15 m; dirt, 0.10 m; coal, 0.23 m. However, in the north-east a single parting is universally developed. At Woodhouse Pit 0.56 m and 0.66 m upper and lower leaves are separated by a 0.08 m parting. Boreholes north-east of Granville Colliery (Figure 21) record a parting 1.80 m to 6.32 m thick, thickest at Childpit Lane and Lilleshall No. 2; it comprises seatearth above and mudstone below, in places with ironstones and thin sandstones. The upper and lower leaves of coal hereabouts are both 0.4 m to 0.8 m thick.

The measures between the Big Flint Coal and Yard Coal are traditionally subdivided using old mining names, and the divisions can be traced tolerably well throughout the coalfield. The classic sequence is as follows, taking as an example the generalised succession proved between Old Park and Hollinswood:

	Thickness m
Quoiceneck or queceneck (seatearth of Yard Coal); grey-black siltstone and mudstone with plant remains and coaly partings	0.35
Blue Flat; medium grey to black mudstone with ironstone beds and nodules, plant fragments, roots, and mussels	2.00
Pitchy Bass; black mudstone, fissile, silty and pyritic; fish teeth	0.60
White Flat Coal; shaly and pyritic	0.15
Pitchy Bass; black shaly mudstone, micaceous and pyritic; fish scales including *Rhabdoderma*, also *Anthracosia* spp.	0.50
White Flat; grey mudstone with ironstone nodules and mussel bands	5.00
Flint Coal Bass; dark grey to black mudstone with carbonaceous coaly wisps, shaly ironstone nodules and mussels	0.20
Total	8.80

This succession persists south of the Lightmoor Fault, reaching a thickness of about 11 m at Nelson Pit; from here it thins northwards to about 8 m at Granville Colliery (Figure 21) and southwards to 4.92 m at Portley Pit. The White Flat, and to a lesser extent the Blue Flat, have been worked for ironstone over large areas of the Dark Lane, Malins Lee and Langleyfield

estates; where it is devoid of ironstone, the White Flat is often called the Flint Coal Roof. The White Flat Coal is commonly absent, or split into two leaves as, for instance, north and west of Dawley (Figure 21).

In the Dawley area, from Langleyfield to Brandlee, the succession varies only from 5.3 m (Dawley Parva) to 3.6 m (Southall Pit) and is less clearly subdivided. The Flint Coal Bass is 0.13 m to 0.20 m thick at Heath Hill, Paddock, Portley and Barker's Yard pits, but is not distinguished farther south. The White Flat, here known as the Sparstone, varies from 1.22 m to 1.88 m and has been widely worked. The Pitchy Bass mudstones and Blue Flat are not separately distinguished; they vary from 1.1 m of black mudstone at Deepfield and Castle pits to 2.7 m at Dawley Parva, locally including thin coals, but without workable ironstone. Farther to the south and in the extreme west the succession thins further. Only 1.08 m of strata are recorded at Lower Lightmoor Colliery: black bass, 0.46 m; clod, 0.31 m; black bass, 0.13 m. A section in Coalmoor Opencast [654 072] included 1.83 m of pale grey bind overlain by 1.05 m of dark grey to black seatclay. Opencast sites south-east of Little Wenlock showed only 1.2 m to 4.0 m of dominantly argillaceous strata, and drilling at Limekiln Lane [656 099] showed 2.5 m of mainly argillaceous measures between the Big Flint and Yard coals, in part passing into sandstones of similar thickness. However, the strata are rather thicker (4.8 m to 5.6 m) in the area encompassed by the Monroe [673 098], Smalleyhill [663 083] and Spring Village [672 077] opencast sites.

Prestwich's section (1840, p.475) for Wombridge Water Engine Pit (Figure 21) is similar to the sequence in Old Park, but with a sandstone appearing between the White Flat and the barren Flint Coal Roof:

	Thickness m
Yard Coal Poundstone: black clay	0.23
Quoiceneck: greyish black clay with shiny surfaces	0.23
Blue Flat: brownish grey ironstone in clay, nodular above	1.83
Pitchy Basses: black shale	1.52
White Flat: ironstone beds in dark grey clay	1.22
Flint Coal Rock: white fine micaceous sandstone	3.05
Flint Coal Roof: dark grey dry clay	3.96
Total	12.04

At New Hadley both ironstones are missing, the White Flat being replaced by a thick sandstone. Prestwich (1840, p.482) records: Yard Coal; Clod, 0.8 m; Pitchy Bass, 1.5 m; Eight Yards Rock, 7.3 m; strong rock binds, 4.3 m; Flint Coal. This deficiency of ironstone can only be local, however, as both the White Flat and Blue Flat were extensively mined at the Ketley and Hadley collieries. East of Wombridge, the sequence varies in thickness between about 10 m and 13 m; the White Flat is poor or absent and replaced by the Flint Coal Roof, but the Blue Flat is sufficient in quality and thickness to have been worked extensively as far as Waxhill Barracks Pits.

Boreholes north-east of Granville Colliery (Figure 21) show a consistent succession of 7.9 m to 13.3 m of strata, which may be generalised as follows:

	Thickness m
Dark grey to black carbonaceous seatearth mudstone	0–0.05
Blue Flat: mudstones and seatclays with ironstones and mussels; sandstone beds in Lilleshall No. 6 Borehole	1.8–4.1
Black cannelly shale with fish debris and mussels	0.5–1.7

	Thickness m
White Flat Coal	0–0.2
White Flat and Flint Coal Roof: grey mudstones, siltstones and seatearths, with nodular ironstones and local sandstone beds	4.2–8.8
Dark grey to black shale with mussels and fish debris	0–0.7

The Yard Coal is a single seam over most of the area, generally 0.8 m to 1.1 m thick. It is only 0.69 m thick in the Dawley area, as at Paddock Pit; the thickest record for an unparted seam is 1.2 m, at Ketley Grange Opencast [690 100]. At Spring Village North Opencast [671 080] a 0.05 m dirt parting was recorded 0.05 m above the base of the Yard Coal, which was 1.07 m to 1.15 m thick; and in an isolated instance at Limekiln Lane [656 099], in the north-west, drilling proved the Yard Coal to be in six leaves, three each above and below a major parting up to a metre thick, giving a total thickness of up to 6 m. The coal has been heavily worked in the south-west, but not between Snedshill and Donnington owing to inferior quality. Farther north-east it is often parted; at Granville Colliery (Figure 21) an upper leaf (0.51 m) and a lower leaf (0.46 m) are separated by 0.10 m of shale. A single parting is recorded in Lilleshall No. 6, 7A and Childpit Lane boreholes (the thickest being 0.41 m of black carbonaceous shale at the last-named), but an unparted seam is recorded in Lilleshall Nos. 1, 2, 4 and Hollybank Wood boreholes.

The measures between the Yard Coal and Double Coal normally total 1 m to 3 m, thickening north-eastwards. The strata are largely pale to dark grey or black, smooth to silty mudstones, shales and clays, with small rough lenticular yellowish brown nodules of ironstone, frequently with conchoidal fracture, which were locally worked as the Yellowstone. This is underlain by up to 0.3 m of black shale with mussels north-east of Granville Colliery, at Wrockwardine Wood, New Hadley, Dukes Hill, Old Park and in Spring Village North Opencast. *Anthracosia* sp. (cf. *phrygiana*) is recorded at Old Park, and *A. beaniana* and *A. phrygiana* from Wellington Road Opencast, a fauna typical of the uppermost *Modiolaris* Zone and contrasting with the *A. aquilina/ovum* assemblage of the Big Flint Coal horizon. The Double Coal rests on up to 0.91 m of seatearth clay, generally dark in colour and cannelly at Childpit Lane. The seatearth is absent in Old Park and at Langleyfield, where the coal rests upon a metre of sandstone; at Langleyfield 0.91 m of sandstone forms the whole of the interval between Double and Yard.

The Yellowstone has been worked locally in the area between Brandlee, Wombridge and Donnington. In the western part of the coalfield the Yard-Double interval is generally thin and the ironstone wanting. In extreme cases, only 0.3 m of pale clay and dark grey mudstone are recorded in Borehole 1021 at Old Park, and 0.5 m of black shaly mudstone at Swann Farm Opencast [649 063]. At Heath Hill Pit and at Charles Hay Pits [6816 0759], Yard Coal workings run into 'dead ground' and 'Symon Fault' respectively. This suggests an east–west-trending washout, which may be the same sandstone as replaces the Yellowstone at Old Park and Langleyfield, to the east. Farther south, in Dawley and Lightmoor, a thin coal is recorded between the Yard and Double; a typical section at Top Yard Pits is: Double Coal; underclay, 0.94 m; coal, 0.38 m; hard black underclay (barren Yellowstone), 1.52 m; Yard Coal.

The Double Coal is the thickest seam in the whole sequence, generally ranging between 1.5 m and 1.9 m. Because of its thickness and its sandstone roof it has been extensively worked as far north-east as Lilyhurst and Lilleshall Abbey. Where the overlying sandstone is thin or absent the upper part of the coal was left for support; a section at Smalleyhill Opencast [6642 0845] shows:

	Thickness m
Coal, bright	0.10
Coal, poor, fibrous partings, much selenite	0.55
Backfill to old mine workings	0.95

It is thinnest in the Dawley area (e.g. 0.71 m at Castle Pits and 0.79 m at Top Yard); farther south-east, figures for thickness (e.g. 1.45 m at Deepfield and 1.27 m at Lightmoor) apparently include the Three-Quarter Coal. The maximum thicknesses for unparted seams are 2.31 m at Watling Street Grange Pit (Figure 21), 2.13 m at Nelson Pit (overlain by 0.5 m of underclay and 0.46 m of 'Sill Coal') and 2.0 m at Lawley Opencast [679 083]. At Swann Farm West Opencast [645 062] a worked coal 3.66 m thick was believed to be the Double, Three Quarters and Top run together. A single thin grey clay parting is commonly recorded within the Double Coal throughout the area, apparently randomly distributed. It may lie within the lower, middle or upper part of the coal. This parting thickens markedly in certain of the boreholes north-east of Granville Colliery, reaching 2.26 m in Childpit Lane, where the section is: coal, 0.21 m; black silty mudstone, 0.79 m; pale fine sandstone, 0.10 m; grey listric mudstone with ironstone nodules below, 1.32 m; coal, 1.83 m. Multiple partings are not known north of the Limestone Fault.,

The Double Coal Rock accounts for the whole of the interval between the Double and Three-Quarter coals over most of the area. It is a pale grey or cream, fine-grained ganister, often laminated or silty. In general it thins south-westwards, but it is subject to widespread local variations; thus it was 0.10 m to 2.57 m thick in the Granville Colliery workings and 0.6 m to 3.8 m in Donnington Colliery, thinning to only 0.1 m in places at Freehold Pit. Whitehead et al. (1928) record very hard sandstone cropping out in a stream [7215 1416] between Muxton Bridge and Lilleshall Grange. In the west the sandstone is locally replaced by argillaceous measures, for example 0.20 m of black shale at Top Yard Pit and around 0.3 m of fireclay or shaly mudstone in a belt stretching between Monroe [673 098] and Dog-in-Lane [6630 0775] opencast sites. No parting at all is recorded between Deepfield Pit and Dawley Parva and at Swann Farm West Opencast [645 062]. The parting thickens north-east of Granville Colliery (Figure 21) to a maximum of 13.9 m at Childpit Lane Borehole. The Double Coal Rock itself thins north-eastwards from 4.52 m at Hollybank Wood Borehole to nothing at Childpit Lane; the bulk of the interval is there formed of siltstones and silty mudstones, generally becoming sandy upwards and with a little ironstone. In Brickkiln Plantation and Lilleshall Nos. 2 and 4 boreholes, *Carbonicola* and fish remains occur in these beds. In this part of the area the Three-Quarter Coal rests on about 1 m of clay seatearth.

The Three-Quarter Coal is consistently 0.4 m to 0.7 m thick over most of the coalfield. It is known to have been worked at Rose and Crown Colliery, Oakengates, and taken with the Double at Horsehay Common where the Double Coal Rock is thin. The Royal Commission on Coal Supplies (1905, p.39) refer to contemporary workings in this seam, 0.36 m to 0.46 m thick, using an electric coal-cutting machine. The greatest thickness appears to be 1.24 m at Trough Opencast [670 094] near Arleston, although 2.8 m of coal with two or three partings at Limekiln Lane Opencast may also represent this seam. Otherwise, a parting within the Three-Quarter is only recorded in boreholes in Old Park, where a lower leaf 0.40 m to 0.57 m thick and an upper leaf 0.17 m to 0.58 m thick were separated by 0 m to 0.15 m of hard fine-grained pale grey sandstone and 0.2 m to 1.5 m of seatclay. Within the exposed coalfield the Three-Quarter Coal is only 0.23 m thick at Monroe [673 098] and Ketley Grange [690 100] opencast sites. The seam is absent at Heath Hill Pits, north-west of Dawley Police Station, and is joined to the Double from Deepfield Pit to Lightmoor and at Swann Farm West [645 062]. In boreholes north-east of Granville Colliery (Figure 21) the seam usually comprises only 0.15 m to 0.20 m of dirty coal, but it is absent at Lilleshall No. 4 Borehole, and at Brickkiln Plantation, Childpit Lane and Lilleshall No. 6 it is represented by up to a metre of black carbonaceous mudstone with thin coals.

The measures between the Three-Quarter Coal and the Top Coal are thin and dominantly argillaceous. Throughout the area south-west of Donnington they comprise grey to black fireclays and mudstones, locally with ironstones, and commonly include a basal black shale. *Anthracosia planitumida?* was collected immediately below the Top Coal at Old Park. A thin coal known as the Foot or Tow Coal occurs locally within these measures, in an area from Little Wenlock and Madeley to Ketley and Muxton Bridge. This is most likely to be a lower leaf to the Top Coal, and usually comes near the top of the interval, although at Wombridge, Prestwich (1840) described 0.30 m of Foot Coal immediately overlying the Three-Quarter Coal. The Foot Coal is thickest at Portley Pit, Dawley, where the succession is as follows: Top Coal; pricking, 0.33 m; Foot Coal, 0.51 m; black slums, 2.44 m; Three-Quarter Coal. Locally these measures are very thin or absent, and the Top Coal rests directly on the Three-Quarter at New Hadley (Prestwich, 1840), Ketley Colliery, and Swann Farm West Opencast [645 062]. Conversely, the measures expand considerably in a small area of Dawley, where the Three-Quarter Coal is not recorded. At Heath Hill Pits, the measures between the Top and Double coals total 18.26 m; a similar thickness is recorded in a borehole [6821 0785], showing alternating silty mudstones and argillaceous siltstones with abundant fragmentary *Calamites, Neuropteris* and *?Linopteris.*

Around Donnington and in Granville Colliery workings, the Three-Quarter Coal is overlain by grey ganister similar to the Double Coal Rock. The thickest recorded section of this is north of Granville shaft, where 10.0 m of strata are recorded above the Three-Quarter Coal: Top Coal; soft fireclay, 0.10 m; fireclay and coal 'slums', 1.45 m; sandy fireclay, 1.65 m; sandstone, 5.25 m. The sandstone is thinner in the Donnington area, and farther south at Nelson, Westcroft and Malins Lee Hall pits. Sandstone is not recorded in the boreholes north-east of Granville Colliery (Figure 21); in most cases the Three-Quarter and Top coals here are only separated by about 1.7 m of seatclay, underlain in Brickkiln Plantation and Lilleshall No. 1 boreholes by 2.21 m and 0.30 m of dark shale with ironstone. In No. 6 the strata are expanded to include 6.40 m of grey silty mudstone underlying 2.13 m of siltstone.

The Top Coal is generally 1.1 m to 1.9 m thick, rarely thinner except around Old Park where it is 0.61 m at Ketley Colliery Rock Pits. It is one of the most valued seams in the sequence, but has been less widely worked than the Double Coal because it is absent from large areas beneath the unconformable base of the Hadley Formation or beneath later Middle Coal Measures washout strata (Figure 22). The thickest record is 2.06 m at Nelson Pit. At Dog-in-Lane Opencast [6630 0775], 1.98 m of hard coal with some large pyritous concretions were recorded. Generally the Top Coal is the cleanest in the sequence, with dirt partings recorded at only two places, including one or two thin partings in 1.8 m of coal at Limekiln Lane [656 099].

The measures between the Top Coal and the Gur Coal resemble those between the Big Flint and Yard, in that they include two workable ironstones, separated by black shales, and locally a thin poor coal. However, over a wide area a sandstone lying high in the sequence develops into a major washout. The measures vary in thickness from about 16 m (in Wombridge) to 40 m (Snedshill; Prestwich, 1840, p.478).

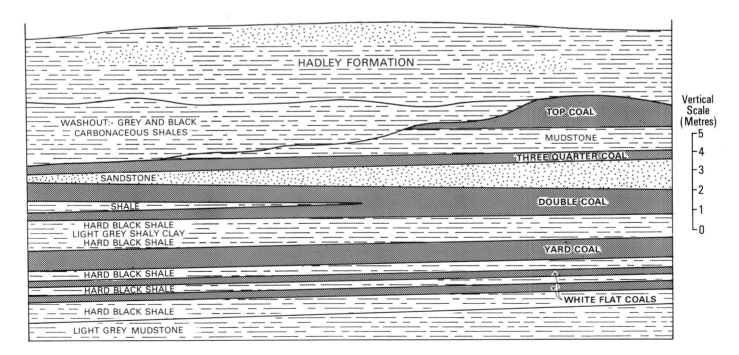

Figure 22   Diagrammatic section showing the Top Coal washout and Hadley Formation basal unconformity at Spring Village North opencast site.

In the centre of the area, around Old Park and Hollinswood, the general succession is:

	Thickness m
Gur Coal	—
Sandstone, thickening northwards; downcutting base	at least 0.7
Brickmeasure Roof: pale to dark grey silty to sandy mudstones; pyrite recorded in Old Park OP5 Borehole	
Brickmeasure ironstone: pale to dark grey mudstone with tabular, regularly jointed masses of dark brown ironstone	up to 8.0
Bind Bass: dark grey to black silty fissile shale, often canneloid, carbonaceous or pyritic; mussels, fish, ironstone nodules; thickening northwards	0.15–1.7
Bind rock and Ballstone Roof: pale grey fine sandstones, siltstones and silty mudstones, becoming more argillaceous upwards; base apparently gently downcutting	0–1.8
Ballstone ironstone: bluish grey mudstone with two or three layers of rounded to ovate ironstone nodules up to 1m across and 20 cm thick; thickens northwards	2.74–7.6
Top Coal Roof; black shales, locally canneloid; *Arthracosia atra* recorded preserved in brown ironstone, also fish spines and scales	0.15–0.46

The Ballstone was widely worked between Dawley, New Hadley, Snedshill and Granville Colliery; in productive areas the lower part was referred to as Dun Earth and was not always worked. **The Brickmeasure** was worked between Ketley and Donnington.

In the west of the area these strata are rarely preserved but the sequence appears to be similar, as the following section was measured on the north face of the Smalleyhill Opencast [6642 0845]:

	Thickness m
Mudstones, sandy, with sandstone beds (Brickmeasure Roof)	c.3.0
Mudstone, medium grey weathering pale grey; two worked ironstone beds in middle (Brickmeasure); yielded *Anthracosia* cf. *atra*, *A.* cf. *caledonica*, *Anthracosphaerium* sp., *Naiadites* sp., and *Rhizodopsis* sp. (fish scale)	c.4.0
Shale, black; pyritic plant remains; very fissile (Bind Bass)	c.2.0
Sandstone, finely laminated (Bind Rock)	1.2
Mudstone, grey; many ovate ironstone nodules, small in lower part but larger and in layers in upper part, up to 1 m long by 0.2 m deep (Ballstone)	c.3.5
Shale, black; *Rhizodopsis*, palaeoniscid and platysomid scales (Top Coal Roof)	0.10
Top Coal	—

Nearby, in Wellington Road Opencast, *Anthracosia* cf. *aquilina* and *Naiadites alatus* were collected 6.55 m above the Top Coal, presumably from the Brickmeasure. Other mussels collected at the same level but within the Ketley Fault belt are: *Anthracosia atra*, *A.* cf. *fulva*, *Anthracosphaerium radiatum*, *A. propinquum*. This fauna is typical for the middle of the Lower *Similis-Pulchra* Zone.

At the Dog-in-Lane Opencast [6630 0775] 0.13 m of black slaty shale with fish remains, above the Top Coal, was overlain by at least 4.57 m of Ballstone, with *Naiadites angustus* and *Spirorbis* 1.4 m above the base. Adjacent to the Little Wenlock Fault in the Swann Farm Opencast, the 'Bind Rock' expands to 6 m and cuts down into the Ballstone:

	Thickness m
Deep Coal	—
Mudstone, medium grey; scattered plant fragments; ferruginous siltstone beds; upper part grey-brown seatearth	about 5.0
Obscured by scree	2.0
Mudstone, dark grey to black; mussel fragments, ferruginous siltstone lenses (Bind Bass)	2.1
Mudstone and siltstone, interlaminated; plant and mussel fragments (Ballstone Roof)	2.1
Sandstone, orange; upper and lower parts ferruginous and massive; central parts pale, fine-grained, laminated, flaggy and silty, strongly micaceous, with shallow cross-bedding (Bind Rock)	up to 6.0
Mudstone, dark to medium grey, many rounded ironstone nodules (Ballstone)	2.0
Top Coal	—

The fauna includes *Anthraconaia ellipsoides*, *A. librata* and *Anthracosia atra*, typical of mid Lower *Similis-Pulchra* Zone.

To the north-east, in Spread Eagles Opencast [652 068], the Bind Rock cuts out the Ballstone completely and rests directly on the Top Coal. The Bind Rock is at its thickest in the north-west, in Prestwich's (1840) section for New Hadley Colliery: Gur Coal; grey rock, 6.40 m; Brickmeasure, 1.07 m; clunch, 0.91 m; bind, 0.61 m; bass, 0.61 m; Bind Rock, 7.32 m; Ballstone, 1.83 m; Dun earth, 2.44 m; total, 21.19 m.

Throughout the Donnington Colliery workings the succession is generally similar to that at Old Park and totals around 21.0 m to 23.4 m. Even in the far north-east, at Granville Colliery and in the Lilleshall boreholes (except No. 6 and Hollybank Wood), the subdivisions can be distinguished within a sequence varying from 17.9 m (Granville Colliery, Figure 21) to 23.0 m (Lilleshall No. 1 Borehole):

	Thickness m
Seatearth, generally with ironstones and commonly silty	up to 2.7
Sandstone (present at Granville Colliery, Brickkiln Plantation and Lilleshall No. 1 boreholes)	0–6.8
Mudstone, grey; silty and sandy, no ironstone; Brickmeasure Roof	up to 4.27
Mudstone, grey, smooth to silty, with tabular jointed masses of ironstone; Brickmeasure	up to 2.69
Black shale, cannelly and carbonaceous; fish at Brickkiln Plantation and Lilleshall No. 7A, mussels at No. 2, 0.08 m of inferior coal at Childpit Lane; Bind Bass	up to 2.29
Seatearth with ironstone; Brickkiln Plantation, Lilleshall Nos. 2 and 4 and Childpit Lane only	0–2.2
Mudstone, grey, silty, thickening north-east; Ballstone Roof	1.9–5.8
Sandstone; Lilleshall Nos.1 and 2 only; Bind Rock	1.6–3.9
Mudstone and seatearth, blue and grey, locally silty, with nodular ironstones, thickening to the north-east; Ballstone	4.4–9.5
Black shale, cannelly and carbonaceous; *Anthracosia atra*, *A.* cf. *aquilinoides*, fish scales including *Rhizodopsis* and palaeoniscids	up to 0.5

At Granville the Ballstone is further subdivided into the Dun Earth below (3.15 m, brown clay with valuable ironstone nodules) and the Ballstone Clod above (1.45 m, pale shale with two or three layers of large smooth nodules).

Throughout the area so far described, thin arenaceous measures are locally developed between the Brickmeasure and the Gur Coal; however, from Dawley to Snedshill and Sheriff Hales these develop into a major washout, comprising sandstones, siltstones and mudstones (Figure 23). The washout is orientated north-east to south-west and lies wholly north-west of the Limestone Fault. The thickest strata are found in the north-east, reaching 30.3 m at Hollybank Wood Borehole, while in the south-west the base of the washout is strongly downcutting and rests on strata as low as the Yellowstone. Incrops of coal seams into the base of the washout are shown in Figure 39; many cease against the Lightmoor Fault, suggesting that the fault was active at the time of formation of the washout.

North-west of the Lightmoor Fault the washout does not cut down as low as the Top Coal, and variations of the thickness of the washout strata imply that the Old Park/Hollinswood area lay at the edge of the washout. In Malins Lee No. 2 Borehole, the Brickmeasure and Gur Coal are separated by only 0.7 m of sandstone, but in Borehole DDD 1 [6868 0866], 6.2 m of gently cross-bedded sandstone with black coaly wisps and layers of coarse grit, together with mudstones incorporating layers of

coarse sand, rest on only 3.30 m of Brickmeasure. At Malins Lee No. 4, similar sandstones and mudstones rest only 0.30 m above the Top Coal.

In Old Park Borehole OP5 (Figure 23), 3.66 m of medium to dark grey, fine- to coarse-grained, cross-bedded sandstone, followed by 1.52 m of dark grey silty beds, lie between the Gur Coal and 5.4 m of Brickmeasure. North-eastwards these measures evidently thicken considerably; at Snedshill, Prestwich (1840) records 31 m of strata between the Brickmeasure and the Gur Coal. To the north-west, washout strata apparently occur as far as Wombridge.

To the south-east of the Lightmoor Fault the maximum degree of downcutting occurs around Malins Lee. There the washout strata are themselves affected by the unconformity below the Hadley Formation; the approximate incrop of the base of the washout into the base of the Hadley is shown in Figure 39. The most southerly shafts at which a complete sequence of washout strata is preserved are believed to be the Top Yard, Deepfield and Portley pits, Dawley, where respectively 7.6 m, 16.8 m and 12.4 m of sandy shales are recorded overlying the Ballstone, Top Coal Roof and Top Coal respectively. From Dawley Parva to Watling Street Grange the washout strata can be recognised in many shaft sections, although interpretation is hindered by archaic terminology. At Pudley Hill Pit (Figure 21) and at Malins Lee Hall Pit the strata are interpreted as follows:

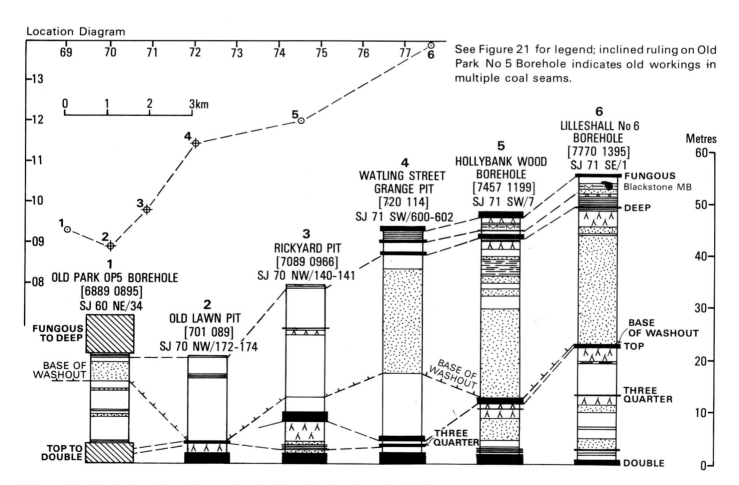

Figure 23   Vertical sections illustrating the Top Coal washout in the Donnington Syncline; compare with normal sequence shown in Figure 21.

	Pudley Hill Pits	Malins Lee Hall Pits
	m	m
Hadley Formation: red and grey mudstone	—	—
Washout strata: sandstones, siltstones, mudstones	18.60	26.58
Brickmeasure	4.12	absent
Bind Bass: dark shales	0.91	2.13
Ballstone Measure	4.57	3.66
Top Coal Bass: carbonaceous shale	thin	0.30
Top Coal	—	—

At Rickyard Pit (Figure 23), a coal is present within strata interpreted to lie within the washout: Hadley Formation; carbonaceous shale, possibly equivalent to the Gur Coal; 'arenaceous shale', 8.08 m; coal, 0.23 m; black shale, 0.38 m; underclay, 1.27 m; argillaceous and arenaceous shales, 7.24 m; Ballstone and Brickmeasure ironstones, 6.38 m; black shale, 0.30 m; Top Coal.

North-eastwards the washout strata thicken; at Watling Street Grange Pits (Figure 21), 20.07 m of 'grey rock' and 2.77 m of 'metals' underlie the Deep Coal. Finally, at Hollybank Wood and Lilleshall No. 6 boreholes, 17.0 m and 22.7 m of sandstone rest upon the Top Coal. At Hollybank Wood the sandstone is overlain by 11.5 m of generally silty measures with sporadic ironstones, succeeded by 1.82 m of grey seatearth with ironstones, but in Lilleshall No. 6 this seatearth (3.05 m) rests directly on the sandstone.

The Gur Coal is thin, commonly shaly, and not known to have been mined. It reaches 0.7 m to 0.8 m around Wrockwardine Wood, Donnington Wood and Muxton Bridge, thinning to 0.6 m to 0.7 m in Wombridge, 0.3 m in Hadley, and 0.2 m to 0.5 m in Old Park. To the north-east (Figure 21) it thins from 0.66 m at Granville Colliery to 0.05m in Childpit Lane Borehole. At Nelson, Rickyard, Portley, Deepfield and Top Yard pits the Gur is believed to be represented by carbonaceous coaly shale, and in all but Nelson Pit this is overlain immediately by the Hadley Formation. The Gur is similarly represented by black shale at Hollybank Wood and Lilleshall No. 6 boreholes and is absent at Watling Street Grange and Woodhouse pits.

The Gur Coal is overlain by dark grey to black coaly seatearth clays, locally including black shale below, around New Hadley (0.30 m thick), Wombridge (0.84 m to 1.22 m), Snedshill (0.75 m to 1.25 m in TDC boreholes ECPR(N) 7, 8 and 10), Cockshutt Piece (1.98 m), Wrockwardine Wood (0.71 m), Donnington Wood (0.75 m) and Muxtonbridge (1.3 m). In Old Park, Borehole 1046 records 0.13 m of coaly seatearth overlying 1.15 m of pale grey mudstones which contain *Neuropteris* as well as ironstone nodules and layers up to 0.14 m thick. Granville Colliery, Lilleshall No. 7A and Brickkiln Plantation boreholes (Figure 21) record 1.0 m to 1.7 m of carbonaceous listric seatearth, with ironstone, but Lilleshall Nos. 1, 2 and Childpit Lane boreholes farther north record only 0.2 m to 0.4 m of dark shale.

The Deep or Stone Coal is generally a single seam, 0.8 m to 1.4 m thick. In places it is thinner, for example 0.7 m at Ketley Manor Pit and 0.3 m or less along a line through Lilleshall boreholes 7A, 4 and 6. It is rarely parted, but 1 km north-east of Granville Colliery shafts, 0.04 m of dirt separates a lower leaf (0.92 m thick) from an upper leaf (0.46 m thick). At Granville and Woodhouse pits, the lowest 0.25 m and 0.23 m are referred to as Tow Coal, while in Old Park Borehole 1046, 1.72 m of combined Blackstone and Deep coals are separated from an underlying 0.13 m of Tow Coal by 0.15 m of coaly seatearth. At Spring Village North [671 080] and Lawley [679 083] opencast

sites in the west, the Gur and Deep combine as a single seam 1.7 m to 1.9 m thick. A section [6495 0665] in the north-eastern corner of Swann Farm Opencast, adjacent to the Coalbrookdale Road, recorded a metre of Deep Coal forming the base of a washout and thinning laterally into black coaly mudstone (Figure 24). Despite its consistent thickness and the availability of the Blackstone ironstone for simultaneous extraction, this coal has not been widely worked; Prestwich (1840) described it as a good coal at Wombridge, but at Granville it is poor. At Daisy Pit, Dawley Bank, the Deep Coal was 1.27 m thick and was worked up to its incrop into later washout strata.

Measures between the Deep Coal and the Blackstone Coal are locally absent at Limekiln Lane [656 099] and Old Park (borehole 1046); elsewhere south and west from Ketley they never amount to more than 0.8 m of dark grey to black ferruginous or sandy mudstone. However, between Ketley and Sheriff Hales they vary up to around 5 m of dark grey to black seatclay, mudstone and shale, with ironstone nodules and a few thin sandstones. These measures typically commence with up to 3.8 m of black mudstone, pyritic or canneloid, and commonly with fish or mussel remains; scales of *Elonichthys* sp. and *Rhizodopsis* sp. were collected from Borehole DDD(N) 13A [6947 1201]. In some cases this makes up the whole interval, although rarely this may comprise as little as 0.6 m of dark grey to black seatearth, as at Hollybank Wood Borehole (Figure 21).

The Blackstone ironstone, which rests on the black mudstone or on the Deep Coal, is a sporadic development of tough, dark clay with small shiny almost black ironstone nodules. It has been widely worked where present from Hadley to Muxton Bridge and Granville Colliery, where 2.21 m of 'Blackstone and spladers' are recorded. At Lodgewood, Donnington, 1.73 m of Blackstone overlies 1.07 m of 'spladers' and 1.22 m of bass. 'Spladers' are not explained, but have been worked for ironstone occasionally where the Blackstone is barren. The Blackstone ironstone is generally overlain by up to 0.6 m of clod, seatearth or sandstone below the Blackstone Coal; sandstones are sometimes present where the Blackstone is absent, as in the thick sequence in Lilleshall Nos. 4 and 6 boreholes, in the extreme east.

The Blackstone Coal, known as the Foot Coal in Wombridge and Donnington Wood, has not been worked. It is generally 0.3 m to 0.5 m thick wherever this part of the sequence is preserved, from Swann Farm Opencast [6495 0665] to north-east of Granville Colliery. It thickens to 0.6 m at Mannerley Lane and Lawley, where it includes much specular pyrite and ironstone nodules; up to 0.75 m is recorded at Limekiln Lane. At Borehole DDD(N) 13A near Wombridge [6947 1201] 0.12 m of cannel overlies 0.48 m of coal. In the extreme east, the seam thins to 0.16 m in Hollybank Wood Borehole and is absent in Lilleshall Nos. 2 and 6 boreholes, but 0.6 m of cannel appears to represent this seam in Lilleshall No. 4. In Old Park and at Limekiln Lane, the Blackstone Coal is locally joined to the Deep Coal.

The measures between the Blackstone Coal and the Fungous Coal generally thicken north-eastwards, from 0.76 m (New Hadley and Hadley No. 12 pits) to 3.5 m (Lilleshall No. 4 Borehole). The lower part includes the Blackstone Marine Band, up to 1.4 m of dark grey to black, silty, micaceous, pyritic, fissile mudstone with *Lingula mytilloides* and fish remains (*Rhadinichthys*) as well as sporadic ironstones. Foraminifera including *Glomospira* are recorded from Borehole DDD(N) 13A [6947 1201]. The *L. mytilloides* in this marine band are typically 5 mm to 6 mm long, larger than the average for the Pennystone and Chance Pennystone marine bands; they are also more abundant and better preserved, often with both valves in contact. At Granville Colliery they have been collected from 0 m to 0.9 m above the Blackstone Coal, overlain by nonmarine ironstone with *Car-*

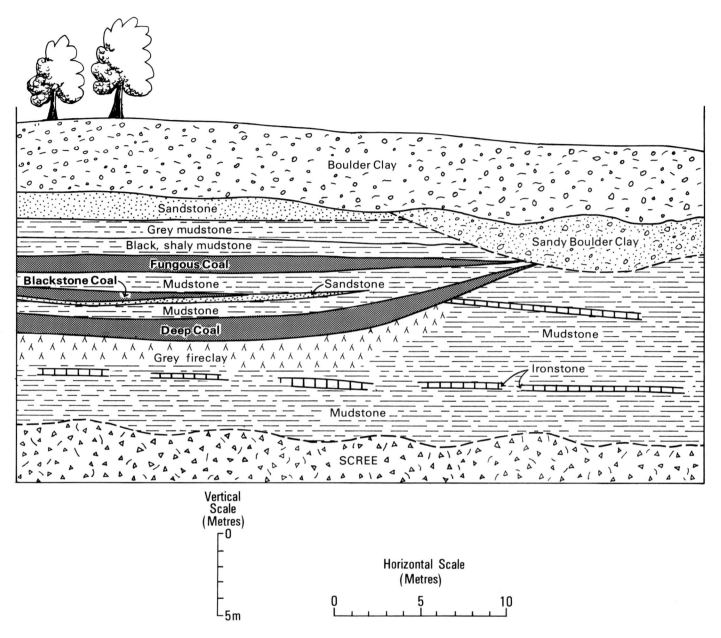

Figure 24 Diagrammatic section showing the Fungous Group coals within a Middle Coal Measures washout, Swann Farm opencast site.

bonita humilis. The marine band appears to be persistent throughout the area, although *Lingula* has not been recorded south-west of the Lawley Opencast [679 083].

The upper part of these measures comprises dark grey to black silty seatclays and mudstones, with sandstones at Limekiln Lane and Wombridge. Ostracods, fish remains, *Naiadites* and *Neuropteris* are known from this level. Rough, irregularly shaped, black ironstone nodules occur between Lawley and Sheriff Hales; these have been worked as the Ragged Robins Ironstone in Ketley and New Hadley (Prestwich, 1840, p.437), and possibly as far as Donnington.

The Fungous (or Marquis or Donnington Wood) Coal is of excellent quality, but is present over only a limited area owing to erosion beneath later washout strata and the Hadley Formation. In the west of the area isolated occurrences are recorded at several opencast sites: Swann Farm (0.7 m thick, weathered), Spring Village North (0.64 m), Lawley (up to 1.25 m) and Limekiln Lane (up to 0.8 m). Old Park Borehole 1046 revealed 0.12 m preserved below washout measures. From its outcrop at Ketley it has been worked extensively as far as Donnington, Granville and Woodhouse collieries, usually being 0.9 m to 1.2 m thick and unparted. It crops out in stream sections east of Muxton (Whitehead et al., 1928, p.77). Boreholes north-east of Granville (Figure 21) record a single seam up to 1.12 m thick (in Lilleshall Borehole No. 1) but reduced to 0.38 m and 0.46 m in Lilleshall Nos. 4 and 6.

The measures between the Fungous Coal and the Chance Pennystone Marine Band are best known in the north-east of the coalfield, but are preserved locally as far south-west as the Swann Farm Opencast [6495 0665] near Little Wenlock; there the coal is overlain by 2.5 m of dark grey to black fissile mudstone and 1.5 m of sandstone. Drilling for the Lawley Opencast [679 083] revealed 5 m to 8 m of wispy-bedded, sandy micaceous mudstone in a washout which cut down through the Fungous and Blackstone coals. A shaly coal up to 0.3 m thick occurs locally about 3 m above the base of the washout. The latter is apparently aligned south-west to north-east, and is seen again in Old Park, where coarse-grained yellow and brown sandstones, shaly and silty mudstones and siltstones cut down to the Gur Coal. The washout cannot be traced further, as borehole ECPR(N) 8A [7006 1043], at Snedshill, records 9.1 m of predominantly dark mudstone overlying the Fungous Coal. A pyritic coal 0.23 m thick occurs 2.5 m above the Fungous, and the measures there pass conformably up into the Hadley Formation.

Drilling for the Limekiln Lane Opencast [656 099] records up to 6 m of sandy grey shale and sandstone, unconformably overlain by the Hadley Formation. However, shaft sections and boreholes around New Hadley show that equivalent grey measures here are overlain conformably by the Hadley Formation (Figure 25). The Fungous Coal is directly overlain by the Fungous Coal Rock, which is thickest, 11.0 m, at Wombridge Water Engine Pit; it is a grey to buff sandstone, fine-grained and silty, with argillaceous partings and coaly wisps, but becoming coarser in its upper part. It is overlain by 0.15 m to 0.45 m of poor coal or black coaly shale, and then by the **Chance Pennystone ironstone**, which has been extensively worked. The ironstone comprises up to 4.6 m of grey, silty to sandy mudstone with siderite beds up to 0.08 m thick in its upper part and siderite nodules and finely disseminated pyrite in its lower part. At Bye Pit it is overlain by 1.8 m of seatclay and 0.1 m of coal, then sandstone, but elsewhere in Wombridge and Hadley the ironstone is overlain directly by the Chance Pennystone Rock. This is a fine-grained, evenly laminated, micaceous, silty sandstone, about 0.6 m to 1.6 m thick.

East of Wombridge, black shale appears between the Fungous Coal and the overlying sandstone, which splits into two. A representative section for the interval at Donnington Colliery (Staffordshire Archives, ref. D593/N/17/5) is (in ascending order): Fungous Coal; Bass, 0.23 m; shale with ironstone nodules, 1.04 m; Fungous Coal Rock, 7.09 m; shale, 1.83 m; Seven Yards Rock, 6.10 m; Coal, 0.15 m; Chance Pennystone ironstone, 1.83 m; Chance Pennystone Rock, 1.37 m. The ironstone was sporadic and rather thin, but of workable quality, yielding 32 per cent of iron.

Variations in the succession east of Donnington are shown in Figure 26; the strata range in thickness from 11.1 m (Lilleshall No. 7A Borehole) to 24.6 m (Childpit Lane Borehole), and include three coals. The coals in the measures above the Fungous are here referred to as Chance Pennystone Coals 1 to 8; the three considered here lie below the Chance Pennystone Marine Band, and five others overlie it. Coal No. 1 is believed to correlate with that known in Hadley and Donnington and ranges up to 0.71 m in thickness. Coal No. 2 is possibly that known at Bye Pit, and reaches a thickness of 0.26 m at Childpit Lane. Coal No. 3 is not known farther to the south-west; it is up to 0.25 m thick and immediately underlies the Chance Pennystone Marine Band. The strata between the coals are very variable (Figure 26). The Fungous Coal is overlain by black shale in most cases, but directly by the Fungous Coal Rock in places. This sandstone is very variable in thickness and is absent from three of the boreholes. Where present it comprises a lower unit of pale grey sandstone with a little ironstone, passing up into siltstone and mudstone with sandstone beds and some iron-

stone. A further sandstone occurs above the No.1 coal in several places; this is thickest, 4.7 m, in Lilleshall No. 1 Borehole. In Lilleshall No. 6 a further sandstone, 3.9 m thick, lies between Coals 2 and 3.

The Chance Pennystone Marine Band is best documented in Lilleshall No. 2 Borehole, where 3.58 m of dark mudstone with ironstone contain *Lingula*, productids, lamellibranchs and fish remains. At Childpit Lane it also contained *Orbiculoidea* and gastropods. The minimum thickness recorded for the marine band is 0.08 m in borehole No. 7A, while at Granville shaft it may be represented in 0.33 m of dark clod above No. 3 Coal (Figure 26). At New Hadley and at Wombridge Water Engine Pit this marine band is represented by up to 1.5 m of grey silty mudstone, with a marine fauna (*L. mytilloides*, *Dunbarella*?, fish debris including cochliodont tooth) recorded in three boreholes (Blockleys' Nos. 2, 5 and 9, Figure 25). Ironstone layers were recorded up to 0.03 m thick, and in one borehole pebbles up to 1 cm in diameter.

The measures overlying the Chance Pennystone Marine Band in New Hadley comprise 0.5 m to 1.1 m of interbedded siltstones and fine-grained sandstones, overlain by the Four Feet Rock, 1.1 m to 1.8 m of hard grey fine-grained sandstone or siltstone. In Blockleys' Borehole No. 9 (Figure 25) this is succeeded by 0.1 m of coal and further mudstones and a 0.7 m sandstone beneath the Hadley Formation, but elsewhere in New Hadley and at Wombridge Water Engine Pit the grey measures pass conformably up into the Hadley Formation at about the top of the Four Feet Rock (Figure 25). Bye Pit, Wombridge is difficult to correlate; if the two uppermost sandstones in the grey measures there are the Chance Pennystone Rock and the Four Feet Rock, the sequence has expanded considerably, compared with Water Engine Pit nearby.

Nothing is known about grey measures above the Chance Pennystone Marine Band in Donnington, but variations in these strata eastwards from Watling Street Grange and Granville pits are shown in Figure 26. The apparent wide differences in thickness between boreholes results both from internal variations and from the diachronous changes from grey measures conformably up into the Hadley Formation. These grey measures contain five coals, the Chance Pennystone Coals Nos. 4 to 8, although no more than four are recorded in any particular borehole. The strata are thickest (40 m) at Childpit Lane, where all the coals except No. 5 were intersected. The strata comprise a variety of sandstones, siltstones, mudstones, seatearths and black shales; little correlation is possible except for the tentative numbering of the various thin coals. The highest coal, No. 8, is only found at Childpit Lane and Lilleshall No. 6, while in Lilleshall Nos. 1, 2 and 4 and Brickkiln Plantation boreholes the measures pass into the Hadley Formation above a sandstone which appears to be that beneath Coal No. 8 at Childpit Lane. At Granville Colliery the change to red-bed facies occurs rather lower, just above a coal which is either No. 6 or Nos. 6 and 7 combined. At Watling Street Grange and Lilleshall No. 7A boreholes the facies change occurs lower still, below Coal No. 6 or lower (Figure 26).

MADELEY AREA

Lower Coal Measures

Strata below the Lancashire Ladies Coal, probably including arenaceous strata of Namurian age, crop out widely in the south-west of the area. Strong features with much sandstone brash are seen west of Benthall Hall [658 026] and Posenhall [657 017], and at Barrow [657 000]; boreholes south-south-east of Posenhall show the Lancashire Ladies Coal to be 12 m to 15 m above

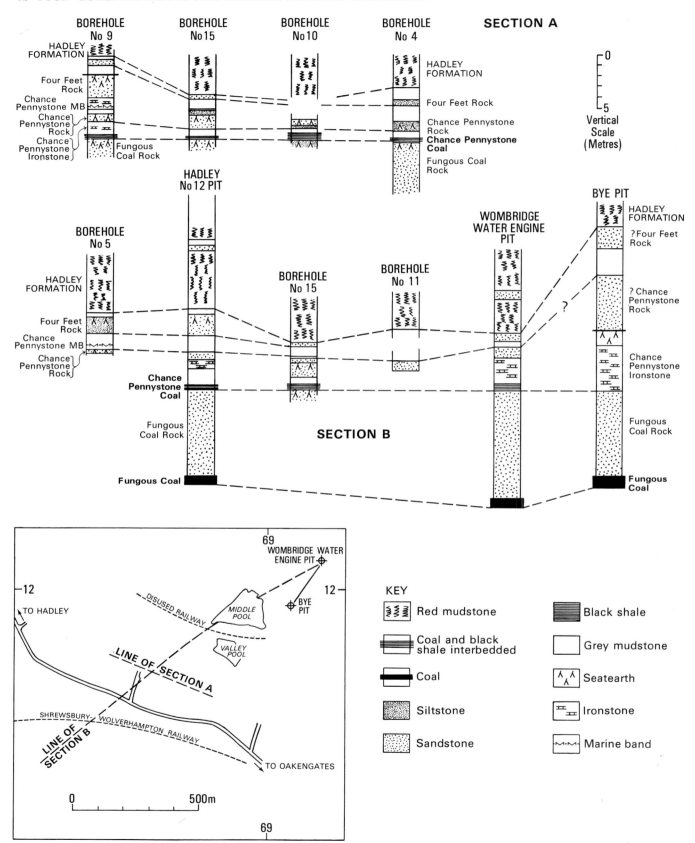

Figure 25   Uppermost Middle Coal Measures and their relations with the Hadley Formation in the Hadley–Wombridge area. Boreholes sunk by Messrs. Blockleys Ltd. Further details (including sites) are confidential.

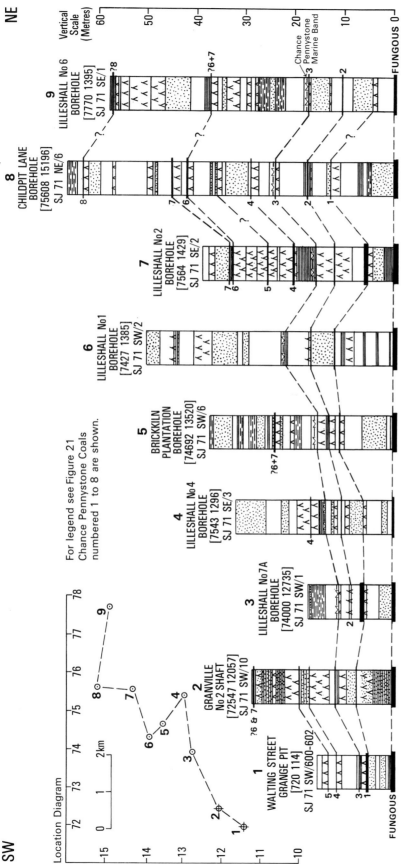

Figure 26 Comparative vertical sections of the productive measures above the Fungous Coal, in the north-east of the Donnington Syncline. In all cases the strata are overlain conformably by the Hadley Formation.

the base of the Coal Measures, which here rests on Ludlow shales. Ferruginous pebbly sandstone brash between Posenhall and Barrow shows a southward increase in pebble content. A disused quarry [6635 0015] east-north-east of St Giles Church, Barrow, showed 3 m of cream to orange, flaggy, coarse-grained very pebbly sandstone. The pebbles are of angular to sub-rounded quartzite, commonly 5 mm and exceptionally up to 40 mm in size. Well-rounded quartzite pebbles up to 7 cm in diameter were found in sandstone blocks on the banks of a tributary of the Dean Brook [6755 0032], and pebbles up to 20 cm across occur in brash at an outlier at Highfield Plantation [SO 670 999] south of the Telford sheet. In the banks of another tributary of the Dean Brook [6840 0038] 600 m north-east of the Dean, arenaceous strata are exposed, dipping gently northwards:

	Thickness
	m
Sandstone and conglomerate, very ferruginous, with quartzite pebbles in slightly friable, coarse-grained orange to purple sandy matrix	c.3
Mudstone, orange and red, weathered	up to 2
Sandstone, orange, flaggy, forming slight waterfall	up to 2

Further strata, to the base of the Coal Measures, are obscured.

At Styches Pit, Coalport Tileries, the Lancashire Ladies was underlain by: clunch, 1.98 m; dark clod with ironstone, 0.91 m; rock with ironstone, 1.37 m; dark parting with ironstone, 0.20 m; gritty rock, 6.78 + m. Fine-grained white pebbly sandstone is recorded 1.5 m thick at Hills Lane (Prestwich, 1840) below the Lancashire Ladies Coal; however, that seam rests directly on Silurian rocks at Madeley Meadow Pit. Exley's Pit, also at Coalport Tileries, records below undoubted Hadley Formation: stone and rock, 0.3 m; fireclay and rock, 4.0 m; grey rock, 1.1 m; fireclay, 1.5 m; rock, 1.2 m; fireclay, 2.7 m; rock and stone, 2.7 m; tar stone, 0.6 m; ballstone, 1.2 m; fireclay, 1.1 m; tar rock, hard, with dark colours, 5.2 m; reddish binds with trilobites (Silurian), 5.5 + m. Most of this succession must be Lower Coal Measures, but as no coal was recorded it might lie partly or wholly above the Lancashire Ladies Coal.

Borehole G3 [6956 0295] at Hay Farm, Coalport, penetrated 28.0 m of strata between the Hadley Formation and Silurian rocks; these were recorded as grey to brown siltstones with thin sandstones, clays and coals, with a basal bed of 'marl fragments'. Thin coals occur 5.6 m, 6.4 m, 12.7 m, 18.1 m and 20.6 m above the base. These measures could be wholly older than the Little Flint Coal, but alternatively they might represent an impoverished sequence in which the seams represent the Best, Randle, Clod, Little Flint and Lancashire Ladies coals.

In the north-east, strata below the Lancashire Ladies Coal were intersected in Madeley Wood Nos. 1, 3, 4, and 6 and Lilleshall No. 5 boreholes (Figure 27), but the base of the measures was only penetrated in two of the boreholes. The strata comprise pale grey to cream, fine-grained, massive sandstones, with thin conglomerates, silty mudstones, seatearth clays and ironstones. A coal seam, 0.84 m thick in No. 1, 0.51 m in No.4, 0.13 m in No.6 and in two thin leaves in Lilleshall No. 5, is present.

The Lancashire Ladies Coal is more variable than in the Dawley area. It is thickest (1.0 m) at Blists Hill (Figure 27), and 0.6 m thick in a trench at Willeypark Wood [6716 0062]. It was absent at Rudgewood [SO 684 992] and at Lodge Farm Borehole [6756 0370]. South-south-east of Posenhall, 0.15 m of smutty coal was found at outcrop across ploughland. In the north-east (Figure 27) it is believed to be absent at Lilleshall No. 5 Borehole, and poorly developed in the Madeley Wood

boreholes: 0.1 m of carbonaceous mudstone with coal streaks in No. 4; 0.33 m of cannelly carbonaceous shale and coal in No. 3, and 0.03 m of black coaly pyritous shale in No. 1. The latter was overlain by dark grey silty mudstone with *Lingula*, the **Lancashire Ladies Marine Band**, implying that the coal correlates with the lower of the two Lancashire Ladies coals in the other Lilleshall boreholes (see Dawley area, Figure 19).

The Crawstone Flint accounts for the whole of the interval between the Lancashire Ladies and Crawstone coals around Madeley (Figure 27). It thins from 7.5 m at Blists Hill and 5.3 m at Madeley Meadow Pit, to 1.7 m at Hills Lane and 3.05 m at Kemberton. At Benthall Potteries, 0.4 m of fireclay intervenes between it and the Crawstone Coal, and at Styches Pit 1.83 m of 'New Mine' (ironstone) is recorded between it and the Lancashire Ladies Coal. Sandstone overlain by seatearth is recorded between the Lancashire Ladies and Crawstone coals in the boreholes to the north-east (Figure 27), these measures increasing in thickness to a maximum of 10.9 m in Madeley Wood No. 3 Borehole.

The Crawstone Coal is more consistently developed here than in the Dawley area, although it is not present at Kemberton Pit, Rudgewood [SO 684 992] and Lilleshall No. 5 Borehole. It varies between 0.1 m and 0.3 m, being thickest at Hills Lane Pits, and it is underlain by 0.08 m of black carbonaceous shale at Madeley Wood Nos. 1 and 4 boreholes. Two thin coals are recorded at the Lodge Farm Borehole [6756 0370], 0.07 m lower and 0.10 m upper leaves separated by 0.7 m of seatearth mudstone with ironstone nodules. The upper coal here is overlain by 0.50 m of medium grey smooth mudstone with *Lingula*, the only known occurrence of the **Crawstone Marine Band** in the coalfield. At Madeley Wood Nos. 1, 4 and 6 boreholes and in a level recently discovered [6707 0361] near St Luke's Church, Ironbridge, the Crawstone Coal is overlain by up to 0.15 m of black carbonaceous or cannelly shale; no marine fauna is recorded.

The Crawstone ironstone is recorded throughout the area and has been widely worked in the exposed coalfield. In the level near St Luke's Church, Ironbridge it was 0.45 m to 0.55 m thick, with ovate ironstone nodules up to 0.8 m long and 0.3 m thick (often forming continuous linked beds) in a matrix of soft carbonaceous material. Sections at Benthall Potteries, Madeley Meadow Pit and Blists Hill suggest the same lithology and thickness, while at Hills Lane it is 0.91 m thick, pale brown and bituminous. In Lilleshall No. 5 Borehole the ironstone appears to be represented by 1.22 m of grey fireclay with sphaerosiderite, underlain by 0.91 m of grey fine-grained sandstone.

The Little Flint Rock is a massive fine-grained cream sandstone as in the Dawley area, its lower part being well exposed in the level near St Luke's Church:

	Thickness
	m
Sandstone, finely laminated; large tree trunks, with coalified bark enclosing laminated sandstone	0.3 +
Mudstone, carbonaceous, very friable; coaly films as long plant impressions; mussel fragments	up to 0.1
Sandstone, massive; roots in upper part, small ironstone nodules, flaggy central part with coaly films	up to 1.0

The Little Flint Rock was 3.2 m thick in the Lodge Farm Borehole, but thinned eastwards at Blists Hill and Madeley (Figure 27). Farther east it is well developed in Madeley Wood boreholes No. 4 (4.8 m thick), No. 1 (7.01 m) and No. 3 (11.13 m). At Lilleshall No. 5 in the far north-east, 6.4 m of coarse-grained brown sandstone with shale partings were over-

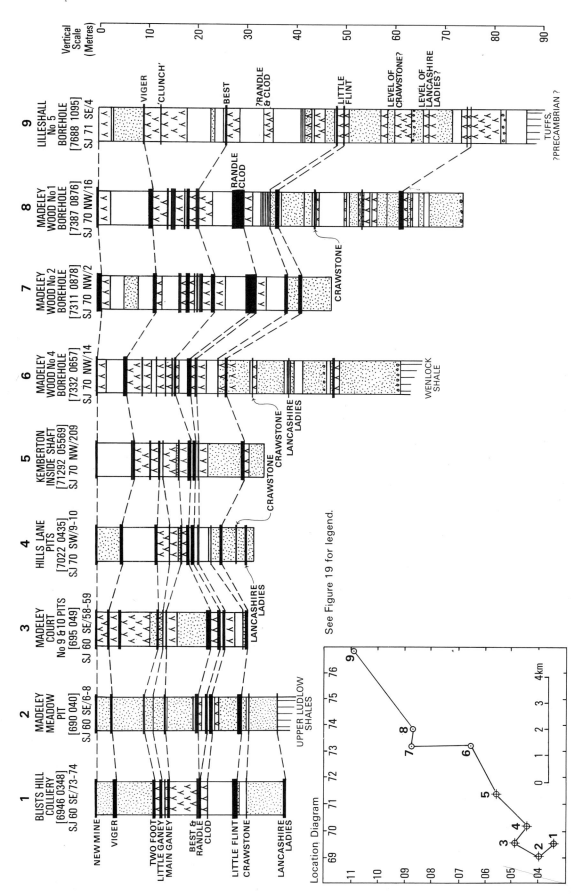

Figure 27 Comparative vertical sections of Lower Coal Measures in the Madeley Syncline.

lain by 0.7 m of grey sandy fireclay with ironstone nodules, but at Madeley Wood No. 6 in the south-east the Little Flint Rock is represented by only 1.7 m of grey seatearth with pale green sandstone layers. A borehole [SO 6841 9920] south-east of Rudgewood Crossroads proved that the strata beneath the Little Flint Coal comprise 11.3 m of yellow sandstone with layers of clay, underlain by 1.83 m of soft yellow conglomeratic sandstone resting on Downtonian rocks. It is possible, here, that the Little Flint Rock has cut down through the Crawstone and Lancashire Ladies coals; or alternatively that these lowest coals may never have been present this far south.

The Little Flint Coal is 0.5 m to 0.8 m thick in Broseley and is present at shallow depth over large areas south-west of the Broseley Fault; it has been widely worked despite its thinness. Eastward and southward from Broseley it thickens to 0.9 m at Amies Field, Caughley and Shirlett Hill [SO 66 98], 0.75 m to 1.15 m at the Caughley [6915 0015] and Ganey [688 000] opencast sites and 0.9 m to 1.1 m in sites around the Linley Green crossroads [SO 6838 9922]. Trenches there revealed three leaves of coal, two upper leaves 0.2 m to 0.3 m thick and a lowermost leaf 0.5 m thick separated by 0.01 m to 0.04 m of black shaly clay; this is the only record of the seam being parted. North of the River Severn the coal is 0.5 m to 1.0 m thick, between Lincoln Hill and Kemberton, and has been widely worked. In most of the Madeley Wood boreholes it is 0.6 m to 0.9 m thick, but thins to around 0.2 m in Madeley Wood No. 3 and Lilleshall No. 5, and is absent in Madeley Wood Underground Borehole No. 6.

The measures between the Little Flint Coal and the Clod Coal are mainly arenaceous below (the Little Flint Coal Rock) and argillaceous above, but the proportions vary considerably. South of the River Severn the Little Flint Coal Rock is absent at Benthall Hall Opencast [6595 0245] but is present elsewhere, ranging up to a maximum thickness of 7.0 m to 8.0 m [SO 688 991] near Rudgewood. Generally it comprises orange, brown and grey, fine-grained, flaggy to massive sandstones and siltstones; it rests directly on the Little Flint Coal except in two areas. At Broseley (?Cockshot Pit) 0.9 m of argillaceous shale was recorded with ironstone nodules beneath it; at the opencast sites around the crossroads at Linley Green [SO 6838 9922], 0.7 m to 2.4 m of black clay occur. At Rudgewood No. 2 Opencast [SO 682 993], the Little Flint Coal Rock is coarse-grained and pebbly, and its base is manifestly erosive, cutting down through the black clay and the Little Flint Coal. Throughout the area south of the Severn the Clod Coal is underlain by up to 2 m of argillaceous measures, typically fireclay above and mudstone with ironstone below. At Amies Field, Prestwich (1840) recorded: Clod Coal; pricking, 0.31 m; Clod Coal Pennystone (i.e. ironstone measures), 0.91 m; black shale, 0.69 m; hard stone (Little Flint Coal Rock), 0.91 m; Little Flint Coal. Locally the Clod Coal seatearth becomes a workable fireclay; on the banks of the Ironbridge Gorge the Ladywood Fireclay Pit worked 0.6 m of 'Clod Clay' until 1953, while the Viger Drift worked 1.07 m of 'Viger Clay' at this level.

North of the Severn the sequence is rather variable; the Little Flint Coal Rock is absent at Lincoln Hill and Blists Hill but 3.4 m thick at Madeley Meadow Pit, where it is underlain by 0.4 m of clod. Conversely, the overlying argillaceous strata, generally up to 2 m thick, are absent at the Lodge Farm Borehole [6756 0370] but reach 4.3 m at Blists Hill, where they include large masses of ironstone. At Madeley Court and Hills Lane pits a thin (0.10 m to 0.17 m) coal is found between the Little Flint and Clod, resting upon 0.15 m to 2.4 m of Little Flint Coal Rock and overlain by argillaceous strata. At Halesfield and Kemberton pits the extra coal is not recorded; the Little Flint Coal Rock is 6.9 m thick at Kemberton and overlain by 1.75 m of fireclay. In boreholes to the north-east, this additional seam

reappears, up to 0.36 m thick and resting upon 1.0 m to 2.4 m of Little Flint Coal Rock, which here comprises fine-grained pale grey sandstone below, with rootlets and coaly films, and grey sandy seatearth above, with ironstone nodules. The additional, unnamed, coal is overlain in the Madeley Wood boreholes by a consistent 3.00 m to 5.69 m thickness of strata; the lower part of this is grey mudstone with ironstone nodules and beds, becoming darker grey to black below, with mussels and fish fragments; and the upper part is grey sandy seatearth and mudstone with ironstone nodules and roots. At Lilleshall No. 5 Borehole these strata are believed to thicken to 14.07 m (Figure 27), and to be made up largely of sandy fireclays and sandy mudstones; they also include shaly sandstones below, beds of black shale and ironstone, and various mussel and fish horizons.

The Clod Coal, south of the Severn, is generally a single seam ranging in thickness from 0.45 m (Yew Tree Pit) to 0.86 m (Benthall Hall Opencast [6598 0238]). However, at one section measured in the Benthall Hall Opencast [6594 0250], a lower seam 0.91 m thick and an upper seam 0.56 m thick were separated by 0.20 m of clay. At Broseley Opencast, boreholes indicated 1.50 m of combined Clod and Randle Coal. The Clod Coal has been worked with the Randle Coal at Madeley Meadow Pit and Madeley Court (Figure 27); it is 0.40 m to 0.76 m thick in Ironbridge and Madeley, thinning north-east to 0.33 m at Foster's Pit, 0.2 m to 0.3 m at Halesfield Pits and 0.25 m at Kemberton Pit. It thickens north-eastwards to 0.91 m and has been worked from Kemberton Pit. In the area of Madeley Wood boreholes Nos. 4 to 6 it is 0.4 m to 0.8 m thick, thickening northwards to 0.9 m in Madeley Wood No. 1 and Madeley Wood Underground No. 11; it is combined with the Randle in Madeley Wood No. 2 (2.24 m thick), No. 3 (2.03 m) and Underground No. 9 (1.98 m). However, it is difficult to distinguish in Lilleshall No. 5, where only 0.05 m of coaly mudstone apparently represents the Randle and Clod.

The parting between the Clod Coal and the Randle Coal south of the River Severn generally comprises up to a metre of grey fireclay, except at Broseley Opencast, Ladywood and Amies Field, where the coals are in contact, and Yew Tree Pit and Broseley (? Cockshot Pit), where it thickens to 2.75 m and 3.66 m respectively. In the latter case the lower part includes ironstone nodules. Boreholes in Ironbridge revealed 0.55 m to 1.45 m of grey-brown mudstone, partly silty or sandy, with roots and scattered ironstone nodules. Shaft sections around Madeley show a rather variable parting of clod or clunch, 0.15 m to 1.12 m thick, but the boreholes to the north-east show only 0 m to 0.46 m of seatearth clay.

The Randle Coal south of the Severn varies between 0.30 m (Benthall Potteries) and 1.07 m (Ganey Opencast), but it combines with the Best Coal at Caughley, Yew Tree Pit and Turner's Yard Pit. North of the river it has been worked with the Best Coal at Ironbridge. Around Madeley and in the boreholes to the north-east it is consistently 0.75 m to 1.1 m thick, except at Madeley Court Nos. 2, 3, 7 and 8 shafts (where it thins to 0.23 m) and at Lilleshall No. 5 Borehole (see above).

The parting between the Randle Coal and the Best Coal south of the Severn comprises up to 0.9 m of grey fireclay, except at the sections mentioned above where there is no parting. Between Roughpark, Blists Hill and Kemberton pits the parting is generally 0.1 m to 0.3 m of bass, except at Madeley Meadow and Madeley Court pits where it is thicker; at Madeley Court Nos. 7 and 8 shafts it reaches 4.7 m, whereas both the Randle and Best coals have thinned considerably. A parting of up to a metre of black carbonaceous mudstone or seatearth occurs to the north-east, in the area worked from Kemberton Pit and in Madeley Wood No. 6 and Madeley Wood underground boreholes Nos. 7, 9, 11 and 14, but a thicker (2.05 m to 6.95 m) parting is recorded in Madeley Wood boreholes Nos. 1, 2, 4, 5, Underground No. 5 and Lilleshall No. 5. In contrast to the situation at Madeley Court, there is here no inverse thickness relationship between the Randle and Best coals and the parting. The thick parting here is lithologically consistent and can be generalised as follows: seatearth, locally with ironstone, up to 2.2 m; mudstone, smooth to silty, with ironstone and plants, up to 5.4 m; black shale with fish, up to 0.15 m.

The Best Coal is very variable in thickness; south of the Severn (Figure 28) it ranges from 0.15 m to 1.22m. At Ganey and Caughley opencast sites it is split, with a lower leaf 0.58 m to 0.65 m thick and an upper leaf 0.30 m to 0.35 m thick separated by 0.19 m to 0.30 m of pale grey-brown fireclay. Shaft sections north of the Severn show variation between 0.61 m at Roughpark and 0.99 m at Lloyds Water Engine Air Pit, but only 0.25 m at Madeley Court and Madeley Wood collieries. The seam thickness is also variable in the boreholes to the northeast. At Madeley Wood boreholes Nos. 4, 5, and 6 it is split, with a lower leaf 0.33 m to 0.58 m thick and an upper leaf 0.20 m to 0.43 m thick separated by 0.08 m to 1.04 m of dirt. Elsewhere it is a single seam, which ranges from 0.18 m of coal on 0.15 m of black coaly mudstone at Madeley Wood Underground Borehole No. 11, to 0.84 m of coal in No. 7, and 0.29 m of coal and dirt on 0.80 m of coal in No. 9.

The strata between the Best Coal and the Two Foot Coal are thicker in the Madeley Syncline than elsewhere. In Benthall, Posenhall and Willeypark, the Best Coal Rock is up to 4 m thick and is overlain by thinner sandy fireclays; a thin canneloid coal locally rests upon the Best Coal Rock north of Benthall Potteries [662 020]. The fireclays above the Rock were worked as 'Bottom Fireclay' (0.54 m thick) at Deerleap Mine. A section was recorded on the high wall in the north-east part of Willeypark Opencast [675 009] in 1944:

	Thickness m
Yellow-grey sandy clay and fireclay with ironstone nodules	3.66
Sandstone, yellow, lenticular	0.30
Shale, sandy, with lenticular sandstone beds; fireclays near base	2.44
Best Coal	—

The Best Coal Rock thickens to 5.48 m at Yew Tree Pit, and it is well developed in Ironbridge and Madeley. It is thickest (7.4 m) in Madeley Court Nos. 2 and 3 shafts and generally overlain by up to 1.8 m of fireclay. In Jockey Bank No. 2 Borehole [6786 0349] the Rock comprised coarse-grained, pale grey-brown sandstone with red and green siliceous rock fragments up to 2 mm across (possibly from the Uriconian), as well as angular fragments of quartzite up to 5 mm across. Elsewhere north of the Severn the Rock is not represented, the equivalent interval being composed of dark indurated clay called 'Linseed Earth'. This is 0.9 m thick in the Roughpark and 0.8 m to 5.2 m thick in the area between Lloyds Pit and Kemberton Pit. Similar clays occur in the Madeley Wood boreholes, and 7.6 m of sandy mudstone and fine-grained sandstone occur in Lilleshall No. 5 in the extreme north-east.

The Two Foot Coal of the Donnington Syncline is represented by two or three coals in the Madeley Syncline. The lowest of these is called the *Main* or *Lower Ganey*, the highest is called the *Upper Ganey* or *Two Foot*, and a *Little Ganey Coal* is locally developed in between. The successions in localities south and north of the Broseley Fault are shown in Figure 28. All three coals are represented in the Posenhall and Benthall outliers and around the Ladywood Fireclay Mine. The Main Ganey Coal is 0.3 m to 0.7 m thick, overlain by up to 1.5 m of workable fireclay around Benthall and Ladywood. The Little Ganey Coal is 0.15 m to 0.45 m thick, overlain by up to 2.0 m of fireclay and up to 0.5 m of Upper Ganey Coal. South of Benthall, in Broseley and at Caughley (Williams, 1846), only the Lower and Upper Ganey coals are present, respectively 0.4 m to 0.9 m and 0.5 m to 0.6 m thick and separated by 3 m to 8 m of mixed sandstones and fireclays. In the Caughley Opencast [6915 0015] a coal believed to be the Main Ganey (0.6 m thick) lay at the base of a washout cutting down into the Best Coal Rock. The upper part of the coal was canneloid and overlain by 4 m of mudstone with scattered ironstone nodules above. The Main Ganey Coal (0.5 m thick) similarly rested at the base of a washout in the Ganey Opencast [688 000].

North of the Severn the three Ganey Coals are present, closely spaced at the Lloyds, Blists Hill and Madeley Court pits, more widely spaced at Hills Lane and Roughpark. The Main Ganey Coal ranges from 0.31 m (Blists Hill) to 0.51 m (Madeley Court Nos. 9 and 10 shafts). It is overlain at most shafts (Lloyds, Hills Lane, Madeley Court, Blists Hill, Kemberton) by 0.1 m to 0.3 m of sandstone and then by 0.3 m to 2.57 m of fireclays, but the whole interval is sandstone at Roughpark (7.3 m) and Meadow Pit (2.06 m). The Little Ganey Coal thickens north-eastwards, from 0.15 m at the Lloyds and Meadow pits, to 0.23 m at Madeley Court Pits and 0.25 m at Halesfield and Kemberton, but it is apparently absent at Foster's Pits. The strata between it and the Upper Ganey normally consist of clunch 0.51 m to 3.05 m thick but Meadow Pit records 3.15 m of rock and 0.20 m of pricking, while Lloyds Pit records 1.07 m of pale clunch, 1.12 m of rocky binds and 0.56 m of fireclay. The Upper Ganey Coal ranges in thickness from 0.35 m at Blists Hill to 0.61 m at Madeley Court Nos. 7 and 8 shafts, and it was worked from Madeley Court Nos. 9 and 10 shafts; although only 0.51 m thick at the shafts, it increased west-north-westwards to between 0.71 m and 0.76 m and is a good sulphur-free coking coal.

The measures between the Upper Ganey (Two Foot) Coal and the Viger Coal in the Madeley Syncline are thicker than the equivalent measures between the Two Foot and Clunch coals in the Donnington Syncline. At Benthall, Ladywood and Ironbridge up to 7.3 m of strata are recorded, comprising sandstones and siltstones passing up into fireclays and mudstones, with some nodular ironstone beds, carbonaceous layers and thin coals (Figure 28). Towards the top a fireclay, the Viger Clay, has been worked below the Viger Coal at Benthall and Ladywood Fireclay Mine; at the latter, 0.72 m of 'Two Foot Clay Top' has also been worked immediately above the Two Foot Coal. Between Roughpark and Blists Hill, a sequence of sandstones and mudstones, referred to as the Two Foot Rock, is 4.0 m to 9.6 m thick (thickest at Lloyds Pit) and includes ironstone nodules at Blists Hill and Madeley Meadow pits. At Madeley Court Pits the Two Foot Rock is represented by only 1.2 m to 3.6 m of sandstone overlying the Two Foot Coal, and is itself overlain by 1.7 m to 8.3 m of fireclays which include a coal seam 0.15 m to 0.40 m thick. Farther east at Foster's, Halesfield and Kemberton pits the Rock is absent, the sequence comprising 2.4 m to 4.6 m of fireclay including a coal 0.15 m to 0.30 m thick. This seam is called the 'Clunch Coal' at Madeley Court Pits, but it is not the Clunch Coal of the Donnington Syncline, which is equivalent to the Viger. Megaspores were abundant in the roof of the Two Foot Coal at Caughley Opencast.

In boreholes north-east from Kemberton Pit, the measures between the Best and Viger coals are mostly seatearths including up to 5 coals. These evidently equate with the four coals which farther south include the 'Clunch' and the three Ganey seams, but no exact correlation can be made. The thickest seam recorded is 0.79 m in Madeley Wood Underground Borehole No. 7. Black carbonaceous mudstones are common; three

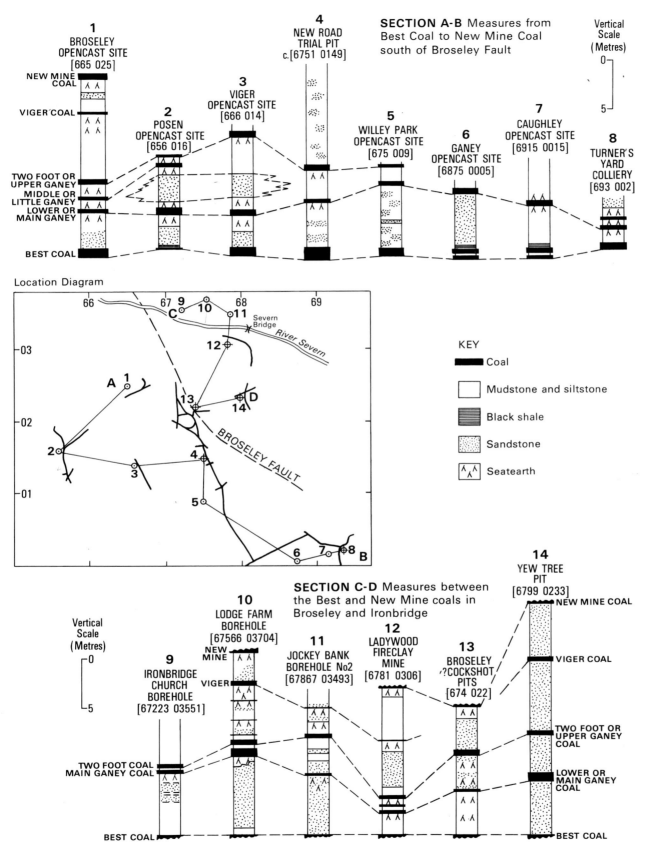

Figure 28 Comparative vertical sections in the Lower Coal Measures in the south of the exposed coalfield.

occur in Madeley Wood Underground Borehole No. 7, with megaspores above the Two Foot Coal in Madeley Wood No. 4. Grey mudstones occur, particularly above the highest coal, but ironstones are rare.

The Viger Coal is a single seam throughout the Madeley Syncline, and is considered to equate with the Clunch Coal of the Donnington Syncline. It is only 0.15 m thick at Benthall, Jockey Bank No. 2 Borehole [6786 0349], Ladywood Fireclay Mine and Roughpark, but thickens steadily north-eastwards to a maximum of 1.09 m in Madeley Wood No. 3 Borehole. However, it then thins to 0.23 m at Lilleshall No. 5 in the far north-east. It has been worked north-east of Halesfield, where it is 0.76 m to 0.84m in thickness.

The measures between the Viger Coal and the New Mine Coal in the Madeley Syncline are more arenaceous than those between the equivalent Clunch and New Mine coals in the Donnington Syncline. Only at Madeley and Halesfield is the interval wholly of fireclay; this is thickest (5.7 m) at Madeley Court No. 5 Shaft, where two thin coals are included. Conversely, between Blists Hill and Roughpark it is wholly of fine-grained grey sandstone, the Viger Coal Rock; this is thickest (4.9 m) at Hills Lane Pits. Elsewhere, in Ironbridge, south of the Severn and north-east from Kemberton Pit, thin fireclays overlie sandy shales and siltstones with lenses of massive sandstone. These dominantly arenaceous measures thicken southwards and eastwards from 2 m to 3 m at Roughpark to 5.5 m at Yew Tree Pit, Broseley (Figure 28) and to 10.3 m at Madeley Wood Borehole No. 2. The lower part of these measures is the Viger Coal Rock, while the upper part has locally been worked as the New Mine Clay at Benthall. The strata in the Madeley Wood Boreholes can be generalised as follows: New Mine Coal; fireclay seatearth, 0.8 m to 3.0 m; grey silty mudstones and siltstones, commonly with ironstone nodules and beds of fine-grained pale grey sandstone, Viger Coal Rock, 3.6 m to 8.9 m; dark grey mudstone with fish remains, 0 m to 0.15 m; Viger Coal.

The New Mine Coal was 0.3 m to 0.5 m thick in the outlier at Benthall [666 024]. Coal seen at outcrop on the banks of a pond at Dungegrove [6784 0085] is probably the New Mine, but north and east of there is lost beneath the Hadley Formation unconformity. At Broseley (?Cockshot Pit) 0.46 m of New Mine Coal was recorded, and a 0.69 m thickness was mined at the Ladywood Sulphur Coal levels between Jackfield and Ladywood. From Ironbridge to Kemberton Pits the seam is only 0.30 m to 0.46 m thick, but was worked with the Pennystone at Hills Lane Pits. In Madeley Wood boreholes north-east of Kemberton Pits, it ranges from 0.15 m (No. 4 Borehole) to 0.66 m (No. 2); farther to the north-east, at No. 3 Borehole, it splits into a lower seam 0.28 m thick and an upper seam 0.43 m thick with a seatearth parting 0.61 m thick, and at Lilleshall No. 5 Borehole it is absent.

Middle Coal Measures

The strata between the New Mine Coal and the Big Flint Coal comprise the Pennystone Measures (including the Pennystone Marine Band) and the Big Flint Rock. *The Pennystone ironstone* is recorded as 1.83 m thick in Yew Tree Pit, Broseley, and 3.0 m to 3.5 m of shaly mudstone with ironstone nodules and lenticular beds were proved in boreholes for Broseley Opencast [664 022]. Between Ironbridge and Kemberton Pit the ironstone varies in thickness from about 1.2 m to 2.5 m; it has been worked at adits along its outcrop in the Ironbridge gorge [as at 6745 0351], and at Hills Lane Pits where it is described as 1.22 m of dark shale with small flattish ironstone nodules. The ironstone includes the **Pennystone Marine Band**; in workings from Kemberton Colliery, *Ammodiscus* sp. and *Lingula mytilloides* were collected 0 m to 0.05 m above the New Mine Coal, and

these species plus *Orbiculoidea* cf. *nitida* and *Rhabdoderma* sp. were found in backfill to Pennystone ironstone workings. In Madeley Wood boreholes, north-east of Kemberton Pit, mudstones ascribable to the Pennystone Measures thicken from 2.26 m (Underground Borehole No. 7) to 5.91 m (Borehole No. 2). The lower part (varying from 1.06 m in Borehole No. 4 to 1.93 m in Underground Borehole No. 5) is dark grey, generally smooth but locally silty, normally with ironstone nodules, and containing *Lingula mytilloides* and *Orbiculoidea* cf. *nitida* below and mussels and fish remains above. The upper part (0.38 m in Underground Borehole No. 7, but up to 4.57 m in Borehole No. 2) consists of grey silty mudstone with ironstone nodules.

The Big Flint Rock was exposed in a small opencast south of Benthall [6630 0178]; 2 m of deeply weathered and reddened sandstone, coarse-grained with many laminated bands of espley-type grit, were overlain by a metre of sandy fireclay below the Big Flint Coal. North of the Broseley Fault, massive sandstone is recorded at Yew Tree Pit (5.5 m) and Ladywood Fireclay Mine (4.0 m); this sandstone forms a prominent feature above the gorge in Ironbridge and causes rapids where it crosses the River Severn [6845 0315]. An exposure [6736 0354] shows medium- to coarse-grained, massive grey sandstone, wispy bedded and very ferruginous towards the base. Jockey Bank Borehole No. 1 [6789 0358] recorded 0.6 m of fireclay overlying 3.5 m of Big Flint Rock; farther east the sandstone is generally around 5 m thick but reaches 9.6 m at Madeley Court Nos. 9 and 10 shafts. At Hills Lane it is described by Prestwich (1840) as fine-grained white sandstone with a few patches of petroleum.

North-east of Kemberton Pit, measures ascribed to the Big Flint Rock vary widely, the sequence being thickest (10.95 m) at Madeley Wood Underground Borehole No. 7:

	Thickness m
Big Flint Coal	—
Seatearth, grey-brown, silty	1.19
Siltstone, pale grey, scattered plants, sandy beds, silty mudstone beds	2.92
Mudstone, grey, silty, scattered plants, ironstone beds	2.95
Siltstone, grey, sandy wisps and layers, oily layers	3.25
Sandstone, fine- to medium-grained, bedded, oily impregnation	0.64
Pennystone Measures	—

Nearby, Underground Borehole No. 6 records a similar sequence, but includes a thicker (4.72 m) oily sandstone at the bottom. Farther south the mudstone thickens at the expense of the sandstone and Madeley Wood Borehole No. 4 records 0.91 m of pale grey sandstone below 7.01 m of grey silty mudstone with ironstone nodules. In the north-east, pale grey massive sandstones are found, 5.99 m thick in Madeley Wood Borehole No. 1 and 2.44 m in Lilleshall Borehole No. 5 (Figure 29). Madeley Wood Borehole No. 5 in the south-east revealed the thinnest sequence in the area:

	Thickness m
Big Flint Coal	—
Seatearth, very sandy, with rootlets	0.15
Big Flint Rock: sandstone, pale grey, dark carbonaceous wisps	0.08
Pennystone Measures	—

The following fauna was collected 'from base of Flint Coal' from the tip heaps of Kemberton Colliery: *Spirorbis*, *Anthracosia aquilina*, *A.* sp. intermediate between *aquilina* and *phrygiana*,

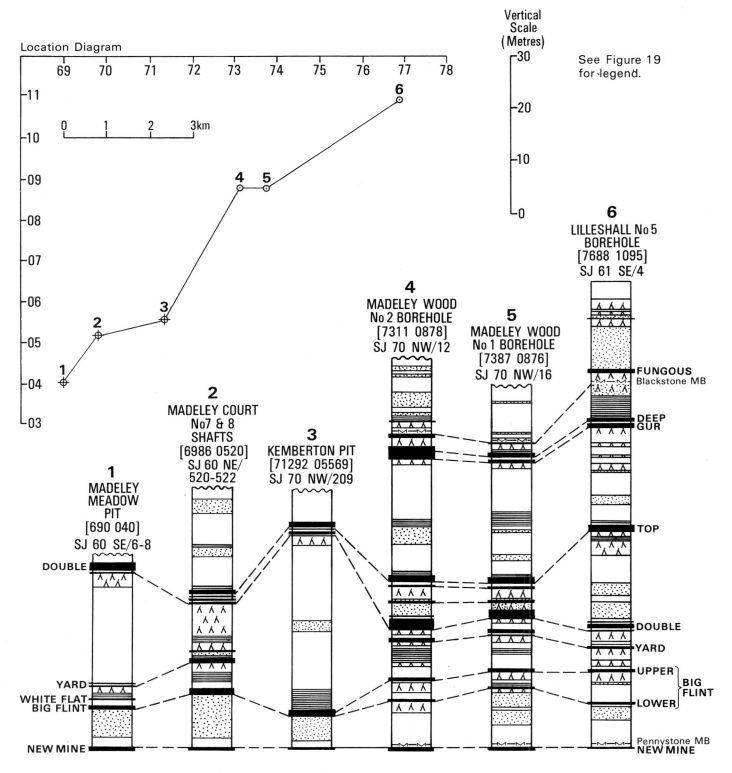

Figure 29   Comparative vertical sections of the Middle Coal Measures in the Madeley Syncline.

Anthracosphaerium sp. (juv.), *Naiadites* sp., *Carbonita humilis*, and fish scales including *Megalichthys*, a platysomid and *Rhizodopsis*.

The Big Flint Coal was extensively mined and worked opencast, in outliers north and south of Benthall Potteries [662 020], where the coal was about 1.5 m thick. In Yew Tree Pit, Broseley, it is present as 0.9 m of 'Bottom Coal'. In the Ironbridge Gorge the coal crops out between the River Severn [6848 0314] and Ironbridge Church [at 6729 0359], beyond which it is cut out by the Hadley Formation. It was widely worked between that incrop and Madeley, being 0.91 m to 1.11 m thick. At Hills Lane, 1.52 m of coal were separated from the base of the Hadley Formation by about 2 m of shale, while Prestwich (1840) records the shale but no coal, suggesting that, in places, the latter was removed by oxidation below the unconformity. It was worked from both Halesfield and Kemberton pits; thicknesses quoted range from 1.22 m to 1.42 m (single seam) to split seams with 0.51 m to 0.64 m (lower leaf) and 0.51 m to 0.53 m (upper leaf).

Madeley Wood boreholes north-east from Kemberton Pits all record a split seam, too thin to work (Figure 29). The lower leaf thickens north-eastwards, from 0.20 m at Borehole No. 4 to 0.16 m (overlying 0.15 m of shaly coal) at No. 3. The parting similarly thickens from 1.12 m at Borehole No. 4 to 3.68 m at No. 3. It comprises 0.33 m to 1.22 m of dark grey silty mudstone with ironstone nodules below, and 0.87 m to 2.41 m of grey seatearth mudstone with ironstone above. The upper leaf of coal thickens from 0.36 m in Borehole No. 4 to 0.66 m in No. 3. Lilleshall Borehole No. 5 shows a lower leaf 0.30 m thick and an upper leaf 0.61 m thick separated by a parting 5.49 m thick (Figure 29), and Madeley Wood No. 5 Borehole, to the south-east, contains two coal leaves 0.30 m thick with a parting 6.17 m thick.

The measures between the Big Flint Coal and the Yard Coal are largely absent south of the River Severn, but thin black shales and mudstones survive below the Hadley Formation unconformity at Yew Tree Pit and north of Benthall Potteries [6620 0200]. North of the river the measures are also much affected by the Hadley Formation unconformity and by a washout later than the Yard Coal. Where the whole of this interval is preserved, it correlates well with the standard succession in the Dawley area, although it is thin, only 3.7 m at Madeley Meadow Pit (Figure 29). The White Flat is not mentioned by name and is absent at Madeley Court Nos. 9 and 10 shafts, but from Blists Hill to Kemberton Pit it is represented by up to 1.22 m of dark mudstone with ironstone nodules. This is overlain by 1.3 m to 2.8 m of black bass, including 0.20 m to 0.25 m of White Flat Coal (known hereabouts as the Sill Coal) at Blists Hill, Meadow Pit and Madeley Court. At Madeley Court Pits, Nos. 7 to 10 shafts (Figure 29), 1.37 m of Blue Flat are recorded overlain by 0.30 m to 0.46 m of seatearth to the Yard Coal. North-east of Kemberton Shaft, *Anthracosia* aff. *aquilina*, *A.* cf. and aff. *phrygiana*, *A.* cf. *ovum* and *A.* aff. *regularis* are recorded in the shales 0 m to 0.1 m above the Big Flint Coal, indicating the *Modiolaris* Zone. North-east from Kemberton Pit, Madeley Wood boreholes reveal a sequence which thickens from 4.78 m in Borehole No. 4 to 8.13 m in No. 3; it is consistently divisible into four units:

	Thickness m
Yard Coal seatclay, grey below, black and carbonaceous above	0.48–2.54
Dark grey to black mudstone with ironstone nodules (Blue Flat)	2.50
Black shale with ironstone, fish, mussels, ostracods; often cannelly	1.04–1.50
Medium grey to black mudstone; ironstone nodules (White Flat), mussels, fish	1.14–2.90

Farther north, Lilleshall No. 5 Borehole contains a less carbonaceous parting; 0.38 m of grey mudstone with fish and mussels underlie 3.28 m of grey to black ferruginous mudstone and fireclay.

The Yard Coal is recorded as 'layers of coal and slum' at Madeley Meadow Pit by Prestwich (1840); it is 0.76 m to 1.07 m thick. The coal is 1.0 m thick at Madeley Court Nos. 7 to 10 shafts, but is cut out by later washout strata south of the Severn and at Madeley Court Nos. 2, 3 and 5 shafts, Halesfield, Kemberton and Foster's pits. North-east of Kemberton Pit the Yard Coal is everywhere present, as a split seam. The lower leaf thickens from 0.38 m at Madeley Wood Borehole No. 4 to 0.58 m at No. 3, overlain by 0.08 m to 0.15 m of dirt or carbonaceous mudstone and a further 0.48 m to 0.64 m of coal.

The measures between the Yard Coal and the Double Coal are represented south of the River Severn, and in Madeley, by a washout succession of sandstones, siltstones and mudstones (Figure 30). The overall structure of the washout is similar to that which occurs above the Brickmeasure ironstone in the Dawley area: the channel is orientated north-east to south-west (in this case along the axis of the Madeley Syncline), with maximum erosion in the south-west and maximum deposition in the north-east. Boreholes for Broseley Opencast [664 022] show massive coarse-grained sandstone, gently unconformable on black shales overlying the Big Flint Coal. Shaft sections for Yew Tree Pit, Broseley (?Cockshot Pits), and Ladywood Fireclay Mine, all appear to show washout strata beneath the Hadley Formation. At ?Cockshot Pits, these rest upon the Pennystone, this being the lowest level they reach (Figure 30). The Lodge Farm Borehole [6756 0370] proved 8.02 m of washout strata beneath the Hadley Formation. These strata comprise fine-grained sandstones normally very carbonaceous, and mudstones, containing abundant plant debris and scattered ironstone nodules. The mudstones were smooth to silty or sandy. Some 20.8 m of washout strata overlie the Yard Coal at Madeley Meadow Pit, and this thickness increases to 31.52 m at Madeley Court No. 5 Pit (Figure 30). The considerable thickness variation in the various shafts for Madeley Court Pits suggests that these lie along the margin of the washout; thus, only 10.3 m are recorded at Nos. 7 and 8 shafts. At Halesfield, Kemberton and Fosters pits, around 30 m of washout strata rest respectively on the Big Flint Rock, the Pitchy Bass and the Big Flint Coal. Boreholes from the Wyke to Haughton record a much thinner (1.56 m to 2.00 m) interval, more like the standard sequence of the Dawley area. The sequence at Madeley Wood No. 7 may be taken as typical:

	Thickness m
Seatearth, silty, dark grey, listric surfaces	0.18
Mudstone, dark grey; plant fragments, rootlets, listric surfaces	1.30
Mudstone, dark grey with mussels	0.15
Mudstone, pale grey, plant fragments	0.20

Anthracosia phrygiana is recorded in the roof of the Yard Coal in Kemberton Colliery workings. The sequence thickens northwards to 2.44 m at Madeley Wood Borehole No. 3 then to 3.1 m at Lilleshall No. 5 (Figure 29), where ironstones are recorded at the level of the Yellowstone:

	Thickness m
Soft grey fireclay	1.83
Mudstone, pale grey; ironstone beds, plants	0.61
Coal	0.03
Very soft grey fireclay	0.51
Shale, black; faintly micaceous, fish fragments	0.15

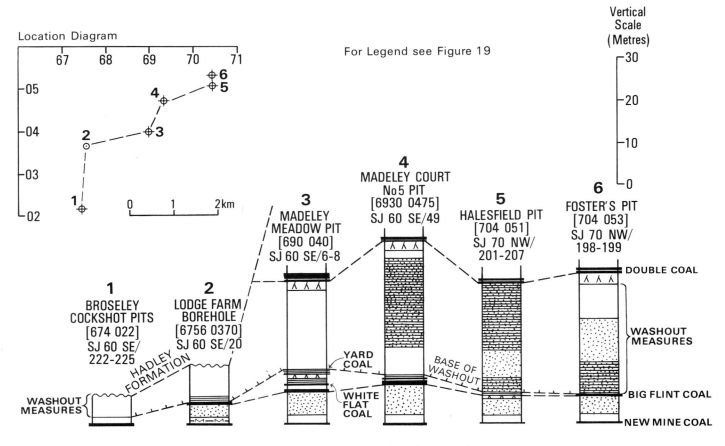

Figure 30 Comparative vertical sections showing the Yard Coal washout in the south-western part of the Madeley Syncline, compared with the standard sequence shown in Figure 29.

The Double Coal is a split seam throughout the area; it has been worked at Madeley Meadow and Madeley Court collieries, but has not been mined north of Kemberton Pit. From Brick Kiln Leasowe to Kemberton Pit it comprises a lower leaf 0.15 m to 0.64 m thick, separated by a 0.08 m to 0.23 m parting of sandstone from an upper leaf 0.45 m to 0.63 m thick. North-east of Kemberton Pit it is split into three to five leaves; the thickest leaf reaches a maximum thickness of 2.32 m in Madeley Wood Borehole No. 2. The total seam thickness ranges from 1.83 m (Lilleshall No. 5) to 3.13 m (Madeley Wood No. 3); the combined coal thickness ranges from 1.29 m (Madeley Wood Underground Borehole No. 6) to 2.63 m (Madeley Wood No. 2).

The parting between the Double Coal and the Three-Quarter Coal from Brick Kiln Leasowe Pits to Kemberton Pit comprises only 0.08 m to 0.23 m of dark carbonaceous clay. However, Madeley Wood boreholes 1, 2 and 8 record 1.07 m to 2.62 m of Double Coal Rock in this interval, consisting of pale grey or cream, fine-grained and silty sandstone. This is separated from the Double Coal by 0.30 m of black coaly mudstone in Borehole No. 8, while fish fragments are recorded in dark sandy mudstone overlying the Double Coal in Lilleshall No. 5.

The Three-Quarter Coal is 0.22 m to 0.58 m thick throughout the area, thickest in Madeley Wood No. 2 Borehole. It is locally but incorrectly known as the Foot Coal between Brick Kiln Leasowe and Kemberton pits, where it is separated from the Top Coal by only 0.05 m to 0.20 m of dark clay. In Madeley Wood boreholes 1, 2 and 8 the parting is thicker and the true Foot Coal of the Dawley area is recorded:

	Thickness m
Top Coal	—
Seatclay, dark grey to black, carbonaceous	0.13–0.43
Foot Coal; with dirt bands	0.30–0.48
Seatclay; pale grey to black, carbonaceous, silty	1.50–2.21
Three-Quarter Coal Rock; sandstone, white, cream, grey, fine-grained	0.20–0.53
Three-Quarter Coal	—

At Lilleshall No. 5 Borehole this parting is apparently even thicker, but difficult to delimit as the Foot and Three-Quarter coals are not known.

The Top Coal is a single good quality seam throughout the area, 1.1 m to 1.7 m thick, and has been worked up to its incrop from Madeley Meadow Pit to Shifnal.

The measures between the Top Coal and the Gur Coal are similar to the standard sequence in the Dawley area. The sections for the Madeley Court Pits can be generalised as follows, overlain by the Hadley Formation in all cases:

	Thickness m
Mudstones and shales	up to at least 2.3
Sandstone	0.6–2.7
Brickmeasure; ironstone and mudstone	1.9–6.0
Black shale	0.3–0.7
Sandstone and binds	0.9–5.8

	Thickness m
Ballstone; ironstone and mudstone	1.9–6.0
Black shale and cannel	0.2–0.5

Farther north-east along the Madeley Syncline, the Hadley unconformity removes most of these measures. Throughout the Top Coal workings north-east of Kemberton Pit the Top Coal roof comprises 0.30 m of black bass packed with mussels (*Anthracosia* cf. *aquilinoides* and *Anthracosphaerium radiatum*) preserved in brown ironstone, beneath mudstone or blue bind. However, in some places there is evidence of washout conditions below this normal roof. The coal thins from the top downwards, often to only a few centimetres, and is cut by intrusive dykes of grey sandstone, which are up to 0.3 m across, slightly sinuous, and branch off into horizontal sill-like lenses. The dykes trend east-south-east and have been recorded also in the Double Coal.

North-east of Haughton Farm the diachronous base of the Hadley Formation rises rapidly and all the measures below the Deep and Gur coals are recorded in Madeley Wood boreholes 1 to 3 and 8, and Lilleshall No. 5. This interval ranges in thickness from 18.7 m (Lilleshall No. 5) to 25.4 m (Madeley Wood No. 3), and can be generalised as follows:

	Thickness m
Seatearth; grey silty mudstone (ironstone nodules in Borehole No. 2; black and coaly above in No. 1)	1.0–1.3
Sandstone, pale grey, fine-grained; (Borehole 8 only)	0.13
Mudstone, grey, silty; ironstone nodules (Brickmeasure)	8.5–10.7
Black silty shale; mussels, fish remains, ironstone nodules (Bind Bass)	1.5–2.4
Pale mudstones and sandstones; lower strata are pale to dark grey silty mudstone with ironstone nodules, lenses and beds (Ballstone), passing upwards in all but borehole No. 8 into 3.4–7.1 m of pale fine-grained sandstone and silty mudstone (Bind Rock)	8.3–10.0
Black shale with mussels preserved in ironstone (cannelly in borehole No. 1, fish fragments in Lilleshall No. 5)	0.15–0.7

The Gur Coal is part of the Deep Coal in Madeley Wood boreholes 2 and 3, but is present as a separate 0.7 m seam in No. 1 and Lilleshall No. 5 boreholes, overlain by 0.2 m of dark coaly dirt. **The Deep Coal** is 0.84 m thick in Lilleshall No. 5 and 1.17 m in Madeley Wood No. 1, but 2.29 m and 1.42 m thick in Nos. 2 and 3, where it includes the Gur. It is succeeded by 1.9 m to 2.5 m of dark grey to black seatearth in Madeley Wood Nos. 1, 2 and 3, but by the following 6.55 m sequence in Lilleshall No. 5: Blackstone Coal or Marine Band; grey sandy fireclay and sandstone, 2.59 m; black fireclay with ironstone (Blackstone), 0.15 m; black cannelly mudstone with fish and mussels, 3.81 m; Deep Coal. **The Blackstone Coal** is around 0.4 m thick at Madeley Wood, but absent in Lilleshall No. 5 Borehole. It is overlain by

the Blackstone Marine Band, which contains fish and *Lingula*; this is 1.30 m to 1.37 m thick in the south, but only 0.61 m at Lilleshall No. 5. The overlying beds are 1.4 m to 1.7 m thick, fireclays above and dark grey mudstone with ironstones and fish fragments below. **The Fungous Coal** measures 0.13 m at Madeley Wood Borehole No. 2, 1.07 m at No. 3 and 0.61 m at Lilleshall No. 5, but is absent in Madeley Wood No. 1 (Figure 29).

Grey measures above the Fungous Coal are preserved only in Madeley Wood 1, 2 and 3 and Lilleshall No. 5 boreholes. In the first two, the measures are truncated by the base of the Hadley Formation below the level of the Chance Pennystone Marine Band, but in No. 3, 30 m of strata are recorded up to the marine band:

	Thickness m
Mudstone, with *Lingula* in lowest 0.9 m; **Chance Pennystone Marine Band**	3.35
Carbonaceous shale with coal streaks; seatearth, mudstone, sandstone, mudstone	7.47
Coal, 0.03 m; seatearth, 0.84 m; inferior coal, 0.13 m; black mudstone, 0.23 m; coal, 0.13 m	1.35
Mudstone, with ironstone and sandstone beds, mussels towards base	8.79
Fungous Coal	—

Lilleshall No. 5 Borehole records the Fungous Coal, overlain by 8.4 m of grey and brown striped sandstones, followed by 8.5 m of mudstones, fireclays and shales. The Chance Pennystone Marine Band is not recorded, but the strata appear to pass conformably up into the Hadley Formation (Figure 29).

Secondary reddening of the productive measures

Logging of the Madeley Wood Colliery boreholes revealed oxidation and reddening of the productive measures to a maximum of 14.3 m below the Hadley Formation unconformity. In boreholes Nos. 2 and 4, respectively 3.8 m and 14.3 m of measures younger than the Fungous Coal were reddened. In No. 8, 8.4 m of strata were reddened, and the Fungous to Gur coals were removed by oxidation. In No. 7 the Top Coal had been similarly removed although only 2.2 m of measures were reddened. In No. 5, 11.7 m of measures were reddened, the Top Coal was replaced by siderite and hematite, and the Double Coal was removed.

In Madeley Wood Underground Boreholes Nos. 8 and 10, the Hadley Formation rested on reddened strata as low as the level of the Yard and Big Flint coals. The oldest secondarily reddened strata in the Madeley Wood boreholes were revealed in No. 6, where only 15.8 m of Lower Coal Measures seatearth and mudstone were preserved above the Best Coal, with the highest 11.4 m reddened. A thin seam of inferior coal occurred 3.66 m above the Best Coal, but all higher coals had been removed by oxidation. In this borehole, red-brown slickensided and hematitised mudstone, with pink grit fragments, was seen to overlie a seatearth 3.81 m below the base of the Hadley Formation; this was interpreted as indicating destruction of the Viger Coal and collapse of the overlying mudstones.

FIVE

Upper Coal Measures: details of stratigraphy

The Upper Coal Measures (or barren measures) are divided stratigraphically into four formations: Hadley Formation and the equivalent Ruabon Marl; Coalport Formation and equivalent Coed-yr-Allt Beds; Keele Beds; and Enville Beds. Description is based on three geographical areas (Figure 31) — the Madeley area and the Dawley area, as in Chapter 4, and the Wellington area north of the Boundary Fault, where some of the terminology from the Shrewsbury district is used. Within each of these areas the strata are described from south-west to north-east.

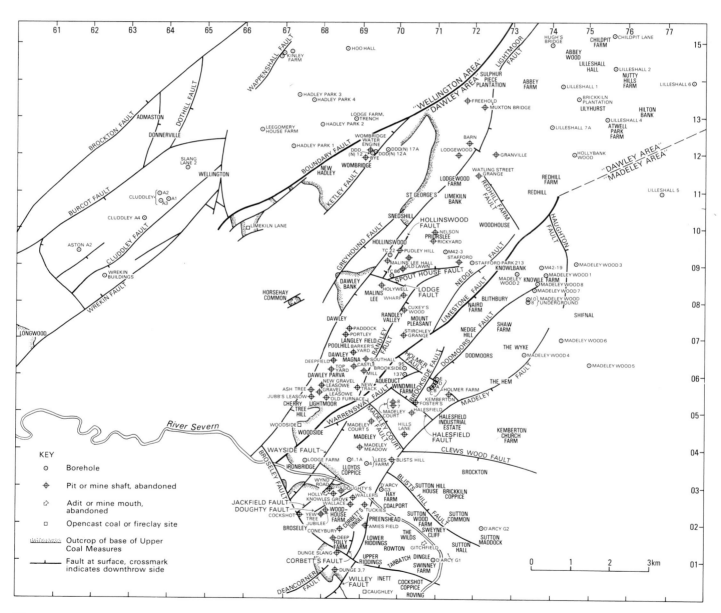

Figure 31 Localities of shafts, adits, boreholes and opencast sites in Upper Coal Measures (except Crow Hayes Pit [7402 1568], and Lilleshall No. 3 Borehole [7570 1598], which lie to the north).

HADLEY FORMATION

Madeley area

South of the River Severn the Hadley Formation is up to 55 m thick (Figure 12), and rests unconformably on Silurian strata or productive measures. The formation consists of roughly equal amounts of sandstones and argillaceous strata; the former are partly espleys, and partly laminated or flaggy, grey or ferruginous sandstones, lacking angular megaclasts. The term 'Rough Rock' is widely used to describe the espleys. Although the term has been used to imply a single stratigraphical horizon (e.g. Randall, 1873), up to three lenticular sandstones are recorded at various localities and there is no one continuous bed. The argillaceous strata are mostly red or purple and have been extensively worked, both underground and opencast, for brick- and tile-clays.

In the Caughley Opencast, the working face in 1972 [SO 6915 9995] exposed more than 18 m of Hadley Formation, including three espleys, 3.0 m to 3.5 m thick; the lowest of these lay at the base of the formation, and was overlain by 7 m of grey, purple, blue and red mottled clays worked for the manufacture of refractories. In the Slang Shaft at Dunge Colliery [6840 0122] 20.4 m of Hadley Formation again included three sandstones separated by a brick clay and a tile clay, but Borehole G1 [7094 0104] beside the River Severn records only 6.8 m of multicoloured marls between the Main Sulphur Coal (conventionally taken as the base of Coalport Formation) and the Silurian. Several mines worked brick clays and tile clays; for example the following section was measured in the Gitchfield Level [7070 0148]: Main Sulphur Coal; clay, 1.5 m; brick clay, 3.05 m to 4.3 m; red tile clay, 1.8 m to 3.7 m; rock with seam of calaminker, 7.3 m to 7.6 m; fireclay, rather purplish, probably transitional to Lower Coal Measures, 0.9 m to 1.2 m. At Yew Tree [6799 0233], Deep [683 016] and Amies Field [approximately 6915 0195] pits, a single sandstone up to 17 m thick is recorded within the formation, and associated brick clays and tile clays were worked both here and at the Tuckies [691 025] and Wallers [688 027] pits near the Severn.

Between the Doughty and Jackfield faults (Figure 31), numerous small mines worked red tile clays. These tile clays are 1.98 m thick at Knowles Pit, 1.83 m at Wynd Road Pit and Holly Grove Level, 1.52 m at Jubilee Pit and 3.1 m at Doughty's Mine, overlain and underlain by sandstone in all cases. North of the Jackfield and Broseley faults the Hadley Formation includes three mappable sandstones and at least four worked clay horizons. In Ironbridge at least two sandstones occur, one at the base of the formation and one within it. Lodge Farm Borehole [6756 0370] was situated on the outcrop of the higher bed and recorded:

	Thickness m
Glacial Drift	—
Espley sandstone; pale grey, fine- to medium-grained, containing pale green and pinkish grains of Uriconian tuff and rhyolite, chips of red and grey mudstone and limestone fragments, together with conglomeratic layers largely composed of subrounded to angular quartzite pebbles up to 13 mm; bituminous impregnation; thin beds of bluish grey mudstone throughout	6.18
Mudstone, siltstone and clay; bluish grey, mottled red and purple; micaceous; a few ironstone nodules	17.47
Sandstone; grey and brown, medium-grained, evenly laminated, fairly micaceous, with partings of smooth-bedded mudstone and siltstone	7.61
Middle Coal Measures	

Farther east a composite section of Lees Farm boreholes 1 and 1A records the complete sequence, which here totals only 18.4 m:

	Thickness m
Main Sulphur Coal	—
Mudstone seatearth, pale grey, passing into	0.22
Mudstone, medium grey, smooth to silty; including a 0.37 m bed of sandstone	4.30
Sandstone, pale grey, fine-grained, hard and massive, micaceous	1.60
Mudstone, pale greenish grey, silty, massive, red stained	5.60
Sandstone, rather muddy, pale greenish grey, fine-grained, cross-bedded	1.90
Mudstone, pale grey, with thin beds of siderite and sandstone	c.3.61
Mudstone, grey, red, olive and black; listric	1.17
Middle Coal Measures	—

Shaft sections around Madeley record a similar sequence, ranging from only 13.1 m at Foster's Pits to 33.1 m at Hills Lane. The lowest recorded sandstone rests directly on Middle Coal Measures at Madeley Meadow Pit and Hills Lane, but elsewhere is underlain by up to 11.6 m of shales and clays, including a basal coloured clay or 'calaminker' as at Lees Farm. The formation commonly includes two major sandstones, separated by a tile clay equivalent to the upper red mudstones at Lees Farm; both sandstones contain breccia bands with angular quartz fragments, though these are more important in the upper unit. However, at Foster's Pits only one sandstone, 7.9 m thick, occurs; three are recorded in Madeley Court and Meadow Pit, and four at Hills Lane. Tar is recorded in the sandstones at Blists Hill, Hills Lane, Kemberton, and Madeley Court. The higher mudstones immediately beneath the Main Sulphur Coal range from 2.2 m to 9.6 m thick; they are colloquially divided into the 'Brickman's Measure' below (a further red clay or calaminker) and 'Potato Butt' above (a pale mudstone with ironstone not of economic importance).

Borehole G2 [7221 0191] at Sutton Maddock includes two sandstones in 25.9m of Hadley Formation. The strata are less highly coloured than around Madeley and include a *Spirorbis* limestone below the lower sandstone:

	Thickness m
Main Sulphur Coal	—
Clay, light grey; silty with calcareous nodules	1.5
Sandstone, grey-green, pyritic; thin coaly streaks	1.8
Clay, greenish grey; 'race' nodules	5.5
Sandstone, grey-green, fine-grained above, coarse-grained below with tar impregnation	8.8
Limestone, grey and brown; *Spirorbis* and fish fragments; silty and clayey partings	2.1
Shale and clay, grey, purple at base; streak of coal near top	6.1
Upper Ludlow Shale	—

Madeley Wood boreholes 5 and 6, east of Kemberton, record only 5.5 m and 4.2 m of Hadley Formation, resting unconformably on reddened productive measures above the Top and Viger coals respectively. The strata here are largely dark grey sandy mudstones and seatearths, with a little greenish and red-brown mottling, but both boreholes include two bands of typical espley sandstone. In Madeley Wood Borehole 4, the Hadley Formation comprises 3.6 m of pale grey sandstone, partly impregnated with oil, passing up into 3.4 m of pale grey, red-brown and variegated siltstones and silty mudstones. Boreholes 7 and 8 proved 12.6 m and 11.5 m of Hadley Formation strata, resting unconformably above the Top and Fungous coals. At Borehole 2, red-brown and pale grey mudstones, 26.5 m thick, include three beds of espley sandstone, and thin nodular limestones near the top. Similar strata were found at No. 1 Borehole, but were only 15.1m thick. Lilleshall Borehole No. 5 in the far north-east passed through 29.6 m of Hadley Formation, largely red, yellow and grey mudstones, with two espley beds. This is the only borehole in the Madeley Syncline in which there is no obvious unconformity between a basal Hadley Formation espley sandstone and the underlying, secondarily reddened productive measures; it appears that the grey measures pass conformably up into primary red mudstones, although minor erosion surfaces may exist within the Hadley Formation, below one or both espley sandstones.

Dawley area

At the Woodside Opencast [674 046] a section in 1970 on the southern face revealed 14.4 m of Hadley Formation:

	Thickness m
Main Sulphur Coal	—
Mudstone, grey to black; fireclay texture in upper part; scattered ironstone nodules in lower part	1.35
Mudstone, pale to dark grey, mottled dark red-brown, purple and orange; silty below; pyrite nodules near top	2.70
Sandstone, grey, some purple mottling, fine-grained, finely laminated; erosive base	0.30
Mudstone, grey, mottled brown; silty to sandy	0.40
Sandstone, grey, ferruginous tints; flaggy in upper part, massive in lower part; gritty to pebbly; erosive base	0.50
Mudstone, grey, much random red-brown and greenish mottling	4.15
Sandstone, grey, bituminous impregnations, fine to coarse, flaggy; becoming conglomeratic in lower part with rounded to subangular chips of quartzite and Uriconian rocks, and angular chips of coloured Coal Measures mudstones	up to 5.0
Unconformity on productive measures	—

At Lightmoor the Hadley Formation similarly comprises a thick basal sandstone overlain by brick clays and tile clays, which have been worked at Cherry Tree Hill Brick and Tile Works [674 051] and at Ash Tree, Jubbs Leasow, Gravel Leasow and New Gravel Leasow pits. Between the Lightmoor and Limestone faults from Dawley Parva to Hollinswood, these strata are known in 18 shaft records, from New Track Pits [6894 0565] to Pudley Hill [700 094]. They are thinnest at Langleyfield (11.6 m) and thickest at Old Lawn (25.8 m). New Track, Castle, Southall and Old Lawn pits show two sandstones in the formation; all the others show only one, referred to as 'Rough Rock', between 2.4 m (Holywell) and 15.6 m (Pudley Hill) thick. This is underlain by red and grey mudstones (in places including poor ironstone), referred to as 'calaminker' and thickest at 11.3 m in Paddock Pit. The sandstone is overlain by further red and grey mudstone and by the clay seatearth of the Main Sulphur Coal.

North-west of the Lightmoor Fault at Dawleybank the Hadley Formation is preserved in a gentle faulted syncline. In its deeper part, adjacent to the Lightmoor Fault, boreholes proved a maximum thickness of 22.4 m. The proportion of sandstone in the sequence increases from south-west to north-east; the sandstones are grey or white, stained purple, yellow, brown and black. They form hard, massive units up to 8.0 m thick, and show rare cross-bedding and local flaggy beds. Pinkish white espley grits occur widely, both within the sandstones and the mudstones, as discrete layers and as disseminated material. The clasts are mainly angular quartz fragments up to 1.5 cm; red and green Uriconian fragments and pale grey mudstone flakes also occur. The associated mudstones are pale grey, stained red, purple, brown, yellow and green, usually poorly bedded, and contain coarse-grained sand as well as grit layers. Unbedded mudstones become more common south-eastwards. North of the Greyhound Fault, 2.5 m of pale orange-brown sandstone crop out beside Princes End Road [6828 0870].

In the outlier of Hadley Formation at Horsehay Common, [673 080], the uppermost 15 m to 20 m of 40 m of barren measures are described as 'rainbow marls', with hard orange sandstones that are wedge-like and up to 5 m thick. A large outlier occurs south-east of Wellington [659 098 to 667 107]; boreholes drilled in that area for the Limekiln Lane Opencast proved up to 49 m of 'sandy coloured measures' and sandstones, which were later seen in the high wall of the opencast excavation to lie unconformably on Middle Coal Measures, at the level of the top of the Fungous Coal.

At New Hadley, boreholes show the Hadley Formation to be conformable on the grey Middle Coal Measures at, or not far above, the level of the Chance Pennystone Marine Band (Figure 25). *Spirorbis* was recorded in one of these boreholes. Blockley's brick pit [683 117] is taken as the type locality for the Hadley Formation. About 34 m of strata are exposed up to the Main Sulphur Coal at the base of the Coalport Formation, but the productive measures underlying the Hadley Formation were not exposed. Espleys occur as lenticular channel-fill sandstones, 30 m to 40 m wide and commonly aligned north-west to south-east. The section measured in 1964 was:

	Thickness m
Main Sulphur Coal	—
Mudstone–seatearth, soft and friable, pale to dark grey; passing down into	1.8
Espley, fawn and grey mottled; large angular limestone and green mudstone fragments in calcareous matrix; passes down into conglomeratic sandstone, pale grey, weathering fawn, with green mudstone fragments and large angular or poorly rounded espley fragments	2.2
Mudstone, purple and grey mottled, becoming pale fawn and grey below; seatearth texture above, with roots; hard, calcareous, silty with gritty fragments	1.5
Espley, pale grey; coarse fragments in argillaceous matrix; lenticular bedding	1.5
Mudstone, purple and green, calcareous, rubbly bedded, few grit fragments; partly obscured	13.1
Sandstone, purple and fawn, cross-bedded; gritty beds below; erosive base	2.4
Mudstone, purple and green mottled, rubbly, gritty breccia beds	2.4
Sandstone and mudstone, purple and green, cross-bedded and lenticularly bedded	9.1

To the north-east, the Hadley Formation dips beneath the Coalport Formation; shaft sections record thicknesses of 40.8 m at Bye Pit and 52.7 m at Wombridge Water Engine Pit, resting conformably on the Middle Coal Measures. The strata are similar to those at New Hadley, with a high proportion of espley sandstones. The highest espley was exposed in a now overgrown quarry [6900 1221] (Whitehead et al., 1928). East of the Ketley Fault, Borehole DDD(N)17A [6967 1212] records 16.5 m (not bottomed) of mostly unbedded coloured mudstones, with some penecontemporaneous mudstone-breccias, layers of angular quartz and rock fragments, and a 0.4 m bed of fine-grained grey sandstone. There is also a black slickensided seatearth 0.1 m thick with a well-preserved and diverse miospore assemblage dated as Duckmantian or Bolsovian but not Westphalian D, confirming the probable Bolsovian age of the Hadley Formation.

North-north-eastwards from Snedshill the proportion of espley sandstone in the sequence decreases; at Snedshill it is rather lower than at New Hadley. At an old brick pit at Snedshill, Whitehead et al., (1928, p.91) described 23.8 m of strata, mostly mudstones, but thick espleys higher in the sequence are now visible in a roadstone quarry higher up the hill [7008 1041]:

	Thickness m
Sandstone, pale yellowish grey, coarse, massive; pockets of espley grit to 10 cm	2.0
Mudstone, purple and brick red, also pale grey; silty, blocky, unbedded; layers of espley grit with angular fragments to 3 cm	3.0
Sandstone, as above; flaggy and thinly bedded near top, pockets and lenticles of espley grit with rock fragments up to 7 cm across; cross-cutting beds of purple and yellow mudstone	2.5
Mudstone, as above	1.0
Sandstone, pale yellowish grey, brown iron staining, rather massive and thinly bedded; scattered thin espley grits, fragments to 3 cm; purple and yellow mudstone partings	1.5
Mudstone, purple, also yellowish	1.5
Sandstone, pale yellowish grey, brown and black staining, coarse, massive and flaggy; a few fine espley grit beds and thin partings of purple mudstone	0.5 to 1.5
Mudstone, purple, brick-red and yellow	2.0

A borehole within the pit shows the Hadley Formation overlying grey Middle Coal Measures conformably.

The old pit at St. George's Brickworks (Whitehead et al., 1928, p.89) is now overgrown, but a larger pit has been worked immediately to the south-west of it [710 113]. This reveals 40 m of silty, blocky, unbedded brick-red mudstone. In the middle of this sequence is a laterally persistent bed of pale grey, fine-grained, hard and recrystallised sandstone 0.35 m thick. A similar bed, 0.40 m thick, occurs as a lens 5 m above it [7095 1131]. Lenses of pale pink espley grit, up to 1.5 m across and 0.5 m thick, occur within these sandstones and are crowded with angular or subangular fragments, up to 5 cm across, of Uriconian rocks, quartz and mudstone. Lenses of espley material, up to 1.2 m thick, also occur within the brick-red mudstone. Farther north-east the Hadley Formation attains its greatest thickness in the Coalbrookdale Coalfield (Figure 12); Prestwich (1840) records 60 m at Lodgewood Pits, and at Muxton Bridge the total thickness is estimated to be 100 m to 120 m.

From Dawley Parva to Hollinswood, the Hadley Formation is only 11.6 m to 25.8 m thick, including one or two sandstones, but farther north-east the sequence thickens, the sandstones increase in number but form a smaller proportion of the total thickness, and the unconformable base of the formation rests on higher levels of the Middle Coal Measures. At Nelson and Rickyard pits, respectively 26.0 m and 26.6 m of strata include four sandstones interdigitated with red, white and grey mudstone (Figure 14). The 35.0 m of strata at Watling Street

Grange Pit are largely red, yellow and white mudstone, but include five thin sandstones. At Granville Colliery, the 35.74 m sequence includes three breccia bands each up to 4.11 m thick. At the latter two collieries the Hadley Formation appears to be conformable on the productive measures, just above the level of the Chance Pennystone Marine Band. Boreholes north-east of Granville reveal typical espley sandstones and coloured mudstones, also conformably overlying productive measures (see Lilleshall No. 1 and Childpit Pit Lane boreholes on Figure 14). The strata thicken north-eastwards from 20.3 m at Hollybank Wood Borehole to 68.6 m at Childpit Lane; the conformable base of the formation also rises north-eastwards, so that at Childpit Lane 40 m of grey measures lie between the Chance Pennystone Marine Band and the base of the Hadley Formation. An impure clayey coal 0.15 m thick is recorded near the base of the Hadley Formation in Hugh's Bridge Borehole, and there is a coal 0.08 m thick in the lower part of the formation at Lilleshall No. 6 Borehole.

Wellington area (Ruabon Marl)

Strata assigned to the Ruabon Marl were not previously recorded in this area. Pocock et al. (1938, p.159) noted that the measures in the lower part of the Slang Lane No. 2 Borehole resemble the Etruria Marl, but assigned them to the Keele Beds, because no overlying Coed-yr-Allt Beds were identified. However, the more recently drilled Wrekin Buildings Borehole [6231 0871] proved red beds of the Ruabon Marl overlain by thin Coed-yr-Allt and then by Keele Beds. It is also likely that the Ruabon Marl crops out beneath the drift at Longwood [603 071], but it is not exposed.

In the Wrekin Buildings Borehole 12.9 m of the Ruabon Marl were proved, overlying Uriconian rocks. The strata were reddish brown to pale greyish green mudstone, and contained pebbles up to 5 mm across of dark green tuffaceous rocks, pellets of red mudstone, and beds of pale calcareous siltstone. The upper part contained closely spaced layers of limestone nodules, from which a single Spirorbis was obtained.

COALPORT FORMATION

Madeley area

The Main Sulphur Coal, at the base of the formation, is thin and sulphurous compared to seams in the productive measures, but it has been widely worked south of the River Severn. Not only is it at its thickest there, but few workable lower seams are present in this area, due to erosion beneath the sub-Hadley unconformity. Its slow-burning properties made the seam a suitable fuel for the brick and tile industries based on the clays of the Hadley Formation. At Deep Pit, Broseley the following descending section is recorded: coal, 0.10 m; pricking, 0.23 m; coal, 0.18 m; clod, 0.23 m; Sulphur Coal, 0.48 m; pricking, 0.15 m; coal, 0.14 m. On Williams' (1846) section for Broseley (?Cockshot Pits) the 1.83 m coal (including partings) named Big Flint at 69.1 m depth is believed to be the Main Sulphur. Other shafts south of the Severn record a single seam, between 0.38 m (Dunge No. 7 Pit, No. 3 Shaft) and 1.02 m thick (Coneybury), as do Borehole G1 [7094 0104] (0.3 m thick) and boreholes for a new sewage works [708 014] (0.6 m thick). Fragments of coal were noted in the stream [7057 0031] below Cockshot Coppice, and in the stream bed of Tarbatch Dingle just below the footbridge [7064 0111].

North of the River Severn, coal was recorded in foundations for a garage [6773 0435] on Woodside Housing Estate, and Lees Farm No. 1 Borehole (Figure 32) records four leaves:

	Thickness m
Coal	0.03
Mudstone, dark grey, smooth; plant fragments; coal partings near top	0.15
Coal, highly pyritic	0.25
Mudstone seatearth, medium to dark grey, soft, listric; plant fragments	0.63
Coal, highly pyritic	0.09
Mudstone seatearth, as above	0.06
Coal, highly pyritic	0.33

Samples from two of the leaves of coal yielded diverse and well-preserved assemblages of miospores. The presence of *Vestispora costata*, which is unknown above the Bolsovian, and the absence of characteristic Duckmantian forms which die out within the Bolsovian, implies a late Bolsovian age.

Mine shafts in the Madeley area reveal further variations. A single seam is recorded at Fosters Pits (0.61 m) and Kemberton (0.71 m). Two leaves, 0.40 m to 0.91 m apart, are recorded at Hills Lane and Madeley Court Nos. 5, 7 and 8 shafts; the thinner upper leaf is 0.10 m to 0.15 m thick, the lower 0.38 m to 0.61 m. Five shaft records distinguish three separate leaves with thicknesses ranging as follows: coal, 0.05 m to 0.51 m; dirt, 0.02 m to 0.41 m; coal, 0.05 m to 0.54 m; dirt, 0.05 m to 1.37 m; coal, 0.05 m to 0.52 m. Madeley Wood Nos. 5 and 6 and Lilleshall No. 5 boreholes record single seams of inferior pyritic coal 0.05 m to 0.09 m thick; four other Madeley Wood boreholes record two or three leaves: coal, 0.03 m to 0.20 m; grey listric seatclay with ironstone, 1.03 m to 2.18 m; grey mudstone and siltstone 1.42 m to 3.71 m; coal, 0.03 m to 0.18 m; grey carbonaceous seatclay or mudstone, 0 m to 0.10 m; coal, 0.03 m to 0.08 m.

Strata between the Main and Little Sulphur coals South of the Broseley Fault the White Rock or Main Sulphur Rock lies close above the Main Sulphur Coal. Between the Deancorner and Willey faults a borehole [6835 0081] recorded: soil and red clay, 1.5 m; rock, 0.6 m; fireclay, 3.4 m; rock, 0.6 m; fireclay, 0.6 m; rock (Main Sulphur Rock), 2.4 m; fireclay, 2.4 m; old heading in Main Sulphur Coal.

Farther east a *Spirorbis* limestone lies above the sandstone; blocks of coarse-grained brown flaggy sandstone can be seen in a stream [6926 0029] 300m south-west of Inett, and fragments of pale *Spirorbis* limestone occur in the same stream [6940 0022]. From near Inett [695 005] to beside Roving [705 000] a further sandstone lies upon or closely above the limestone; both sandstones were seen in a stream section [7049 0031]:

	Thickness m
Sandy mudstone, pale brown, with ironstone nodules and few sandstone beds	c.5–7 +
Sandstone, pale greenish brown, fairly calcareous, very micaceous, coarse-grained	c.5.0
Spirorbis limestone, grey; nodules up to 0.2 m with a ferruginous crust, nodules are commonly of limestone breccia in a calcareous matrix	0.6–1.0
Grey sandy mudstone	c.2.5–3.0
Grey sandstone; coarse, cross-bedded, calcareous, rather flaggy and argillaceous	3.0 +

Borehole G1 [7094 0104] recorded the strata below the upper sandstone; these include two thin limestones and rest upon the Main Sulphur Coal at 29.6 m depth. The upper sandstone crops out above this borehole and was seen in a disused quarry [7082 0105] beside Tarbatch Dingle:

	Thickness m
Sandstone, pale orange-brown, wispy bedded and cross-bedded; small ironstone nodules	c.5.5
Sandstone, pale brown, ferruginous, massive	c.0.6
Mudstone, dark grey; micaceous; abundant plant fragments in central part; becomes sandy and pale brown upwards, passes laterally into argillaceous wispy sandstone	1.2
Sandstone, brown; coarse, friable	1.1
Mudstone and shale, very sandy and micaceous; comminuted plant debris in lower part	0–0.4
Sandstone, grey, massive, unjointed, coarse- to medium-grained, scattered ironstone nodules	2.0 +

Farther upstream a gentle fold structure exposes *Spirorbis* limestone below this sandstone.

At Broseley (?Cockshot Pit), Amies Field, Deep Pit and the Wallace Shaft the strata in this interval are 28.7 m to 30.5 m thick. The Main Sulphur Coal is overlain by 1.5 m to 2.6 m of sandy shale, then 3.8 m to 9.6 m of sandstone, locally named Sulphur Coal Rock. This is followed by 0.9 m to 2.5 m of red clay or mudstone, then a further thin sandstone. The overlying *Spirorbis* limestone is 0.9 m to 1.2 m thick and is succeeded by 4.5 m to 5.2 m of sandstone, then 0.7 m to 1.2 m of red clay or mudstone. At all these shafts except Amies Field these are overlain by 4.8 m to 5.0 m of argillaceous beds followed by a sandstone, 1.5 m to 1.7 m thick, and a further metre of underclay or clunch.

Between the Wayside and Limestone faults north of the Severn, temporary sections in Woodside Housing Estate [677 042] show the Main Sulphur Coal to be overlain by several metres of flaggy ferruginous sandstone, then vivid multicoloured mudstone; a trench [6803 0422] encountered sandy pale grey mudstone with *Spirorbis* limestone nodules. At Lees Farm No. 1 Borehole (Figure 32) the strata between the Main and Little Sulphur coals total only 6.06 m of smooth to silty grey mudstone and seatearth, including scattered siderite nodules and shaly coal partings, with *Stigmaria* sp., *Spirorbis* sp., *Carbonita pungens* and fish remains collected from the roof measures of the Main Sulphur Coal. However, several shaft sections between Madeley Meadow Pit, Blists Hill and Kemberton Pit record this interval as 27 m to 38 m thick. The sequence includes a variable proportion of sandstone and a variable number of sandstone beds (Figure 32). Pit sections for Madeley Court and Halesfield show three clearly defined layers of red mudstone, and some of the Madeley Court shafts show a coal up to 0.1 m thick overlying the White Rock. Borehole G3 at The Hay Farm, Coalport (Figure 32), records 24.24 m of clays and micaceous siltstones, usually grey or greenish but also purplish red and brown; there is no basal sandstone, but micaceous sandstone beds occur in the middle of the sequence, with a *Spirorbis* limestone 0.38 m thick. Borehole G2 at Sutton Maddock records 1.22 m of grey sandstone with black tar filling pore spaces, resting on the Main Sulphur Coal and overlain by 28.05 m of grey-green clays and micaceous siltstones.

Madeley Wood Colliery boreholes in the north-east record 23.4 m to 26.1 m of strata, largely grey in colour. The Main Sulphur Coal is overlain by dark grey to black shales and mudstones, in which are recorded *Estheria, Spirorbis, Leaia*, ostracods and fish. The overlying strata were not always cored, but the White Rock can be detected in most of the logs, ranging from 3.0 m thick in No. 1 Borehole to 12.9 m in No. 5 (Figure 32). It was pale grey, fine- to coarse-grained with some oil in No. 5 and No. 6 boreholes, and was overlain by up to 15 m of pale grey and red-brown mudstone with thin sandstones. Farther to the

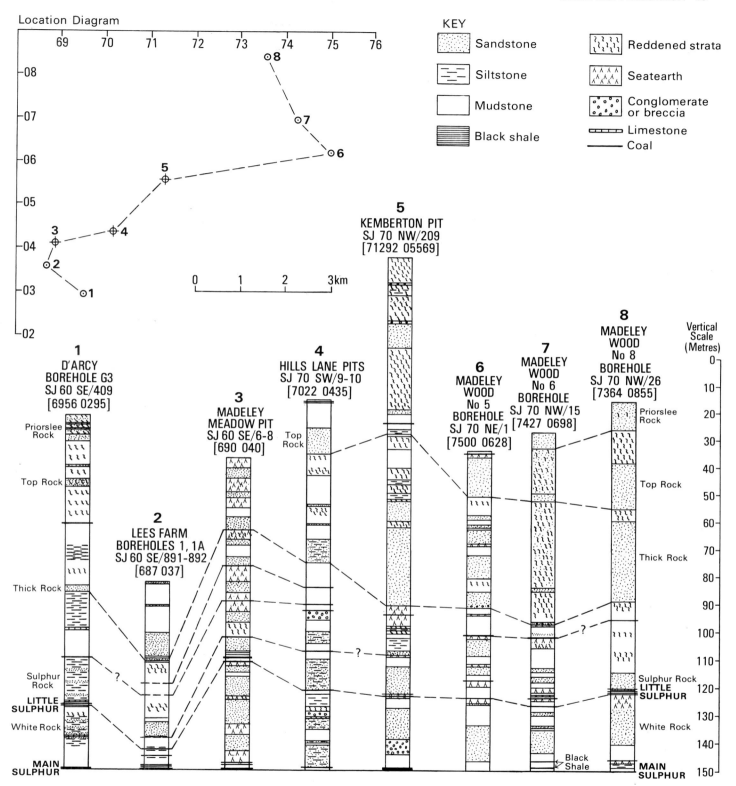

Figure 32 Comparative vertical sections of the Coalport Formation in the Madeley area. (At Lees Farm, Madeley Meadow and Hills Lane, Coalport strata are at outcrop and the section is incomplete; at all others they are succeeded by Keele Beds).

north-east, Lilleshall No. 5 Borehole demonstrates a thickening of the interval to 32.4 m:

	Thickness m
Little Sulphur Coal	—
Fireclay, grey siltstone and sandy shale, also grey, red and green mudstones, passing into	13.59
Coarse-grained micaceous sandstone, grey-green; White Rock	12.40
Dark grey mudstone, striped grey sandy shale, dark grey shale	6.32
Main Sulphur Coal	—

The Little Sulphur Coal   South of the Broseley Fault, 0.61 m of coal was proved beneath drift in a borehole [6860 0070]. Two coals, up to 0.23 m thick, are recorded at Broseley (?Cockshot Pit) and Deep Pit, separated by 1.2 m of clay, and at the Wallace Shaft the following is recorded: gob, 0.45 m; coal, 0.27 m; gob, 1.31 m.

Lees Farm No. 1 Borehole north of the Severn recorded three leaves of coal, 0.06 m (lowest), 0.03 m and 0.33 m thick; a sample from the seam yielded diverse populations of miospores, in a good state of preservation. The presence of *Cirratriradites saturni*, which is unknown above the Bolsovian, and the absence of certain characteristic Duckmantian forms which die out in the Bolsovian, again implies a late Bolsovian age. Three leaves of coal are known at Madeley Meadow Pit and Blists Hill, while two are recorded at Halesfield, Kemberton and Borehole G3 (Figure 32). Various Madeley Court shafts record 0.30 m to 0.41 m (lower) and 0.15 m to 0.23 m (upper) leaves, overlain by black coaly shale, but only a single pyritic coal 0.25 m thick was found at Hills Lane. Madeley Wood No. 7 and Lilleshall No. 5 boreholes in the north-east record single seams 0.08 m thick, but two leaves are recorded at Madeley Wood Nos. 1 and 5, and three leaves at No. 6 (Figure 32): coal, 0.13 m; black mudstone, 0.09 m; coal, 0.06 m; dark grey seatearth, mudstone and shale, 2.06 m; coal, 0.26 m.

The Sulphur Rock and measures below the Thick Rock   South of the Broseley Fault only the lower part of the Sulphur Rock crops out; in the stream running through the northern part of Cockshot Coppice [704 004] about 4.5 m of coarse-grained flaggy sandstone with a central grey-blue clay layer are seen, dipping gently eastwards. North of the Broseley Fault this sandstone forms the feature west of Swinney Farm [7065 0085]. Beside Tarbatch Dingle there are numerous exposures of orange-brown, micaceous, slightly ferruginous sandstone, in part tarry, with shallow-angle cross-bedding. North of Tarbatch Dingle, the outcrop is largely concealed beneath landslip at the Wilds and Preenshead.

Farther west, the sequence is recorded in shaft sections at Broseley (?Cockshot Pit), Deep Pit, Amies Field Pit and the Wallace Shaft; the total thickness decreases eastward and north-eastward, from 30.8 m at Broseley to 25.0 m at the Wallace Shaft. The basal item comprises 5.5 m to 6.5 m of assorted binds, clod, clunch and rock. This is overlain by a coal 0.23 m to 0.25 m thick, then 4.4 m to 4.7 m of blue clunch, clod and rock. Above another, thinner pyritic coal there follow 5.8 m to 8.2 m of sandstone, blue clunch and clod. All these can be referred to the Sulphur Rock, and are overlain by 1.2 m to 2.4 m of red fireclay. Finally, below the Thick Rock, lie 11.3 m of shale and clay, including two thin coals at Broseley and at Deep Pit.

The lower part of the Sulphur Rock in these sections is believed to correlate with that in the sections seen farther east. The sandstone believed to be that part of the Sulphur Rock which overlies the lower two coals crops out in both banks of Corbett's Dingle [6878 0204]; there it comprises 10 m of pale grey evenly laminated sandstone, with occasional purplish or ferruginous bands. The southerly tributary of the dingle shows 6 m to 7 m of grey, blue and red clay, overlain by about 2.5 m of mudstone breccia [6879 0175], which contains subrounded cherryred sandy mudstone pellets and more angular grey porcellanous mudstone fragments in a dark brownish red mudstone matrix. This breccia is equated with the one overlying the 1.2 m to 2.4 m of red fireclay at the Wallace Shaft, Deep Pit and at Broseley.

Lees Farm Borehole No. 1 [6873 0372] (Figure 32) records 31.2 m of mainly grey mudstone, smooth to silty, variously stained red, yellow, brown, olive, purple and mauve. This includes three coal partings, some ironstone, and a 5.1 m bed of pale green-grey Sulphur Rock, massive and fine- to coarse-grained. *Neuropteris* occurred above the Little Sulphur Coal. Shaft sections for Madeley Court, Madeley Meadow and Hills Lane pits record 42 m to 45 m of strata including a very variable amount of sandstone. The sequence includes five thin coals, two in the lower part of the succession and three in the upper, although only four coals are recorded in any one shaft. North of Madeley Court a single bed of Sulphur Rock sandstone, 15 m thick at Halesfield and 9.75 m at Kemberton Pit (Figure 32), rests directly on the Little Sulphur Coal. This is overlain at Halesfield by 17.5 m of blue clod, with two thin coals high in the sequence, and at Kemberton by 21.95 m of grey and coloured shales with a 0.3m coal near the top.

Borehole G3 at Hay Farm, Coalport, encountered very little sandstone, but proved the only two limestones recorded in these strata (Figure 32):

	Thickness m
Silty clay and siltstone, greenish grey	12.8
Argillaceous limestone, pale greenish grey	0.9
Clay, greenish grey, thin coal at base	10.1
Clay, siltstone and fine sandstone, greenish grey	15.8
Limestone, brown; *Spirorbis* and plant remains	0.15

Borehole G2 at Sutton Maddock records 24.7 m of strata: 4.6 m of grey-green sandstone overlain by 20.1 m of grey-green silty clay, locally purple and including one bed of pyritic sandstone.

Madeley Wood Colliery boreholes proved this interval to range from 26 m to 40 m thick and to comprise mainly pale to dark grey, greenish and red-brown mudstones and siltstones. The Sulphur Rock was well developed in boreholes 7, 8 and 1, as pale grey, fine- to medium-grained massive or banded sandstones, respectively 8.1 m, 6.1 m and 3.6 m thick, resting close above the Little Sulphur Coal. Two thin sandstones are recorded at about this level in No. 6 (Figure 32), and two sandstones higher in the sequence in No. 5. A single thin coal is recorded high in the sequence in boreholes 5 to 8. Finally, in Lilleshall Borehole No. 5, the Little Sulphur Coal is overlain by 22.7 m of strata, mainly grey sandy shales, but with 7.9 m of red and grey fireclay, grey sandstone, siltstone and mudstone in the middle part of the sequence; immediately below the Thick Rock is a 0.3 m coal.

The Thick Rock and measures below the Top Rock   The Thick Rock, which is the most persistent sandstone in the Coalport Formation, varies widely in thickness, and locally splits into two or three beds. It is generally greenish grey, brownish grey or olive-green, often stained purple, orange, brown, yellow or black, and is medium- to coarse-grained, micaceous, massive below and flaggy above. It contains much carbonaceous material, weathered feldspar and comminuted coal, with scattered plant stems, coal wisps, espley bands, pyrite and hematite. The Thick Rock is overlain by a sequence of mudstones, smooth to silty and blocky or bedded, interbedded with siltstones and thin, flaggy, fine- to coarse-grained sandstones. These are pale greenish or bluish grey, mottled and banded red, brown, purple, lilac and yellow.

South of the River Severn, two sandstones, separated by argillaceous beds, join as a single unit above Tarbatch Dingle [6990 0104]. At an old quarry [7035 0117], 2 m to 3 m of sub-massive to flaggy, coarse-grained, friable, purplish grey sandstone shows abundant small ironstone nodules in its lower part. The Thick Rock thins along the top of the landslipped slopes of the Wilds and Preenshead. It is referred to as the Dingle Rock, 9.0 m thick, in Amies Field Pit; at outcrop between the Madeley and Corbett's faults it is about 15 m thick, pale greenish grey, medium to coarse grained and fairly micaceous. It forms a prominent feature between the Corbett's and Broseley faults, north of Folly Farm [6857 0149], and outliers were found at Broseley [676 020] and near Woodhouse Farm [683 020]. Overlying the Thick Rock are many lenticular sandstones, as at Lower Riddings Farm [6931 0162] and Rowton [6994 0136]. Associated argillaceous beds are mainly red to grey silty clays, but underlying the Top Rock in a stream [6943 0084] east of Upper Riddings Farm, coal fragments indicate the presence of a thin seam.

North of the River Severn the Thick Rock, and the strata immediately above it, crop out along the top of Lloyds Coppice [6909 0323 to 6837 0364]; at the eastern end it is poorly developed and split into three beds up to 2.74 m thick (Whitehead et al., 1928, p.96), but at the west end of the coppice [6848 0363], 6.0 m of grey and brown sandstone, massive, micaceous and with disseminated carbonaceous material, pass up into grey mudstone. Lees Farm Borehole No. 1 (Figure 32) [6873 0372] revealed the following:

	Thickness m
Boulder clay	—
Mudstone, pale to medium grey, smooth and silty, micaceous; hematite and siderite; thin sandstone at top	8.32
Sandstone, medium grey, coarse, unbedded; becoming sideritic ironstone	0.19
Mudstone, pale to medium grey, brown and yellow staining, smooth to silty; a little white mica, few sandy wisps	9.81
Thick Rock; sandstone, pale to medium grey, olive and brown, stained yellow, purple and black; massive; fining upwards; very coarse and gritty at the base with mudstone clasts, dark and white mica, pyrite crystals, hematite veins	10.76

Lees Farm Borehole No. 4 [6918 0363] penetrated 24.5 m of strata immediately above the Thick Rock; these were largely grey mudstones, with some brown and red mottling, a few thin siltstone and sandstone beds, and one thin coaly parting. North-east of the Madeley Court Fault no beds lower than the Top Rock crop out, but north-west of the Warrensway Fault the Thick Rock and beds above were exposed in a trench [6920 0546] dipping north-west at up to 32°.

The Thick Rock is represented by three sandstones separated by clunch at Madeley Meadow and Hills Lane pits (Figure 32). At the latter the succession is given as: sandstone 0.9 m; clunch, 6.2 m; sandstone, 0.3 m; clunch, 4.9 m; sandstone 9.0 m. The lower two of these sandstones join to give a single bed 6.4 m to 16.5 m thick at Madeley Court Colliery, and all three sandstones join to form a single unit, 28.0 m thick, at Halesfield Pit.

The Thick Rock is overlain in these two shafts by mudstones, mostly dark grey, greenish and blue, but including up to four red bands and one thin coal seam.

At Coalport (Borehole G3) and Sutton Maddock (Borehole G2) the Thick Rock may be represented respectively by 2.1 m of calcareous micaceous sandstone (at 72.2 m depth in G3), and by 6.1 m of fine-grained grey-green sandstone (at 204.8 m in G2), overlain by mudstones, siltstones and thin sandstones which include a 0.3 m coal in Borehole G3.

At Madeley Wood the full interval was cored in Borehole No. 5 (Figure 32); the 39.85 m of strata included three thick sandstones:

	Thickness m
Mudstone, mainly pale greenish grey, also brown above; becoming more silty below, with beds of pale grey, micaceous sandstone	11.35
Sandstone, pale grey, fine-grained	5.33
Mudstone, pale to dark grey, commonly carbonaceous; beds of dark seatearth above, and of pale grey sandstone below; brown ironstones; plant fragments	5.84
Sandstone, pale grey; medium-grained; black carbonaceous wisps	6.96
Mudstone, greenish grey and brown; ironstone beds	4.57
Sandstone, grey, coarse above, fine below with mudstone and ironstone; conglomerate bed; plant fragments	5.79

Similar strata were revealed in Borehole No. 4, totalling 38.1 m. However, at Borehole No. 6 (Figure 32) 45.6 m of strata, which are tentatively ascribed to this interval, mainly comprise red, purple and green-grey mudstones and seatearths with a grey conglomeratic sandstone, 1.1 m thick, at the base.

In Borehole No. 7, 10.7 m of pale grey medium-grained sandstone (the Thick Rock), are overlain by 18.8 m of variously coloured mudstone. Borehole No. 8 (Figure 32) records 29.0 m of pale grey fine- to medium-grained sandstone, overlain by only 4.6 m of red-brown mudstone. However, the thickness of sandstone here, compared to No. 7, may be an error of logging as neither borehole was cored. Borehole No. 2 records 33.5 m of red-brown and grey sandstone, interbedded with red mudstone above, and then overlain by similar red mudstones ascribed to theKeele Beds. Borehole No. 3 records a similar thickness of Thick Rock, with a lower sandstone 24.4 m thick and an upper sandstone 6.1 m thick, separated by 6.1 m of argillaceous strata and overlain by 9.1 m of mainly grey mudstones beneath the red marls of the Keele Beds. In contrast, Lilleshall No. 5 Borehole in the far north-east records only 7.3 m of Thick Rock; this is coarse-grained and grey below, becoming calcareous, red and grey above, and is overlain by Keele mudstones.

The Top Rock and measures below the Priorslee Rock The Top Rock lithologically resembles the Thick Rock, although rather paler and finer grained; it is overlain by an argillaceous sequence similar to that below it. South of the Severn, these strata are the highest preserved; they form an outlier at Rowton [699 014] and an arcuate outcrop around Upper Riddings Farm [6905 0090]. There, the Top Rock is about 10 m thick, including a lenticular upper leaf, and is overlain by a similar thickness of red, purple and grey mudstone.

Boreholes G2 (Sutton Maddock) and G3 (Coalport) each record 2.7 m of sandstone interpreted as Top Rock, overlain by respectively 16.5 m and 13.5 m of clay, siltstone and sandstone (Figure 32). These beds crop out beside the River Severn south-east of the Madeley Fault, grey sandstone with marcasite being recorded [7123 0128], as well as multicoloured mudstone immediately beneath the Priorslee Rock [7027 0225]. Boreholes beside the Severn [704 020] revealed about 20 m of silty slickensided mudstone immediately beneath the Priorslee Rock.

The Top Rock is poorly exposed along the side of the Blists Hill valley northwards from the Madeley Fault [6957 0318], and under a large area of Madeley village. A sewer tunnel penetrated these strata between the Madeley Court Fault [7005 0415] and the Madeley Fault [7038 0428]:

	Thickness m
Mudstone, grey and red, with sandstone, brown and grey	7.6
Coal	0–0.3
Mudstone, grey	4.6
Sandstone, brown and grey	2.4
Mudstone, grey and brown	6.1
Sandstone, brown and grey; Top Rock	7.9 +

In Madeley, 9.1 m to 10.0 m of Top Rock sandstone are recorded at Foster's, Halesfield and Hills Lane pits; two coals are recorded in the overlying shales at Hills Lane. Between the Warrensway and Limestone faults the Top Rock crops out at Aqueduct [695 058] and the overlying argillaceous strata crop out between there and the Holmer Fault. A coal is known about 10 m above the Top Rock; this varies in quality between a black coaly carbonaceous mudstone (Brookside 137 Borehole) and two leaves of coal, 0.3 m and 0.6 m thick, separated by 0.9 m of grey mudstone (Brookside 95 Borehole).

North-east of Halesfield Pits the Top Rock is not well developed. The following strata are recorded at Kemberton Pits:

	Thickness m
Assorted clods and binds; mostly red, also grey	22.86
White rock	1.83
Blue clod, including 0.10 m of coal	5.89
Blue rocky binds; Top Rock?	1.52

The only Madeley Wood borehole which cored these strata is No. 5 (Figure 32), in which the Top Rock is represented by 14.7 m of pale grey fine- to coarse-grained sandstone with a few thin greenish grey mudstone bands. It is overlain by 0.91 m of red-stained grey seatearth and a 0.08 m seam of inferior coal, followed by 9.5 m of mudstones mottled and banded purple, green-grey and yellow; these represent a passage from Coalport to Keele strata. Chippings from No. 4 Borehole suggest that all the strata below the Priorslee Rock are in Coalport facies: 18.3 m of grey, lilac and red-brown mudstone overlay 19.8 m of pale grey to lilac sandstone (Top Rock) with some oil. By correlation with these boreholes, the Top Rock in No. 6 Borehole (Figure 32) is interpreted as 7.6 m of grey-green sandstone passing up into purple mudstone. Borehole No. 8 records a 16.8 m unit of pale grey sandstone, 4.6 m above the Thick Rock, which is probably the Top Rock. This is overlain by 12.2 m of red-brown and purple mudstone beneath the Priorslee Rock.

The Priorslee Rock and overlying measures   Lithologically the Priorslee Rock resembles the Thick Rock, although inclined to be more flaggy. Alternatively it may be very pale, fine-grained and quartzitic, or else stained red and purple, foreshadowing the onset of the Keele facies. A little espley material is locally present. The overlying argillaceous strata include more red beds than do lower members, particularly towards the top, approaching the Brookside Rock, so that it is sometimes difficult to determine the base of the Keele Beds.

Borehole G2 (Sutton Maddock) records the following 25.3 m of strata below the base of the Keele Beds:

	Thickness m
Limestone in greenish matrix	0.3
Mudstone, dark purple; scattered limestone pebbles and beds of race	1.8
Clay, red-brown, some green mottling	6.4
Silty mudstone, dark purple, passing into fine sandstone	1.8
Limestone breccia, hard	0.6
Calcareous clay, red, purple and green; argillaceous limestone nodules, beds of race	6.1
Limestone, grey-green, hard, impure	0.3
Sandy clay, dark purple	3.0
Sandstone, pale grey, bedded, some marly streaks and siderite pebbles; Priorslee Rock	4.9

The Priorslee Rock can be seen along the side of the Severn Gorge [7110 0040] to where it disappears below boulder clay [7130 0130], and at crags [7079 0177] where a large included clast of Ercall granophyre was collected. Crags 3 m high [7047 0199] reveal pale grey and dark olive sandstone, fine- to very coarse-grained, massive and thinly bedded, with knots of weathered organic material up to 3 mm across, white weathered feldspar, and large flakes of brown and white mica. This is overlain by green, grey and red mudstone. Borehole G3 (Figure 32) records 2.44 m of hard pale grey sandstone overlain by 7.32 m of red clay with beds of blue-grey sandstone and of grey and purple limestone.

Strata believed to include the Priorslee Rock and the measures above it, crop out south of the Halesfield Fault at Windmill Farm; a sandstone at least 3.05m thick was proved in boreholes [7000 0549]. Patches of sandstone [at 6991 0581, 6978 0600, 7014 0620 and 7013 0637] are believed to be the Priorslee Rock. Between the Halesfield, Holmer, Brookside and Madeley faults, beds higher than the Priorslee Rock crop out over a wide area; the best exposure seen was in a railway cutting [7054 0539]:

	Thickness m
Keele Beds, basal sandstone	—
Mudstone, pale purple, lilac and brick red, a few pale green bands; smooth, bedded, rather hard	0–1.5
Mudstone, brick red, joints stained yellow; blocky, unbedded, silty, micaceous, small concretions, very hard	1.8
Mudstone, pale greenish and purplish grey, lilac and purple; smooth, hard	1.1

At Kemberton Pits (Figure 32), 9.14 m of 'white rock with water' and 0.91 m of dark espley rock are overlain by 23.16 m of red mudstone, including 0.15 m of 'light strong rock' and 0.76 m of espley. To the north-west, Holmer Farm Boreholes A to D show that the Priorslee Rock has thinned and that the basal Keele sandstone appears to be cutting with gentle unconformity into the strata above it. The Priorslee Rock is recognised in four Madeley Wood boreholes, Nos. 1 (4.6 m thick), 4 (1.5 m), 6 (6.1 m) and 8 (10.7 m), in all cases immediately overlain by Keele Beds.

Dawley area

Main Sulphur Coal   At Woodside Opencast [674 045] a small outlier of the Coalport Formation includes about 1.9 m of Main

Sulphur Coal including partings. Four leaves are recorded at Lightmoor, in descending order: coal, 0.13 m; white clunch, 0.05 m; coal, 0.20 m; clunch, 0.03 m; coal, 0.51 m; clunch and bass, 0.28 m; coal, 0.13 m. Three coals are recorded at Old Furnace Colliery Air Pit and Top Yard Pit. Between New Track Pits [6894 0565] and Paddock Pits [686 073], eight shafts each record two coals, a lower leaf normally 0.07 m to 0.23 m thick and upper leaf normally 0.23 m to 0.75 m thick with a parting 0.23 m to 0.74 m thick. At Holywell Pits [695 985] the seam is similar, but all other shaft sections from Langleyfield to Stafford Pits record either a single thin coal, black shale or nothing at all.

Shaft sections for Watling Street Grange and Granville Collieries again record two seams, 0.05 m to 0.33 m thick (lower leaf) and 0.15 m to 0.30 m thick (upper leaf), with a 3.15 m to 4.88 m parting. Two seams with a thick parting are also recorded to the north-east (Figure 33), in the Brickkiln Plantation, Hugh's Bridge, Childpit Lane and Lilleshall No. 6 boreholes:

	Thickness m
Coal	0.8–0.61
Seatearth, grey; silty, carbonaceous	0.71–0.91
Grey mudstone	0.91–6.73
Black carbonaceous shale with fish and ostracods	0.01–0.10
Coal	0.01–0.46

The black shale contained ?*Estheria* at Brickkiln Plantation and *Spirorbis* at Childpit Lane; it would appear that this bed overlying the lower leaf of coal correlates with that overlying the upper leaf in the Madeley Syncline.

Drilling for the Limekiln Lane opencast site [656 099] proved a faulted outlier of Coalport Formation, at the base of which were two leaves (0.64 m lower and 0.18 m upper) of the Main Sulphur Coal separated by 0.15 m of grey mudstone. A core of the Main Sulphur Coal and its roof measures yielded a miospore flora: the presence of *Triquitrites sculptilis*, *T. tribullatus*, *Punctatosporites minutus*, *P. oculus*, *Endosporites globiformis* and *E. zonalis*, and the absence of certain monolete miospores diagnostic of Westphalian D, indicate a latest Bolsovian age. Two leaves of coal were similarly recorded in borehole DDD (N) 12 [6925 1203] at Wombridge, and single leaves at DDD (N) 12A [6934 1206] (0.5 m thick), at Wombridge Water Engine Pit (0.23 m) and at the entrance to Blockleys' Brick Pit [6828 1183] (0.6 m). A sample from the latter site contained the miospores *Lycospora pusilla*, *Punctatosporites* sp. cf. *P. obliquus* and ?*Apiculatisporis* sp., none of which are of stratigraphical value. The roof measures here yielded the ostracods *Carbonita agnes* and *C. humilis*.

Strata between the Main and Little Sulphur coals

From Lightmoor to Dawley Magna the sequence ranges from 26.4 m to 30.9 m thick. The White Rock is best developed at Dawley Parva, 12.7 m thick and resting directly on the Main Sulphur Coal; to the north it thins and is not recorded at Top Yard, Deepfield and Barker's Yard pits. The remainder of the sequence consists largely of grey, white, blue and red mudstones, with a thin coal at Deepfield (Figure 33), Mill and Barker's Yard pits. Between Dawley and Priorslee the strata vary from 9.9 m (Stirchley Grange) to 34 m (Portley Pit). The sequence commonly includes a single major sandstone, the White Rock; it is thickest, 23.8 m, at Wharf Pit and either rests directly on the Main Sulphur Coal or is separated from it by shales. The White Rock is overlain by rough binds and red clod. At Watling Street Grange and Granville collieries (Figure 33), 23.0 m and 19.4 m of strata include 8.1 m and 8.7 m of

pale grey White Rock, underlain by grey fireclay, shale and sandstone; immediately beneath the White Rock at Grange is 0.05 m of 'magnesian limestone' which may be equivalent to the *Spirorbis* limestone at Coalport. The White Rock is succeeded by shales, clod and bind, including (at Grange) an espley sandstone 0.91 m thick.

Boreholes north-east of Granville record strata ranging in thickness from 19.1 m (Lilleshall No. 6) to 29.7 m (Brickkiln Plantation). The Main Sulphur Coal is overlain by up to 4.8 m of grey, black and lavender shale, fireclay and siltstone. The White Rock is well represented, 4.3 m thick at Brickkiln Plantation and 15.6 m thick at Lilleshall No. 6. Generally, it is pale grey or greenish grey, hard, fine-grained and micaceous; only at No. 6 Borehole does it contain bands of coarse grit and conglomerate. The White Rock is overlain by grey and purple mudstones and siltstones, and then by the dark grey seatearth to the Little Sulphur Coal; however, Lilleshall No. 6 records only 0.46 m of seatearth between the White Rock and the coal, and two boreholes reveal a further sandstone higher in the succession. These are Lilleshall No. 1, where 3.1 m of dark grey fine-grained sandstone immediately underlie the Little Sulphur Coal, and No. 7A, where 1.5 m of fine-grained, silty, grey-green micaceous sandstone are separated from the Little Sulphur Coal by 4.6 m of dark grey seatearth clay with beds of dark grey to black shale with ostracods.

The White Rock sandstone overlies mudstone [716 117] north of Lodgewood Farm, and also farther north [716 127]; similar strata must crop out north of Freehold Pit but have not been recorded. North of Wombridge, boreholes and shafts record the Main Sulphur Coal overlain by 4.2 m to 6.0 m of mudstone and then by up to 8.2 m of sandstone, which crops out at the top of the hill [692 122].

The Little Sulphur Coal

Around Dawley Parva and Dawley Magna, two coal leaves up to 0.30 m thick are recorded 0.3 m to 0.9 m apart. Between Dawley and Granville Colliery, one to three leaves are variously recorded; the thickest single leaf is 0.56 m at Old Lawn Pit, with the thickest complete sequence at Pudley Hill: coal, 0.53 m; rock, 0.46 m; coal, 0.23 m; fireclay, 0.61 m; coal, 0.31 m. Most boreholes north-east of Granville record two leaves of coal, 0.05 m to 0.46 m and 0.01 m to 0.61 m thick and up to 1.78 m apart. The parting is generally grey seatearth clay, but at Lilleshall No. 7A it comprises black to grey shale with mussels, fish and ostracods. The three most north-easterly holes (Lilleshall No. 1, Hugh's Bridge and Crow Hayes) record a single seam 0.15 m to 0.28 m thick.

The Sulphur Rock and measures below the Thick Rock

Shaft sections from Portley (Figure 33) to Stafford pits record a single massive bed of grey or white, pebble-free, Sulphur Rock sandstone, thickest (24.2 m) at Paddock Pit. The Sulphur Rock is overlain by argillaceous strata, ranging in thickness from 14.6 m (Pudley Hill) to 29.0 m (Nelson Pit); these are largely grey but include a distinctive bed, up to 4.8 m thick, of red clod near the middle. Thin coals are recorded above and below the red clod at Stafford Pit, and additional sandstones are recorded at several shafts.

The Sulphur Rock comprises three sandstones at Mill and Castle pits, but only two at Barker's Yard and one (10.6 m thick) at Top Yard Pit. Shaft sections for Dawley Parva and Dawley Magna reveal a maximum of 40.2 m of strata in this interval (at Top Yard Pits). A more detailed succession is available for Deepfield Pit (Figure 33) totalling 37.19 m:

	Thickness m
Thick Rock	—
Red, grey and blue mudstone with beds of sandstone	18.45

	Thickness m
Grey sandstone and white shale	6.86
Coal, 0.10 m; underclay, 1.42 m; black shale, 0.05 m	1.57
White sandstone	1.83
Carbonaceous shale, 1.09 m; coal, 0.08 m	1.17

Underclay, 2.59 m; sandstone, 2.74 m; argillaceous and carbonaceous shales, 1.98 m	7.31
Little Sulphur Coal	—

In this sequence all the strata below the 18.45 m of mudstone would appear to represent the Sulphur Rock, which thus

See Figure 32 for legend.

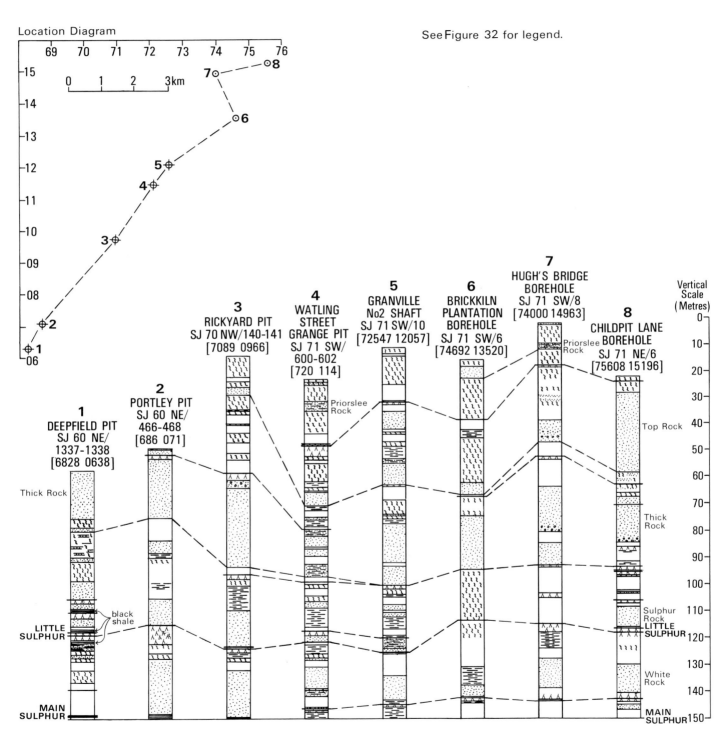

Figure 33 Comparative vertical sections of the Coalport Formation in the Dawley area. (At Deepfield, Portley and Rickyard, the Coalport strata are at outcrop and the section is incomplete; at all others the sequence is overlain conformably by the Keele Beds).

includes three sandstones and two coals. This correlates well with Madeley and Broseley, the thick red and grey mudstone immediately above the Sulphur Rock probably being equivalent to the red fireclay at this level at Broseley.

The Sulphur Rock thins to 2.4 m and 2.0 m of sandstone at Watling Street Grange Pit and Granville, but the thickness of overlying beds remains substantial, 22.0 m and 23.1 m. These strata are mostly grey shales, but include sandstones and thin coals (Figure 33). The equivalent argillaceous strata are believed to crop out east of Donnington, from south of Barn Pits [7185 1233] to Freehold Colliery, swinging eastwards to strike the Lightmoor Fault between Muxtonbridge Farm [724 133] and Sulphur Piece Plantation [725 139].

Boreholes north-east of Granville Colliery record these strata as ranging from 18.3 m at Brickkiln Plantation to 33.7 m at Lilleshall No. 6. Four boreholes record no Sulphur Rock; for example, at Lilleshall No. 7A Borehole, 21.2 m of pale grey mudstone and silty mudstone were cored. These mudstones contained mussels close above the Little Sulphur Coal, a bastard seatearth in the middle of the succession, and a 0.04 m coal 0.56 m below the Thick Rock. Lilleshall Nos. 1, 4 and 6, Hollybank Wood and Childpit Lane boreholes record 5.5 m to 9.5 m of Sulphur Rock, comprising fine- to medium-grained grey and red sandstone and siltstone, underlain by up to 1.8 m of grey mudstone, which forms the roof of the Little Sulphur Coal. In Lilleshall No. 6 and Childpit Lane boreholes these roof measures contain *Spirorbis*, fish, ostracods and megaspores. The Sulphur Rock is overlain by 15.1 m to 16.8 m of grey, green, red, brown and purple mudstone. These include thin limestones and sandstones in the middle at Lilleshall No. 6; and a bed of rubbly nodular limestone 0.69 m thick near the top, at Childpit Lane. Four coals, 0.01 m to 0.05 m thick, are included in these measures at Childpit Lane (Figure 33) and two thin leaves of coal were found close below the Thick Rock at Lilleshall Nos. 3 and 4.

The Thick Rock and measures below the Top Rock The Thick Rock is exposed in Aqueduct [6942 0596], and the overlying argillaceous strata crop out nearby [691 059, 695 061 and 700 069]. It is recorded as 21 m to 22 m thick at Stirchley Grange and Cuxeys Wood pits, overlain by 13.7 m and 14.6 m of argillaceous measures. Farther west the Thick Rock crops out from Pool Hill [681 068] through Langleyfield and along the Randley Valley [702 082], where it was exposed in a sewer trench:

	Thickness m
Sandstone, dark purple-brown, weathered brown and stained black on joints; coarse-grained, massive, micaceous, well-jointed; much organic material and finely disseminated coal, also coal on bedding planes	5 +
Mudstone, pale grey and yellow; soft, smooth	0–0.3
Sandstone, pale grey-green; coarse-grained, massive, micaceous; some organic material; black staining and brown clay on joints	3 +

The Thick Rock is apparently split into two at Deepfield Pit, Dawley (Figure 33), but most shaft sections from Portley Pit to Rickyard Pit record a single massive sandstone, ranging from 15.6 m at Pudley Hill to 35.6 m at Paddock Pits. The overlying argillaceous strata are thickest (35.0 m) at Pudley Hill, and include a coal 0.20 m to 0.36 m thick close above the Thick Rock at Portley, Old Lawn, Old Dark Lane and Rickyard pits. This coal was exposed [7043 0863] prior to burial during land-

fill operations. The strata immediately below the Top Rock were seen in a sewer trench [7006 0855]:

	Thickness m
Mudstone, deep olive-grey, yellow-brown staining; hard, silty, blocky, unbedded; small concretions; top 75 mm weathered bright yellow	0.40
Mudstone, deep purple-red, deep olive staining, otherwise as above	0.20
Mudstone, pale grey; hard, silty, rather blocky, poorly bedded	1.60
Mudstone, deep purple-red, blocky, hard, silty, unbedded; listric surfaces, small concretions	1.50
Mudstone, pale grey; as above	0.15
Mudstone, deep purple-red; as above	0.90 +

These strata can be traced around the hillside beneath the Top Rock to Hollinswood [701 095], where boreholes revealed brick red, pale yellow and grey, smooth mudstones overlying thinly bedded pale grey-green siltstones with thin sandstones below.

The Thick Rock splits into three beds at Stafford Pit: grey rock, 7.57 m; dark clod, 1.07 m; grey rock, 3.66 m; dark shale rock, 7.39 m; grey rock, 10.11 m. Three sandstones are also known at Watling Street Grange Pit (Figure 33) and two at Granville; these two crop out west of the Lightmoor Fault [720 122 to 724 133]. The Thick Rock is reported as overlain at these three pits respectively by 14.8 m, 9.2 m and 14.9 m of grey, blue and red binds, clods, marls and fireclay, including thin sandstone bands, with a thin coal resting on the Thick Rock at Watling Street Grange.

The Thick Rock is a single sandstone at Crow Hayes Shaft and at Hollybank Wood, Lilleshall Nos. 4 and 7A and Brickkiln Plantation boreholes, being thickest (19.8 m) at the last (Figure 33). It is pale grey and fine to coarse grained, and in No. 7A is capped by a grey conglomerate with coarse gritty matrix. The overlying grey, lilac, red-brown and purple mudstones are thickest (30.4 m) at No. 4 where they include at least two beds of limestone. Lilleshall No. 1, Hugh's Bridge and Childpit Lane boreholes (Figure 33) record a split Thick Rock with the upper part much thicker than the lower, as at Granville:

	Thickness m
Top Rock	—
Grey, lilac, red and purple mudstones with thin sandstones and a thin coal	10.7–16.61
Pale grey sandstone, coarse- to fine-grained; mudstone breccia bands	15.54–16.92
Greenish grey silty and sandy mudstone, some seatearth clay	2.44–7.80
Pale grey sandstone, fine-grained	1.98–8.10

The uppermost mudstones include one *Spirorbis* limestone bed in No. 1, and two at Hugh's Bridge.

The Top Rock and measures below the Priorslee Rock The Top Rock crops out north of Aqueduct [697 065, 694 063 and 700 071], with the overlying argillaceous strata cropping out farther to the north-east; it is recorded as 8.2 m thick at Cuxey's Wood Pits. The strata proved in boreholes for the Randley Valley Sewer [7008 0752 to 7027 0790] are shown in Figure 34. The Top Rock was pale to medium grey, fine to coarse grained, massive and well jointed, with weathered feldspar and carbonaceous material and a conglomerate of mudstone pellets. The overlying strata were mostly bedded mudstones, but also

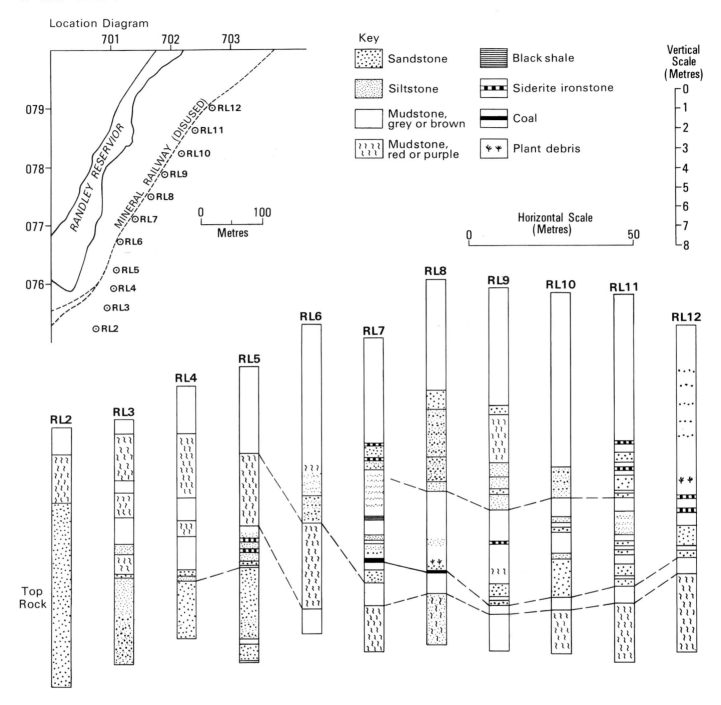

Figure 34 Coalport Formation strata as proved in the Randley Valley Sewer boreholes 2 to 12 [7008 0752 to 7027 0790].

included micaceous siltstones, grey or khaki and stained purple, brown and black. They contain a 0.25 m coal seam, siderite nodules, plant debris, and thin sandstone lenses. East of the sewer section, the Randley Brick Pit no longer exposes the Top Rock, and the following section measured there in 1972 is apparently higher in the sequence than the strata shown in Figure 34. The succession in the brick pit comprises:

	Thickness m
Mudstone, pale grey and olive; silty, bedded, shaly, with thin sandstone beds; brown iron staining	2.5
Sandstone, pale grey and olive, pale brown stained; fine-grained, micaceous	0.2–0.3

	Thickness m
Mudstone, greyish green, stained brown, black and yellow; bedded or blocky, massive, silty, with small concretions	1.5–2.5
Sandstone, pale grey-brown, black and brown stained; dark and white mica; thinly bedded, fine-grained	0.45
Mudstone, variously grey, purple, green, yellow; smooth to silty, blocky and bedded; pale greenish grey cherty layers to 3 cm	4.0
Sandstone, pale grey, stained pale olive and brown; in two beds; fine-grained, micaceous, laminated and cross-bedded	1.5
Mudstone, pale grey, stained yellow and brown; well-bedded, smooth to silty, scattered cherty layers	1.8
Sandstone, as above, in two beds	0.9
Mudstone, pale grey and brick red, stained brown; smooth, well-bedded	1.0 +

Immediately above this section in an underpass [7038 0759], the Priorslee Rock rested on pale grey smooth mudstone with large pyrite nodules.

The Top Rock forms a strong feature from the centre of Dawley northwards through Malins Lee. Between the Lodge and Spout House faults, the Top Rock, about 6 m thick, was exposed in excavations, and on the northern side of the Spout House Fault 5 m of sandstone were seen, overlain by 2 m of red and grey mudstone and more sandstone. A 7 m thickness of this upper sandstone was exposed over a large area excavated for town centre development between the Abbey Villas [6995 0879] and Malins Lee Hall [6976 0899]. The sandstone was horizontal throughout, dark greenish brown, massive, gently cross-bedded and full of coaly wisps, and contained a bed of conglomerate with rolled irregular siderite nodules up to 5 cm in diameter. Borehole TC 86 [6979 0870] records the Top Rock with conglomerate layers, containing angular to subangular clasts of Carboniferous sandstone, mudstone, ironstone and coal.

The Top Rock attains its greatest proved thickness, 17.4 m, at Old Lawn Pit, but at Pudley Hill Pit only 7.3 m of Top Rock are succeeded by 5.7 m of red clunch and blue clod, a 0.3 m coal, and 2.1 m of shale and loose rock. North-west of the Hollinswood Fault, Malins Lee Hall Pits record, below the Priorslee Rock, 13.2 m of red and blue mudstone and 16.5 m of sandstone (Top Rock). Borehole TC22 [6973 0928] records, above the Top Rock: 20.4 m of red-brown, khaki, greenish and grey mudstone, with calcareous beds, plant debris and pyrite.

Boreholes in the Hollinswood Valley [704 092] revealed dark brownish grey and greenish grey, coarse-grained Top Rock sandstone with large biotite and muscovite flakes. Higher strata faulted down to the north and east were largely pale grey, olive and red-brown mudstones and included a 0.3 m coal seen at outcrop [705 090]. The Top Rock is exposed in the railway cutting [707 090], where it is pale yellow, coarse-grained, massive and cross-bedded, with thin shale partings and pyritic concretions. Shafts to the north and east show the Top Rock to be about 3 m thick at Nelson and Rickyard pits, 5 m at Watling Street Grange, and 8 m at Stafford Pits and Granville. It is overlain by 6.5 m to 11.1 m of red, yellow and blue argillaceous strata at Nelson, Rickyard and Stafford pits, but by thicker sequences including a thin coal at Grange and Granville (Figure 33).

These strata were not cored in any of the boreholes northeast of Granville, but the Top Rock can be identified in seven of them, ranging from 4.6 m at Brickkiln Plantation and Hollybank Wood to 30.5 m at Childpit Lane. It is greenish grey, lilac and purple, fine to coarse grained, and in places argillaceous,

with coal layers and pyrite in Lilleshall No. 4. The overlying argillaceous strata are thickest at Brickkiln Plantation, comprising 39.6 m of greenish grey and purple mudstone with a thin coal; this seam is also present at Childpit Lane, Hugh's Bridge and Lilleshall No. 4.

The Priorslee Rock and overlying strata   A section in the Priorslee Rock was measured in an underpass excavation [7039 0758] near Mount Pleasant:

	Thickness m
Sandstone, purple and pale green, well-bedded to blocky; ironstone nodules to 12 mm	0.80
Sandstone lens, blue-grey, coarse-grained, quartzitic	0–0.25
Clayey sand, pale green above, yellow below; wet	0.01–0.02
Sandstone, purple and pale grey; coarse-grained, poorly bedded, partly silicified; siderite nodules	0.15–0.25
Sandstone, pale grey-green; fine-grained, soft, well-bedded, micaceous; siderite nodules, a little pyrite	0.25
Sandstone, grey-green and purple, coarse-grained, silicified, cross-bedded; siderite nodules; much organic material	0.27–0.35
Sandstone, pale grey-green (fine-grained) and dark purple (coarse-grained); siderite nodules	0.30
Sandstone, pale grey, weathered dark purple, yellow, orange and green; coarse-grained, poorly bedded; siderite nodules; base of Priorslee Rock?	1.00
Clay	—

North of the Nedge Brook, in a sewer tunnel [7140 0811 to 7150 0835], the Brookside Rock of the Keele Beds was gently unconformable on the Coalport Formation. Some 13 m of the latter were seen, predominantly pale grey and dark purple-brown mudstones, smooth to silty, blocky and unbedded, in places slickensided or micaceous. They include beds up to a metre thick of flaggy pale grey sandstone, micaceous and pyritic, and thinner beds of massive, coarsely crystalline pale grey limestone. The Priorslee Rock forms a strong feature [708 086] east of the Randley Fault, and passes up by alternation into argillaceous strata.

The Priorslee Rock also forms the feature on which stands Malins Lee Hall [697 090]; the coal mine there records 6.7 m of sandstone. A small sandstone outcrop [7065 1010] near Snedshill is believed to be a faulted outlier of Priorslee Rock, and *Spirorbis* limestone was recorded in the overlying strata [7060 1026].

The following section is recorded from this interval in Stafford Pits:

	Thickness m
'Magnesian Limestone'	1.7
'Red and white wild ground'	9.0
Blue clods and grey rock binds	4.1
Grey rock (Priorslee Rock)	3.4

To the north the Priorslee Rock thickens and forms a discontinous faulted scarp from Stafford Park [711 089] to the A5 road east of St Georges. A shallow borehole for the Telford–Wolverhampton Motorway, No. 3 [7122 0937], was sited at the top of the Priorslee Rock, but did not bottom it:

	Thickness m
Weathered sandstone, pale grey, yellow, grey and brown, coarse-grained, clayey	1.2

	Thickness m
Sandstone, pale olive-green and brown, coarse-grained, micaceous, with carbonaceous specks; poorly bedded; lowest 0.50 m fine-grained, pale greyish green	3.0
Mudstone, lilac and pale olive, silty, micaceous, bedded	0.2
Sandstone, pale grey, also brown and purple; hard, coarse-grained, poorly bedded; pale grey mudstone partings	0.8 +

At Limekiln Bank [7147 1082], brash included coarse-grained sandstone with espley material and mudstone pellets. At Watling Street Grange Pit, the following is recorded beneath the Keele Beds:

	Thickness m
'Magnesian Limestone'	1.5
Blue and purple rock	0.8
Mingled clod, red and blue	6.3
Blue binds and espley; Priorslee Rock	4.2

In Childpit Lane and Lilleshall No. 3 boreholes the Priorslee Rock may be present but in the Keele facies; it is absent from Lilleshall Nos. 1, 6 and 7A, where Keele facies extends to a lower level. At Lilleshall No. 4 Borehole, 3.05 m of grey bedded 'limestone' are recorded below 6.1 m of grey-green shale, which pass up into Keele mudstones; it is possible that the 'limestone' is a calcareous sandstone, the Priorslee Rock. At Brickkiln Plantation (Figure 33), 4.6 m of pale grey, medium-grained sandstone with limestone and mudstone are also inter-preted as Priorslee Rock, while 9.65 m of grey sandstones and multicoloured mudstones underlie the Keele Beds at Hugh's Bridge.

Wellington area (Coed-yr-Allt Beds)

In the Wrekin Buildings Borehole [6231 0871] (Figure 17), 18.0 m of strata resemble the Coalport Formation of Coal-brookdale and are attributed to the equivalent Coed-yr-Allt Beds. A pyritous coal (which may be the equivalent of the Main Sulphur Coal), 0.34 m thick at 134.34 m depth, overlies 0.81 m of seatearth; 3.79 m of beds beneath this coal seam are of Coed-yr-Allt facies and rest conformably upon Ruabon Marl. Plants collected from a depth of 120.1 m to 120.6 m were identified by Professor W G Chaloner as *Calamites* sp. and *Neuropteris* cf. *ovata*. The Ruabon/Coed-yr-Allt boundary has, in this area, been taken at the level of the facies change, although if the coal were the Main Sulphur then the Hadley/Coalport junc-tion would be placed at the base of the coal. The Coed-yr-Allt facies is not recognised in borings north-east of Wrekin Build-ings, where Keele strata rest upon the Uriconian volcanic group.

West of Longwood [6045 0710] the Dryton Coalfield is a long-abandoned outlier of the Shrewsbury Coalfield. Murchi-son (1839, p.39) records that coal had been worked near Long-wood and that two seams were being worked at Dryton, just west of the Telford district. He records the thickness of the lower seam as 0.8 m and that of the upper as 0.6 m, the two being separated by clods and sandstones; a third coal and beds of limestone which occur in the Shrewsbury Coalfield are not recorded. It is believed that the lower coal of Dryton is that found at Wrekin Buildings and is the Main Sulphur Coal of Coalbrookdale. The base of the Keele Beds in this area could be interpreted (p.41) to represent the base of sub-Permian red-

dening, so that, prior to oxidation, all three coals of the Shrews-bury Coalfield might have been present in this area.

KEELE BEDS

Madeley area

Borehole G2 [7221 0191] at Sutton Maddock records a com-plete Keele sequence, 63.7 m thick, consisting largely of purple and red mudstones, but with two thin sandstones in the lowest 7.6 m. West and south-west of there the outcrop is largely obscured by boulder clay but 18 m of strata were exposed at the top of the Severn gorge [7098 0017]:

	Thickness m
Sandstone, pale green and red, hard, medium-grained, massive and thinly bedded; cross-bedded; mudstone beds	3.0
Mudstone, purple above, red below	6.0
Sandstone, as above	3.0
Mudstone, red and purple	6.0

From Sweyney Cliff [7070 0184], where 9 m of purple cal-careous sandstone with layers of mudstone pellet conglomerate are exposed just behind the house, the lowest sandstone is the Brookside Rock, which forms a series of crags to beyond Hay Farm [6961 0316]; Borehole G3 [6956 0295] records 7.0 m of pale grey sandstone. The second major sandstone in the Keele Beds crops out at Sutton Wood Farm [706 022]; 3 m of coarse-grained reddish brown micaceous and feldspathic sandstone can be seen in the old quarry [7063 0211]. Probably the same sandstone forms the feature [700 034] north of the Blists Hill Fault. Road and factory excavations [708 042] revealed green and purple-red thinly bedded sandstones and conglomerates overlying mudstones and siltstones which are brick-red, mottled and banded pale green. Further factory excavations [7124 0505] revealed Keele Beds dipping eastwards at 23° to 45° beside the Madeley Fault:

	Thickness m
Sandstone, purple, mottled pale green, massive, micaceous, not cross-bedded	2.1
Mudstone, brick red and purple, a few pale green and olive-yellow layers	9.0

The Brookside Rock is known from boreholes to crop out north of the Madeley Fault [7117 0502 to 7122 0568], and 13.2 m of red sandstone with two red mudstone partings are recorded at the top of Kemberton Colliery Inside Shaft. West of the Mad Brook Valley, the Brookside Rock and overlying mud-stones are preserved against the Brookside Fault. A 6.0 m section in the Brookside Rock was exposed [7054 0537] during construction of a bridge over the railway:

	Thickness m
Sandstone, pale green, purple stained, thinly bedded, bed thickness increasing upwards; purple mudstone beds near base	3.0
Sandstone, pale green, hard, massive; brown-weathered pyrite nodules, black carbonaceous spots, rare purple staining, red clay on joints	2.2
Sandstone, pale green, also purple; thinly bedded and cross-bedded; layers of mudstone breccia	0.8 +

On the north side of the railway [7053 0541] the sandstone was more massive, coarse-grained, feldspathic and micaceous, with much cross-bedding. It contained barytes veins [7052 0544] and, beside the Brookside Fault [7054 0546], malachite veins.

North of the Brookside Fault, 3.8 m of sandstone in borehole EP47A [7042 0538] are believed to be the Brookside Rock, faulted down by some 13.7 m. The overlying strata crop out between the Brookside, Warrensway, Halesfield and Holmer faults; the following section is generalised from site investigation boreholes and temporary exposures:

	Thickness m
Mudstone, mostly red	3.35
Sandstone, deep purple becoming pale green below; hard, micaceous, thinly bedded, cross-bedded, medium- to coarse-grained; red clay on joints	3.0
Mudstone, purple and khaki, also yellow-brown, blue-grey and pale green; smooth to silty; thin beds of khaki and deep purple hard fine-grained sandstone	4.3
Sandstone, deep purple becoming pale green below, also mottled grey, olive and lilac; hard, feldspathic, slightly micaceous; thinly bedded, cross-bedded, also massive below; medium- to coarse-grained, some organic material, scattered pale green mudstone clasts; red clay on joints; thin limestone beds; knots of malachite and hematite; 0.3 m basal mudstone conglomerate	5.8
Mudstone, multicoloured pale green, lilac, purple, brown, blue, brick red; smooth to silty	2.1
Sandstone, pale to deep purple and green; hard, feldspathic, micaceous and non-micaceous, thinly bedded and massive, coarse- to medium-grained; red clay on joints; beds of purple mudstone pellet conglomerate	5.7
Mudstone, mainly red and purple	15.9
Sandstone: Brookside Rock	—

The Brookside Rock crops out within a fault block at Holmer Farm [709 060]. At its base is a mudstone conglomerate, 0.3 m thick, with tabular clasts of purple and green mudstone in a sandy matrix. Excavations on the edge of the reservoir [7090 0601] revealed 4.0 m of sandstone; it was hard, coarse-grained, massive but with some cross-bedding, and with weathered pyrite cubes up to 8 mm across. Within the sandstone was an erosive-based lens of dark red and purple mudstone up to 1.5 m thick, with thin layers of pale green and purple sandstone. North-east of Holmer Farm the Brookside Rock was seen in a sewer tunnel [7104 0632 to 7124 0681]; it was massive, medium- to coarse-grained, pale green, faintly micaceous and feldspathic with scattered spots of weathered organic material, but it became deep purple towards the top where it passed up by alternation into purple mudstone. Surface excavations [712 063] revealed up to 4.0 m of mudstone, generally silty, calcareous and micaceous, unbedded and blocky, in places very hard. Also present were small (1 mm) ferruginous concretions, some rootlet casts, and beds up to 1.0 m thick of fine-grained, massive purple and pale green sandstone. A normal fault [7121 0645] was mineralised with malachite, calcite, baryte and hematite. Holmer Farm Borehole E [7100 0588] recorded 9.9 m of red mudstone overlying 9.6 m of Brookside Rock.

A sandstone high in the Keele Beds crops out along the ridge [710 063 to 710 073] from Holmer to Lower Brands, with the underlying mudstones reappearing to the east. As exposed in an underpass [711 068] this sandstone is coarse grained, feldspathic, non-micaceous, partly cross-bedded and with beds of mudstone pellet conglomerate. Thinly bedded, fine-grained sandstones at the top of this unit were exposed in another underpass [7073 0704]; these are micaceous, pale grey, green, lilac, brown, yellow and purple, and pass up into mudstones that crop out north of Lower Brands [7086 0692].

The Keele Beds were proved in Madeley Wood boreholes 1 to 8 between Halesfield and Shifnal. The sequence was 137.5 m thick in Borehole No. 5:

	Thickness m	Depth m
Bridgnorth Sandstone and Enville Beds	—	167.6
Mudstone, brick red and purple, silty, micaceous, with pale calcareous patches; sandstone beds	85.4	253.0
Sandstone, purple and grey, fine-grained; 3.05 m mudstone bed; Brookside Rock?	19.8	272.8
Mudstone, purple and red, green mottled; silty and micaceous or smooth; thin sandstone beds; limestone nodules	20.6	293.4
Sandstone, purple, red and grey; fine-grained above, coarse below; Priorslee Rock?	3.0	296.4
Mudstone, purple, mottled green; silty, micaceous, calcareous, passing into	8.7	305.1
Coalport Formation, beds above Top Rock	—	—

Similar strata, 141.7 m thick and including the Brookside and Priorslee rocks, were found in Borehole No. 6. In Borehole No. 4, a sandstone believed to be the Priorslee Rock and assigned to the Coalport Formation, is overlain by 99.1 m of Keele strata. Madeley Wood boreholes Nos. 1, 7, and 8 penetrate 102 m to 113 m of Keele facies strata, mostly brick-red and purple, silty, calcareous mudstones, with the Brookside Rock well developed (Figure 16). In Borehole No. 3, 85.3 m of Keele facies strata passed down into Coalport mudstones 9 m above the Thick Rock. The three sandstones included in the lower part of the Keele Beds here may be equivalent to the Top Rock, Priorslee Rock and Brookside Rock (Figure 16). In No. 2 Borehole, Keele strata apparently rest directly on the Thick Rock; the Keele facies sequence totals about 130 m, predominantly red-brown silty mudstones and sandstones, with more sandstone recorded than in neighbouring boreholes. In Lilleshall No. 5 Borehole, to the north-east, the Keele facies extends as far down as the top of the Thick Rock or even to within it; the top 3.0 m of the Thick Rock is described as 'red and grey calcareous sandstone'; between this and the Brookside Rock are 70.1 m of red mudstones with some green colouration below and a sandstone 6.1m thick towards the top (Figure 16).

Dawley area

The Brookside Rock and overlying mudstones are preserved as a largely drift-covered outlier between the Nedge and Randley valleys north-east of Mount Pleasant [705 075]. Up to 2.4 m of sandstone were recorded as variously pale green, brown and purple, with black manganese staining and finely disseminated, brown-weathered organic material. This sandstone passed up into pale grey and lilac, smooth to silty mudstone. Keele Beds cropping out between the Limestone and Nedge faults are all believed to lie above the Brookside Rock; the sandstone which forms a feature on the eastern side of the valley between the Nedge Brook and the railway is thought to be the one above the Brookside Rock in the local succession. An excavation [7131 0793] adjacent to the Nedge Fault showed this sandstone to be badly broken by subsidiary normal and reverse faults; the rock was mostly deep purple, also lilac and pale green, massive to medium bedded, coarse grained, feldspathic and rather micaceous.

The underlying mudstones were brick red, lilac and pale green, silty, micaceous and blocky. The third Keele sandstone is believed to crop out over a wide area [714 076 to 716 083], and higher strata, seen in a sewer tunnel [7168 0848 to 7175 0850], were mostly smooth, poorly bedded brick red mudstones, rarely purple or pale green, and including beds up to 1.5 m thick of pale, hard, purple and green sandstone.

Between the Nedge and Randley faults the lower Keele strata were seen in the Nedge–Stafford Park Sewer tunnel and boreholes, and in surface excavations. The Brookside Rock ranged in thickness up to 3.5 m, and was pale greenish grey, fine-grained, micaceous, thinly bedded and pyritic. It was overlain by brick red and pale grey mudstones, smooth and silty and generally blocky. The pale grey mudstones were often pyritic. These were overlain by a sandstone, 1.8 m to 3.8 m thick, pale purple and green, coarse-grained and micaceous, thinly bedded and cross-bedded above but more massive below, with mudstone pellet conglomerates and much feldspar and brown-weathered organic material. A knoll of this sandstone reaches the surface through the drift [714 086]. It is overlain by brick red mudstones, and a third thick sandstone was proved in boreholes and drainage trenches [7176 0865 to 7194 0917]. This third major sandstone is at least 6.8 m thick (Stafford Park Borehole 213 [7193 0908]), mostly deep to pale purple and brick red, massive, medium-grained, micaceous and feldspathic, with mudstone partings, pellet conglomerates and a little weathered pyrite.

At Stafford Pits, the Brookside Rock is 4.15 m thick and boreholes nearby show it to be overlain by at least 12 m of mudstone and then a further sandstone. North of the Priorslee–Shifnal Road, the Keele Beds occupy low ground, poorly exposed and partly drift-covered, but the sandstone which reaches the surface at Watling Street Grange [721 111] is believed to be the Brookside Rock. It is brownish green, coarse grained, micaceous and feldspathic. To the west, a fault-block adjacent to the Lightmoor Fault at Lodgewood Farm [7140 1136] comprises bright red mudstones overlain by reddish sandstone in their south-east corner. Watling Street Grange Pit is situated within a smaller fault block and 9.5 m of Keele Beds are recorded, including 3.84 m of Brookside Rock.

Farther north, the exposed Keele Beds mainly comprise red mudstone, with faulted knolls of deep purple and reddish coarse-grained micaceous sandstone [7234 1177, 7210 1178]. At Granville Colliery (Figure 35) the highest 71.6 m of solid strata are assigned to the Keele Beds and are mostly mudstone but include three thin impure limestones. Fine-grained grey sandstone, 5.9 m thick and interbedded with red and grey mudstone 8.1 m above the base of this succession, is interpreted as the Brookside Rock, and there are further sandstones in the upper part of the sequence. North of Granville, three sandstones are mapped within red mudstones. The lowest occurs immediately east of the Lightmoor Fault at Muxtonbridge Farm [724 133] and may be the Brookside Rock; higher sandstones crop out to the south-east [724 129 to 730 132, 724 127 to 727 127]. All are purple, brown and pale green, coarse-grained, micaceous and feldspathic. North of Abbey Farm [735 139] the Keele Beds are largely obscured by drift, but in Crow Hayes trial shaft near Lilleshall [7402 1568] the highest 55.3 m appear to be Keele strata.

Figure 35 shows the Keele Beds as recorded in coal boreholes north-east of Granville Colliery; unfortunately only chipping samples were available so conclusions are tentative. The thickness of the formation and the proportion of sandstone both vary widely. However, one sandstone is persistent in almost all the boreholes, and from its position relative to the sandstones of the

Coalport Formation, beneath, it is believed to be the Brookside Rock. In Lilleshall No. 1 Borehole 137.8 m of Keele facies strata rest on the Top Rock of the Coalport Formation (Figure 35). At Hollybank Wood Borehole, 126 m of Keele strata include a sandstone 15.2 m thick (with parting) near the base, and a 12.2 m bed higher up; neither correlates well with the Brookside Rock, and the lower sandstone here may be the Priorslee Rock. In the Brickkiln Plantation Borehole, Keele facies strata, 99 m thick, appear to rest on Coalport Formation mudstone above the Priorslee Rock. In Lilleshall No. 2 Borehole, 142.8 m of strata are identified as Keele Beds, starting at about the base of the Priorslee Rock, and include a large proportion of brown and grey sandstone interbedded with the red mudstones. At Childpit Lane Borehole 135.6 m of strata are assigned to the Keele Beds, overlying a coal seam above the Top Rock. Two thick sandstones close above the base probably represent the Priorslee Rock, and a 4.6 m sandstone near the middle of the sequence is tentatively interpreted as the Brookside Rock; thin coals are recorded both above and below it. In Lilleshall No. 3A Borehole the base of the Keele Beds is placed at the top of the Top Rock and the sequence is about 91 m thick; 6m of coarse-grained variegated sandstone 3 m above the base is identified as the Priorslee Rock, and a 3 m sandstone, 52 m above the base and overlain by a *Spirorbis* limestone, is interpreted as the Brookside Rock. Finally, in Lilleshall No. 6 Borehole the mudstones of the Coalport Formation pass upwards into Keele facies about 3 m above the Thick Rock, and no less than 259 m of strata are here assigned to the Keele Beds (Figure 35). The Brookside Rock is identified as a 3 m-thick, purple and pale grey sandstone, 97.5 m above the base. Thin limestone beds occur below this rock, and beds of sandstone and limestone with ?*Spirorbis* occur in the highest 73.2 m of the Keele Beds.

Wellington area

South-west of Longwood, powered auger holes [6013 0704, 6026 0683] record boulder clay overlying pale purplish, micaceous fine-grained sand, typical of weathered Keele Beds. At Wrekin Buildings Borehole [6231 0871] 45.8 m of red strata assigned to the Keele facies overlie definite Coed-yr-Allt Beds with apparent conformity (Figure 17). Auger holes Aston A2 [6162 0944], Cluddley A2 [6376 1095], A3 [6377 1074], A4 [6333 1030] and A1 [6397 1080] all proved purple, red or brown mudstones — unconformably overlain by Bridgnorth Sandstone in Cluddley A1.

Water boreholes sunk in the early 1900s indicated (Pocock et al., 1938) that Keele Beds underlie all of Wellington, concealed beneath drift. Slang Lane No. 2 Borehole [6448 1163] (Pocock et al., 1938, pp.158–159) revealed red clay and lavender sandstone at a depth of 22.25 m. In fragments from between 20.7 m and 21.3 m, an insect wing was subsequently referred (Bolton, 1921) to a new species, *Archimylacris pringlei*. From 29.6 m to 31.4 m, fragments of red clay contained the plants *Pecopteris* (*Cyatheites*) sp. and ?*Cordaites*.

West of the Dothill Fault the western outcrop of the Keele Beds is conjectural, but the formation is believed to rest directly on the Uriconian rocks of Wrockwardine. Saline springs occur at Uffington, Donnerville, Kinley Farm and Admaston, where the Keele rests directly on Uriconian rocks, at or near outcrop and beneath little or no drift. A borehole [6696 1474] at Kinley Farm proved 'marl, marly rock and sandstone' to 36.0 m depth below 6.7 m of drift; another borehole [6689 1466] proved 'hard marl and sandstone' to 26.8 m, again below 6.7 m of drift. Finally, the BGS Kinley Farm Borehole [6716 1478] was drilled 150 m south of the Kinley Farm spring. The cores showed that beneath 9.5 m of drift, 29.7 m of Keele Beds were mainly dark purple calcareous sandstones, with chocolate brown

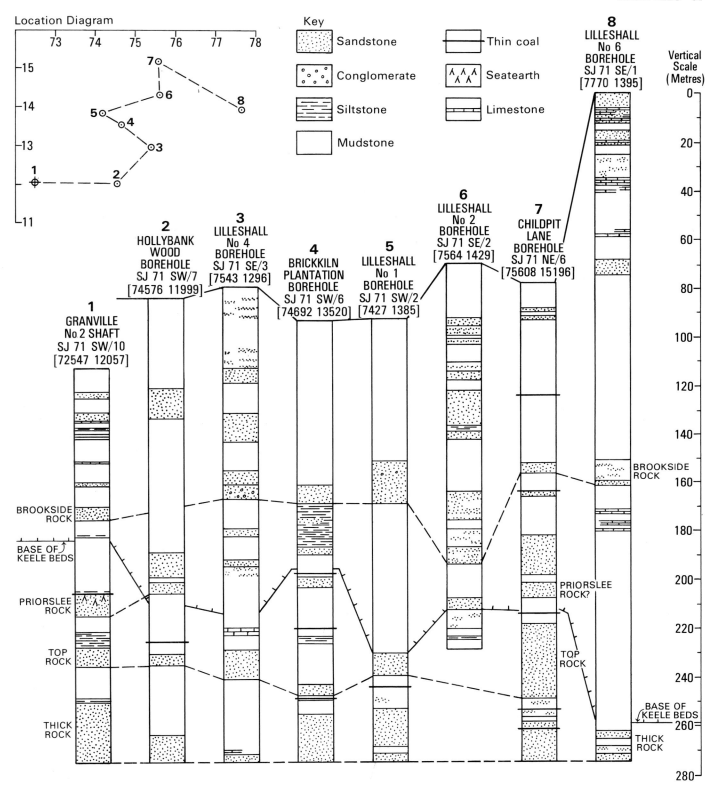

Figure 35 Keele Beds as proved in boreholes for Granville Colliery. The junction with the underlying Coalport Formation is conformable but strongly diachronous; and in all cases except the Granville Shaft, the Keele Beds are overlain conformably by the Enville Beds.

and lavender mudstones. These strata rest unconformably on the Uriconian; at their base were 1.5 m of conglomerate with subangular to subrounded pebbles, up to 30 mm across, of dark green and blue tuffaceous Uriconian rocks, dark brown siltstone, red ferruginous sandstone, purplish sandstone, and pellets of dark brown and purple mudstone. The matrix was dark purple sandstone with well rounded grains.

South of Kinley Farm the Keele Beds are overlain by Bridgnorth Sandstone (Figure 17). The tabulation below shows the thickness of the Keele Beds, and the depth to their top, in recent BGS boreholes and in four other boreholes sunk in Hadley Park between 1860 and 1884. In all boreholes, except Hoo Hall and Wrekin Buildings, the Keele Beds are proved to rest on theUriconian; and in all except Hadley Park No. 4 and Kinley Farm, they were unconformably overlain by Bridgnorth Sandstone:

	Thickness of Keele Beds	Depth to top of Keele Beds
	m	m
Hadley Park No. 1 [6720 1322]	45.72	11.89
Hadley Park No. 2 [6798 1281]	82.56	37.15
Hadley Park No. 3 [6738 1361]	45.11	13.11
Hadley Park No. 4 [6775 1349]	39.33	11.88
Hoo Hall (1970) [6861 1488]	45.65	45.79
Kinley Farm (1971) [6716 1478]	29.69	9.50
Leegomery House Farm (1971) [6638 1268]	93.75	24.99
Lodge Farm, Trench (1971) [6887 1297]	16.64	71.83
Wrekin Buildings (1973) [6231 0871]	45.78	74.32

From these boreholes, a generalised sequence can be compiled; note, however, that the three lowest items pass laterally into Coed-yr Allt facies at the Wrekin Buildings Borehole (Figure 17):

	Thickness m
Sandstones, purple, blue and dark greenish grey, micaceous and slightly calcareous, coarse-grained, slightly friable, commonly cross-bedded; subordinate red to purple mudstones and paler purple, slightly calcareous siltstones; thickest at Leegomery House Farm	up to 33
Mudstones, dark grey to purple, commonly mottled; finely silty; scattered plant remains at Leegomery House Farm	c.5–13
Sandstones, dark greenish grey to purple; coarse-grained, with angular grains; calcareous; graded bedding in the upper parts, more massive and cross-bedded in the lower parts; breccia-beds common at or near the base	8–12
Mudstones, brown and purple, mottled pale green; commonly smooth, but grey calcareous siltstones occur particularly in the south-west; plant-rich beds at Leegomery House Farm and Wrekin Buildings are correlated with 'ironstones' at the same level in the Hadley Park boreholes; *Alethopteris serli* and *A.* cf. *lesquereuxi* collected at Wrekin Buildings	4–11
Sandstones, purplish grey to red; micaceous, slightly calcareous, massive, cores frequently unjointed; several beds with angular, chocolate mudstone fragments; lower part commonly cross-bedded, upper part horizontally laminated and may pass up into brown, smooth, blocky mudstones with thin sandstone beds; strongly erosive base	10–20
Mudstones and siltstones, chocolate brown, red and purple; brown mudstones frequently show organic trails and burrows; finely micaceous, particularly towards the base; a well-developed seatearth occurs in the uppermost part at Leegomery House Farm; these beds become more calcareous towards the south-west, with impure silty limestone nodules common in the middle and lower parts; thickest at Leegomery House Farm	1.0–14.5
Sandstones, red to purple; coarse-grained, micaceous and calcareous; conglomerates at the base and within the lower part consist almost entirely of Uriconian fragments, angular to subrounded, pebble to cobble size	7–19

ENVILLE BEDS

Madeley area

Borehole G2 at Sutton Maddock [7221 0191] records 19.8 m of strata assigned to the Enville Beds below the Bridgnorth Sandstone; these include red mudstones and three beds of purplish red and purplish brown calcareous sandstone. To the south the Enville Beds are cut out below the Bridgnorth Sandstone in the vicinity of Sutton Hall [719 014]; however, to the west the two lowest sandstones crop out on the high ground of Sutton Common [715 021] and Suttonhill House [707 029]. A large, partly overgrown quarry at Brickkiln Coppice [712 029] exposes a sandstone believed to be the lowest in the Enville sequence. The quarry section reveals 3.0 m of dull red-brown, coarse-grained, massive, micaceous sandstone, with much weathered feldspar. Included are thin beds of highly ferruginous conglomerate, with pellets of pale brown and reddish purple mudstone. Two sandstones, believed to be that seen at Brickkiln Coppice and a higher one, were exposed in excavations south of the Clews Wood Fault [711 038], separated by brick red and brown silty mudstones and siltstones, soft, micaceous and well bedded. North of this site the Enville outcrop is offset eastwards by the Clews Wood Fault, forming the topographic gap through which the Mad Brook flows.

North of the Clews Wood Fault the southern half of Halesfield Industrial Estate lies on the lowerpart of the Enville succession, which here comprises massive sandstones with thin mudstone beds dipping generally east-south-east. Excavations for a factory site revealed a section [7138 0470] beside the Madeley–Shifnal Road:

	Thickness m
Boulder clay	—
Sandstone, greenish red, coarse-grained, massive, feldspathic, non-micaceous, some manganese staining; cross-bedded	2.0
Mudstone, bright red, smooth to sandy	0.6
Sandstone, as above, very hard	0.6 +

The lower sandstone forms the floor of a large part of this site. A water-main trench on the western boundary of the site [7128 0475 to 7128 0464] revealed:

	Thickness m
Sandstone, red-brown, also pale green; micaceous, thinly bedded, cross-bedded (lowest sandstone in section described above)	0.6 +
Mudstone, brick red; thin pale green and brown sandstone layers	1.0–1.2

	Thickness m
Sandstone, mostly red-brown, also pale green, purple and yellowish, with a little manganese staining; massive in beds 0.6 m thick, also flaggy and thinly bedded; soft green sandstone at the top, underlain by thinly bedded purple to red quartzitic sandstone and mudstone pellet breccia; below this is a lenticle up to 0.3 m thick of red-brown mudstone with thin dark green sandstones; base very uneven, cutting down into	1.3
Mudstone, red, blocky	up to 3.0 +

North of the factory site, boreholes indicate a downfaulted wedge of mudstones, but north of this the basal Enville sandstones occupy the top of the hill, beneath boulder clay. A deep drainage trench [7142 0510 to 7145 0525] revealed 0.7 m to 1.0 m of brownish red to green, flaggy, cross-bedded, fine-grained, micaceous sandstone underlain by at least 2.5 m of similarly coloured, massive to thinly bedded, coarse-grained and micaceous sandstone with black manganese staining, and beds up to 0.2 m thick of mudstone pellet conglomerate.

East of the sections described above, the strata underlying the wide valley between Brockton [720 035] and The Hem [730 060] are believed to be largely mudstones. The village of Kemberton is built on a ridge of strata in the upper part of the local Enville sequence; west of the fault through Church Farm [7281 0452] these beds are mostly hard red mudstones, but east of the fault there are two thick sandstones. The lower forms a pronounced feature to the north of the village [732 053], with crags up to 3.0 m high of coarse-grained, red-brown and purple calcareous sandstones, with mudstone pellet conglomerates.

Madeley Wood boreholes No. 5, south of Shifnal [7500 0628], and No. 6, south-west of Shifnal [7427 0698], penetrated respectively 70.1 m and 61.0 m of strata considered to be Enville Beds, conformable on Keele Beds and overlain by Bridgnorth Sandstone. Chert and limestone pebbles were recorded in the top 30 m of strata in No. 5 Borehole.

The hill west of Hem Manor Farm [725 058] is formed by the lowest three Enville sandstones, which are cut by at least three minor faults. No evidence has been found for the fault originally postulated through Hem Mill (Whitehead et al., 1928, p.117); the three sandstones cross the valley without a break, and the lowest two form a strong escarpment, trending north-north-west past the Dodmoors to Nedge Hill [718 072]; there, the second of these sandstones is conglomeratic, being the most southerly calcareous chert and limestone conglomerate recorded at outcrop. The third sandstone in the sequence underlies Shaw Farm [726 073], and the fourth sandstone passes through The Wyke [730 068], with a fifth to the north and east. Four sandstones can also be distinguished in the chippings log for Madeley Wood Borehole No. 4 [7332 0657]:

	Thickness m
Sandstone, red-brown, fine-grained, with siltstone	9.14
Mudstone, red-brown	6.10
Sandstone, red-brown, fine- to medium-grained, marly and calcareous in part	7.62
No samples	4.57
Mudstone, red	6.10
Sandstone, pale brown, medium-grained, marly and calcareous in part	16.76
Mudstone, red-brown, with cream to grey spots	9.14
Sandstone, deep to pale red-brown, fine-grained; sparsely conglomeratic below	7.62

Scattered pebbles in the lowest sandstone in this borehole are the only indication of conglomerate within these four sandstones south-east of the Dodmoors Fault. However, the fifth sandstone becomes conglomeratic in its lower part [734 077] north-east of Shaw House. South-west of Knowle Farm [735 085] it forms a strong feature, and old quarries on either side of the Telford–Shifnal Road contain conglomerates with partly rounded pebbles of red and yellow chert, quartz and quartzite, rarely over 3 cm in diameter, in a highly calcareous matrix. Madeley Wood boreholes 7 and 8 record approximately 91 m and 87 m of Enville Beds up to and including this fifth sandstone.

The correlation of individual sandstones north-east from Naird Farm [719 079] is uncertain; that on which the farm stands may be the fourth in the sequence just described, and is underlain by at least 11.7 m of mudstone. The next sandstone up in the sequence crops out east of Naird Farm [721 076 to 728 083], as four outliers on the dip slope between Blythbury [725 081] and Knowlbank [730 090], and east of Castle Farm [729 093 to 732 095]. It contains limestone and chert pebbles, like the fifth sandstone at Knowle Farm.

Madeley Wood Borehole No. 2 [7311 0878] records only 56.4 m of strata interpreted as Enville Beds, mostly sandstones with scattered pebble conglomerates. Madeley Wood Borehole No. 1 [7387 0876] penetrated 109.7 m of Enville strata; at the top is the fifth sandstone, which is about 12.2 m thick in the borehole and is seen in a nearby quarry [7373 0892] to be highly conglomeratic with pebbles, up to 10cm in diameter, of chert, limestone and jasper. North of Haughton Lane, Motorway Borehole 19 [7375 0897] cored 18 m of strata (below 2.5 m of boulder clay), including 7.2 m of the fifth sandstone and 10.8 m of underlying strata:

	Thickness m
Boulder clay?	—
Sandstone, purple; fine- to medium-grained, thinly bedded	0.25
Mudstone, deep purple-brown, silty	0.13
Sandstone, pale green and deep purple; hard, fine-grained, massive below, thinly bedded above	1.12
Conglomerate; chert, limestone and sandstone pebbles, pale purple sandstone matrix	4.50
Sandstone, deep reddish purple; coarse-grained, micaceous, hard, massive	1.20
Mudstone, purple-brown, smooth to silty and micaceous; thin sandstone and conglomerate beds	5.20
Sandstone, purple-brown, mottled green and yellow; hard, massive, medium-grained	0.68
Mudstone, deep purple, hard, silty, micaceous; bed of sandstone as below	1.33
Sandstone, pale green and purple, coarse-grained, massive, micaceous	3.39
Mudstone, brick red, micaceous, silty	0.20

To the east a higher, sixth, sandstone forms a dip slope down to the Haughton Fault. However, Madeley Wood No. 3 Borehole [7464 0906] east of that fault records only 82.3 m of Enville Beds beneath 33.5 m of Bridgnorth Sandstone; this suggests that there may have been considerable erosion of the Enville before deposition of the latter, possibly as a result of contemporary movement on the Haughton Fault.

Dawley area

The basal Enville sandstone forms a strong feature [722 086] just north-west of the Limestone Fault; it is mostly purple-red, but also pale grey, massive, fine-grained and micaceous, with layers of conglomerate containing purple and mustard-coloured mudstone flakes. The lowest two Enville sandstones form a low hill above The Woodhouse [723 101], and a stronger feature against the Redhill Fault at Redhill [726 110]. Boreholes for the reservoir there show at least 10.5 m of the lowest sandstone, which varies in colour from almost white to medium purple; it is coarse-grained and massive, with thin beds of brick red mudstone and a few mudstone pellet conglomerates.

From the Redhill Fault north-eastwards to Lilyhurst [750 133] it is rarely possible to identify individual sandstones or to follow their outcrops for any distance because of the complex-faulting. However, there is little drift cover and the distribution of sandstones and mudstones can be traced by augering. Basal Enville conglomeratic sandstone with chert clasts can be seen in an old quarry [7257 1155] and slabs of ripple-marked sandstone with rain-spot impressions and sun-cracks [7384 1144] occur near Redhill Farm. Hollybank Wood Borehole [7457 1199] was drilled adjacent to the base of the Bridgnorth Sandstone, hence the 74.7 m of Enville Beds recorded must there represent the complete succession. Lilleshall No. 7A Borehole [7400 1273] recorded only 42.5 m of Enville Beds; this sequence was cored and revealed mainly red-brown, fine-grained and commonly micaceous sandstone, with beds of mudstone pellet conglomerate and calcareous marl.

North of Lilyhurst, the strata are less faulted and individual sandstones can again be traced for long distances. Lilleshall No. 1 Borehole [7427 1385] lies within the second sandstone in the sequence; 42.7 m of Enville Beds are recorded including a mudstone, 8.4 m thick, overlying 32.9 m of sandstone with mudstone interbeds, which can be taken as the basal sandstone. The second, thinner sandstone has been much quarried in

Abbey Wood [7446 1477]. This is the lowest sandstone described by Whitehead et al. (1928, p.114); it is coarse-grained and micaceous, and contains small chips of chert and beds of mudstone pellets. Brickkiln Plantation Borehole [7469 1352] records 68.6 m of Enville Beds, mostly mudstones but with two thick sandstones in the lowest 18.3 m.

The two sandstones which trend northward from Lilyhurst [749 132] and Lilleshall Hall [748 144] join to form a single bed at Childpit Farm [753 153], just outside the Telford map area; this was considered to be the second in the sequence by Whitehead et al. (1928), but it now seems more likely to be the third sandstone, or higher. It is coarsely conglomeratic with pebbles of chert, limestone, quartzite and quartz. The next sandstone (also outside the map area) produces a strong feature, with a wide dip slope, from Childpit Lane [756 152] to south of Lilyhurst Road [752 130]. It is sparsely conglomeratic, and includes three thick lenses of red mudstone in its lower part. Childpit Lane Borehole [7560 1519], situated on this sandstone, records 100.6 m of Enville Beds, whereas Lilleshall No. 4 [7543 1296] and No. 2 [7564 1429] start in the overlying mudstone and record thicknesses respectively of 97.5 m and 131.7 m.

The highest Enville sandstone in this region runs north from near Atwell Park Farm [756 128] (where it appears to be cut out below the Bridgnorth Sandstone), through Nutty Hills Farm [759 142]; this contains conglomerates with chert clasts up to 8 cm in length. At Hilton Bank [7633 1324], this sandstone is 15.5 m thick and overlies 17.1 m of mudstone, with a sandstone 23.5 m thick below that. Finally, Lilleshall No. 6 Borehole [7770 1395], some distance to the east, records 112.8 m of Enville Beds between Bridgnorth Sandstone and Keele Beds.

SIX

Permian and Triassic rocks

NOMENCLATURE

The Permian and Triassic rocks of the area were initially termed 'red sandstone and quartzose conglomerate' (Murchison, 1835, 1839) and were correlated with the Bunter Sandstone of Germany. Hull (1860) first distinguished three formations, assigned them to the Triassic System, and named them the Lower Red and Mottled Sandstone, the Pebble Beds, and the Upper Red and Mottled Sandstone. These became accepted as the representatives of the Bunter, in the English Midlands, under the simplified names of 'Lower Mottled Sandstone', 'Bunter Pebble Beds' and 'Upper Mottled Sandstone'. In the Telford area the lowest of the three formations is now termed the Bridgnorth Sandstone Formation and is assigned a Permian age (Smith et al., 1974). The upper two are now called the Kidderminster Formation and the Wildmoor Sandstone Formation, both of which form part of the Sherwood Sandstone Group of early Triassic (Scythian) age (Warrington et al., 1980). Slightly different terms were in use when the Telford map was published, and are retained here.

BRIDGNORTH SANDSTONE FORMATION

In the south-east of the Telford region the Bridgnorth Sandstone has a relatively narrow outcrop, and rests unconformably on Enville Beds and Keele Beds. North-west of the Boundary Fault it crops out over large areas, resting unconformably upon rocks ranging from Uriconian volcanic group to Keele Beds. Lithologically it is a uniform fine-grained sandstone, generally dull red-brown but locally yellow-brown or dull crimson, with some blue-grey, green-grey or black mottling. Strong cross-bedding is ubiquitous. Cement is scanty and the rock crumbles readily to sand, although it stands up well in road cuttings.

The formation thins northwards from about 130 m at Grindle to about 64 m at Crackleybank (Lilleshall Borehole No. 5); in the north-west, beyond the Brockton Fault, it exceeds 100 m, but has been much reduced by erosion in other areas north-west of the Boundary Fault. The wide variation in thickness is partly explained by the very irregular pre-Permian topographic surface, as at Decker Hill, where knolls of Enville Beds protrude into the Bridgnorth Sandstone. Along the Wrekin there is a marked unconformity, the Bridgnorth Sandstone again resting on strata ranging from the Precambrian to the Keele Beds. Wills (1950, p.23; 1956, p.106) suggested that the Permian sands infilled a block-faulted graben, thickening eastwards in the Worcester Basin, but abruptly truncated against the western boundary fault of the South Staffordshire Coalfield; the relative thinness of the deposits east of Telford supports this hypothesis. The increased thickness north-west of the Brockton Fault may imply contemporaneous movement along this fracture also.

An aeolian origin for the formation has long been accepted (Shotton, 1937). This is established by the well-sorted, rounded and polished ('millet seed') sand grains; the rarity or absence of mica, pebble bands and clay partings; and the form of the cross-bedding, which originated in crescentic or barchan dunes (Shotton, 1937, p.553). Barchans imply a constant wind direction (Bagnold, 1941); the cross-bedding in these sandstones suggests a prevalence of easterly winds (Shotton, 1937, p.548), and thus a source of sand in the 'Mercian Highlands' to the east and south-east.

A basal conglomerate, a few centimetres thick and containing pebbles of reddened quartzite and green ?Uriconian rocks, is present at some localities. In the rest of the sequence pebbles are very rare, though dreikanter (wind-faceted pebbles) are recorded by Sherlock (1926, p.9). Heavy minerals from the Bridgnorth Sandstone (Fleet, 1925, 1927) differ from those of the Keele and Enville sandstones; they include garnet, staurolite, apatite and a little mica, indicating erosion of crystalline metamorphic source rocks.

The reddish colour of the Bridgnorth Sandstone is due to the iron oxide that coats each quartz grain; the red mineral was identified as turgite ($2Fe_2O_3, H_2O$) by Dunham (1953). The turgite was deposited before cementation; a pebble of Bridgnorth Sandstone with its turgite-coated grains cemented by calcite is recorded (Shotton, 1956) in the Kidderminster Conglomerate at Wollaston (Stourbridge). Calcite cement occurs at depth in the Bridgnorth Sandstone in the Telford district, and may once have been more widespread.

Wills (1948) considered the Bridgnorth Sandstone to be Permian in age and equivalent to part of the Zechstein sequence; he placed the base of the Trias at the base of the Pebble Beds, which he described as a 'major unconformity', following Wilson (1926, p.49) in the East Midlands. Shotton (1956) correlated the Bridgnorth Sandstone with the Penrith and Collyhurst sandstones, of known pre-Zechstein age and envisaged a 'sand sea' of aeolian dunes extending from north-east Scotland to south-west England. Smith et al. (1974) date the Bridgnorth Sandstone as largely Lower Permian, with a long break before deposition of the Triassic Kidderminster Conglomerate.

KIDDERMINSTER CONGLOMERATE

The Kidderminster Conglomerate crops out in isolated areas in the south-east of the Telford district and in two small areas in the extreme north-west. It forms a prominent feature above the outcrop of the Bridgnorth Sandstone, its relative hardness being due partly to local calcareous or siliceous cementation and partly to its pebble content. Its maximum thickness has not been proved in the district, but is probably about 60 m.

A conglomerate or breccia, up to about 3 m thick, lies at the base of the formation. It includes clasts more angular than in the higher beds, and contains a high proportion of Carboniferous limestone and red marl, indicating dominantly local derivation. It may mark a substantial time break; at Kinver (west of Stourbridge) the base is erosive and cuts down into the Bridgnorth Sandstone (Smith et al., 1974).

The bulk of the formation comprises a sequence of cross-bedded sandstones, pebbly sandstones and pebble conglomerates, similar in colour to the Bridgnorth Sandstone, and long accepted as fluvial in origin. It is believed (see discussion in Fitch et al., 1966, p.301) that the pebbles in the conglomerates were introduced by a major river system flowing northwards from the Hercynian Highlands and joined by tributaries rising in upland areas to the south-east and south-west. The high degree of rounding of the hard quartzite pebbles indicates a distant source, although Wills (1956, p.113) suggested that this was due to their derivation from an earlier conglomerate. Topographic relief was probably greater than in Permian times (Audley-Charles, 1970b, p.49). Both Wales and the Midland 'Mercian Highlands' appear to have been uplifted relative to the Telford district, with the main drainage channels flowing through the Worcester Basin (Fitch et al., 1966, p.305) to disgorge into widespread alluvial fans covering much of Shropshire, Staffordshire and part of Cheshire. Telford lies at the western side of these fans, and the pebbles are fewer and smaller (up to 20 cm diameter) than they are in deposits farther east. Wills (1929, p.115) first suggested that the lack of any long-axis orientation in the pebbles, together with the small amount of stratification, cross-bedding and interstitial sand, indicated deposition on a desert fan rather than a lacustrine delta. He later recognised distinct sedimentary cycles (Wills, 1970, p.229) in which coarse flood gravels, fed by seasonal rains in the uplands, alternated with sandstones and fine-grained sediments showing some signs of dessication. A semi-arid climate with alternating wet and dry periods is implied for the upland source areas to the south, though the climate in the depositional areas may have been more arid (Wills, 1956, p.110; Audley Charles, 1970b, p.68).

Up to 90 per cent of the pebbles in the conglomerates are of quartzite or vein quartz, the former varying from white to dark grey or dull red. The pebbles include fossiliferous Ordovician and Devonian quartzites which can have been derived only from Hercynian uplands to the south — most likely from the Grès de Mai and Grès Armoricain in Northern France (Lamont, 1946). Pebbles of tourmalinised breccia, together with certain quartz-porphyries and rhyolites, can be matched with rocks in Devon and Cornwall (Campbell-Smith, 1963); within equivalent strata in Cheshire, detrital mica dated at 280

to 300 Ma is also believed to point to a southern Hercynian origin (Fitch et al., 1966, p.300). Rocks of more local derivation include Uriconian volcanic rocks, Cambrian quartzite, Llandovery sandstone, ?Upper Carboniferous mudstone and Lower Carboniferous limestones and cherts; the latter are particularly abundant in the area from near Kemberton south to Bewdley (Wills, 1935, p.240), indicating that a tributary drained the area between the Clee Hills, the Forest of Dean and South Wales (Wills, 1948, p.76).

The sand matrix of the Kidderminster Conglomerate contains fresh angular material as well as reworked aeolian sand, and is less well sorted than that in the Bridgnorth Sandstone. The heavy minerals (Fleet, 1923, 1925, 1927) include tourmaline, garnet, staurolite, apatite and anatase.

There is no faunal evidence to indicate the age of the formation, but its base is conventionally regarded as the base of the local Triassic sequence — although, since it overlies an unconformity, older Triassic rocks may be present in more complete sequences elsewhere.

WILDMOOR SANDSTONE

The Kidderminster Conglomerate passes gradationally upwards into the bright red fine-grained sandstones and siltstones of the Wildmoor Sandstone, which is more than 100 m thick in the south-east of the Telford district. Wills (1970) described cycles within the sequence, formed by alternations of cross-bedded and evenly bedded sandstone. The style of the cross-bedding and the presence of mica, clay seams, scattered quartzite pebbles and red mudstone clasts all point to deposition in water, and Wills (1948) considered the deposit to have formed in a shallow lake. Fleet (1923, 1925, 1927, 1929) considered that the petrography of the sandstones implied that they are largely made up of material reworked from the underlying conglomerates.

The formation yields no fauna but there is no reason to doubt a Triassic age.

DETAILS

Bridgnorth Sandstone

Norton to Redhill The Bridgnorth Sandstone emerges through the drift as an isolated knoll [720 001], and other outcrops lie beside the Stockton Fault [729 000; 732 002]. The subdrift outcrop of its base around Old Park Farm [714 006; 718 009] is conjectural, while at St Mary's Church [7189 0138] Bridgnorth Sandstone is clearly faulted against Keele Beds to the west. The sandstone has been augered at surface at Sutton Maddock [7228 0169]; the D'Arcy Exploration Borehole G2 [7221 0191] recorded 4.3 m preserved beneath 25.9 m of glacial gravel and unconformably overlying the Enville Beds.

Between the Harrington Fault and Evelith [744 051] the outcrop widens considerably. The western part of this large area is drift covered, and the base of the Bridgnorth Sandstone can be detected at surface in only a few places, though knolls protrude through the boulder clay south of Kemberton; the eastern half of the area includes drift-free strips of Bridgnorth

Sandstone along the valleys of the Mad Brook and Wesley Brook, and below the Kidderminster Conglomerate north from Havenhills [734 028] and Grindleforge [752 034]. A borehole for water at Grindle [7524 0348], starting just below the base of the Kidderminster Conglomerate, recorded 18.3 m of drift overlying 118.9 m of fine-grained, red and mottled sandstone with two conglomerate beds. Possibly the lowest 15.2 m of this sequence (recorded as 'fine pebble bed' and 'fine red sandstone') belong to the Enville Beds, and the remaining 103.7 m to the Bridgnorth Sandstone, giving an estimated total thickness of about 128 m for the formation in this region.

Good exposures of dune-bedded sandstone can be seen in the gorge of the Wesley Brook [7465 0400] and in road cuttings nearby [7408 0407; 7436 0504]. North of Evelith the sandstone outcrop in the gorge continues to north of Shifnal Manor [7414 0668], and crags of sandstone are visible in the lower faces of the Kidderminster Conglomerate escarpments at Lodge Hill [744 060] and Brimstree Hill [749 058]. Madeley Wood Borehole No. 5 [7500 0628], starting near the top of the Bridgnorth Sandstone, recorded 86.9 m of the formation and Borehole No. 6 [7427 0698] recorded 54.86 m, below drift in both cases. From Hem Farm to north of Haughton [730 060 to 744 092] the junction with the Enville Beds is along the Madeley and Haughton faults, although for a distance north and south of the railway the boundary appears to be an unconformity. Six power auger holes [7360 0673 to 7389 0666] drilled by BGS, each to 14.6 m depth, revealed dark brown, soft, wet, very clayey fine-grained sand, beneath drift. In Shifnal a water borehole [7473 0788] 30.5 m deep revealed Bridgnorth Sandstone below drift, and Madeley Wood Borehole No. 3 [7464 0906] proved the lowest 33.5 m of the sandstone overlying Enville Beds.

Bridgnorth Sandstone overlies the Enville Beds on the eastern dip slope of Decker Hill, where a shallow cutting [7494 0977] reveals soft, coarse-grained, dune-bedded, feldspathic sandstones with a few small chert pebbles. The basal unconformity is very uneven here, and inliers of Enville Beds stand up as knolls [7485 0996; 7500 0996]. The Brewer's Oak Fault, throwing down to the north, moves the unconformity westward by 900 m, and the low-lying area north of this fault and east of Redhill Farm [740 113] is underlain by Bridgnorth Sandstone, partly obscured by thin boulder clay. The Bridgnorth Sandstone/Enville Beds junction east of Redhill Farm appears to be an unconformity, but to the north-east its continuity is broken by faulting. A pit [7421 1091] shows coarse-grained, purple-red sandstone with small, pale, feldspar grains and cross-bedding dipping at 20°. Similar sandstone overlies the Enville Beds in an old marl pit [7414 1128] at Redhill Farm. Farther east, Lilleshall No. 5 Borehole proved a complete sequence of Bridgnorth Sandstone 67 m thick, between the Kidderminster Conglomerate and the Enville Beds.

North-west of the Boundary Fault East of Muxton, Bridgnorth Sandstone rests unconformably on the Keele Beds between the Boundary and Trench faults, although the basal strata are everywhere obscured by drift. Red sand and weakly cemented sandstone were seen in an artificially deepened stream course [7120 1365] adjacent to the Boundary Fault. North of the Trench Fault thick Bridgnorth Sandstone is ubiquitous, but partly drift-covered. A water borehole at Midland Iron Works [7096 1424] recorded a thickness of 87.6 m, not bottomed, below 4.6 m of drift. A BGS power auger hole [7122 1438] recorded soft red and yellow Bridgnorth Sandstone with rounded grains from the surface to 6.4 m depth, on 3.7 m of yellow coarse-grained sand with pieces of hard white silicified sandstone and a few small clayey patches, resting on 0.6 m of dark red clayey sand. Another power auger hole [6911 1386] is believed to have

entered Bridgnorth Sandstone below drift at 13.7 m and a third hole [6884 1439] proved 2.44 m of bright red to red-brown sand believed to be Bridgnorth Sandstone beneath 5.48 m of drift. The Hoo Hall Borehole [6861 1488] proved 34.5 m of Bridgnorth Sandstone between drift and Keele Beds. Parts of the sandstone were pale greenish grey, with minor dark grey-blue mottling; close to the base it was calcareous and included very hard layers, the basal 3 cm containing small pebbles of reddish quartzite and dark greenish (?igneous) rocks. The top 3 cm of the underlying Keele Beds contained wisps of millet seed grains, suggesting some reworking of these beds prior to deposition of the Bridgnorth Sandstone. North of Hoo Hall the Bridgnorth Sandstone crops out around Preston upon the Weald Moors, forming rich red sandy soils in an area previously believed to be underlain by the Keele Beds.

A thickness of 69.4 m of Bridgnorth Sandstone was recorded in the BGS borehole at Lodge Farm, Trench [6887 1297]. The sandstone here was medium to coarse grained, each grain being well rounded and polished. Faint laminations rendered the sandstone friable and flaggy. At its base it was hard and calcareous and contained gritty layers of dark angular sharp grains, and pink or green rock fragments similar to Uriconian rock types. The unconformity with the Keele Beds was sharp and clean; open dessication cracks extending into the top of the Keele strata were lined with millet seed grains.

A borehole [6884 1353] referred to as Hadley Park No. 5 (Whitehead et al., 1928) proved 82 m of 'red-rocks'; probably most, if not all, of this thickness was Bridgnorth Sandstone, which was also penetrated in three other holes sunk in the Hadley Park area. In Hadley Park No. 1 [6720 1322] 4.6 m of wet sand beneath 7.3 m of glacial drift are considered to be Bridgnorth Sandstone. Borehole No. 3 [6738 1361] records 11.1 m beneath 2.0 m of drift. To the south-east, Borehole No. 2 [6798 1281] proves 26.8 m of wet red sand and sandstone beneath 10.4 m of drift.

The BGS borehole at Leegomery House Farm [6638 1268] proved 7.5 m of poorly cemented, very friable Bridgnorth Sandstone beneath 17.5 m of drift. North of the Leegomery Fault the base of the formation is believed to crop out from near Kinley Bridge to north of Kinley Farm [6630 1387 to 6717 1510]. Old well sinkings and recent site investigation boreholes prove the presence of Bridgnorth Sandstone beneath drift at Wellington and Dothill Park [645 125].

The base of the Bridgnorth Sandstone is marked by a feature extending from Ercall Gardens [6480 1125], through Barnfield [6388 1047] to the Cluddley Fault [6360 1014]. The base was proved in a power auger hole [6397 1080], in which red very friable sandstone overlay Keele Beds at a depth of 12.8 m. Bridgnorth Sandstone also crops out between the Cluddley and Wrekin faults, faulted against the Precambrian rocks of the Ercall, but it is locally obscured by scree or hillwash. Wet red sand with coarse spherical grains was proved in three power auger holes north-west of Buckatree Hotel [6400 0975], beneath thin boulder clay. The base crops out south of Wrekin Farm, and a pit [6285 0880] formerly showed a basal breccia made up of angular fragments of Uriconian rhyolite and tuff with some Cambrian quartzite.

The BGS Wrekin Buildings Borehole [6231 0871] proved Bridgnorth Sandstone to 74.32 m, beneath 2 m of head. The sandstone was brownish red with black ?manganese mottling, generally coarse grained, very friable and commonly well bedded. The base rested on an abrupt unconformity with no basal breccia, but with millet seed grains in the top 0.4 m of the underlying Keele Beds. A small quarry [6210 0855] 150 m west of Wrekin Buildings Farm formerly exposed 3 m of bright red sandstone with decomposed feldspar grains and black manganese staining.

East of White Cottage Plantation small overgrown pits [6195 0819] indicate where the Bridgnorth Sandstone has been dug. Its base is believed to crop out at the foot of a prominent feature [6165 0805] through the central parts of the plantation, and is apparently unaffected by a north-west-trending fault that throws Keele Beds against Precambrian and Cambrian rocks. South-west of this fault a small area of Bridgnorth Sandstone overlies the Cambrian Upper Comley Group.

North-west of the Brockton Fault the Bridgnorth Sandstone outcrop is largely drift covered, but there are some small exposures, which produce red, coarse-grained sandy soil with red sandstone fragments. Its thickness has not been proved but is believed to be over 100 m, and it may overlie Keele Beds. West of Marsh Green a larger inlier [602 142] produces rich red sandy soils, separated by an outcrop of glacial lake clays from a narrow belt cropping out on the steep slope rising up to the Kidderminster Conglomerate west of Sugdon. Similar red sands have been ploughed on the steep slopes beneath a Kidderminster Conglomerate outlier at Lower Farm [6215 1490]. Boreholes at Isombridge Farm [6106 1374] and Eyton [6495 1384] record respectively 4.0 m and 83.9 m of Bridgnorth Sandstone, not bottomed, beneath drift.

Kidderminster Conglomerate

Norton to Shifnal South of Norton [729 004] the Kidderminster Conglomerate forms an impressive escarpment running southwards to Bridgnorth. Between the Stockton and Harrington faults the outcrop is anomalously narrow because of the effect of the Sutton Maddock Fault and, apart from two distinctive hillocks, the area is largely drift covered. A knoll [726 011] beside the Bridgnorth–Telford road is capped by coarse gravel of quartzite pebble debris; below this in the roadside [7253 0103] is an exposure of coarse-grained gritty feldspathic sandstone, partly red-brown and rather soft, and partly white and silicified. Similar quartzite debris occupies a knoll at New House [735 016]. A water borehole at Harrington [7477 0156] records 30.8 m of 'coarse red sandstone with small pebbles', interpreted as Kidderminster Conglomerate, underlying 100.3 m of strata believed to be Wildmoor Sandstone.

Between the Grindle and Clews Wood faults, the basal conglomerate forms a pronounced scarp running northwards from near Havenhills [734 027]; it is a hard, flaggy, deep red sandstone, with clasts mostly of mudstone but including some of quartzite. Similar sandstone with coarse quartzite pebble conglomerates underlies a second ridge [742 030], the two forming a faulted outlier. The main outcrop forms a prominent feature just east of the district; the western extremities of this outcrop are included on the Telford map [750 034] near Grindle House, at Evelith Manor [750 051], and at Brimstree Hill [750 057]. Finally, a faulted outlier of basal Kidderminster Conglomerate forms the prominent Lodge Hill which stands above the confluence of the Wesley and Nedge brooks.

North-west of the Boundary Faults The Kidderminster Conglomerate is not known between the Boundary Fault and the Brockton Fault, but beyond here isolated outliers occur at Longdon-upon-Tern and Sugdon. At the former locality, quartzite pebbles abound in the vicinity of Lower Farm [6215 1490]. In a partly infilled quarry [6037 1497] just north of Sugdon, 8 m of pebbly brown sandstone were exposed in 1972; the pebbles are typically of pale liver-coloured to white quartzite, fairly well rounded and 2 cm to 4 cm in size. Some fragments (up to 8 cm) of red mudstone have been recorded. Another quarry [6006 1460] south-west of Sugdon formerly showed 4.5 m of coarse-grained brown sandstone with pebbles up to 5 cm.

Wildmoor Sandstone

Norton to Harrington Hall East of Norton [730 004] the Wildmoor Sandstone is largely obscured by thick deposits of drift, but east of Cotsbrook Farm [747 006] red sand is seen beside the gorge of the River Worfe. A water borehole south-east of Harrington Hall [7477 0156] records 100.3 m of fine-grained red sandstone overlying pebbly strata assigned to the Kidderminster Conglomerate. North of the Stockton Fault the base of the sandstone crops out near New House [737 018 to 741 011]. Massive, coarse-grained cross-bedded red sandstone is exposed in a track cutting [7423 0211] near Harrington Hall, and medium-grained, bright red sandstone, with clasts of red mudstone and small pebbles, occurs in the banks of the Mad Brook [7453 0228].

SEVEN

Structure

FOLDING

Precambrian strata were folded along north-west-trending axes. In the Wrockwardine fault-block, dips are to the south-west at up to 60°; along the Wrekin–Ercall ridge, dips between north-east and north-west also reach 60°. This suggests the existence of a syncline plunging to the north-west with its axis running from the Wrekin [62 08] to Overley Hill [60 10].

Fold axes in the Lower Palaeozoic rocks, south-east of the Boundary Fault and south-west of the coalfield, generally trend north-east; the folding is Caledonian in age, postdating the (Downtonian) Temeside Shales but predating the (Dinantian) Lydebrook Sandstone. Approaching the Wrekin from the south-east the folding becomes more complex, with steepening dips and a greater variation in strike; the Shineton Shales are most affected, with development of isoclinal folds trending eastwards or north-eastwards.

Dinantian strata and Westphalian Lower and Middle Coal Measures are also folded along north-east-trending Caledonoid axes. Dinantian rocks are preserved beneath the Coal Measures in a syncline plunging north-eastwards, as shown in Figure 2. This structure is more open than those affecting the Lower Palaeozoic strata, upon which the Dinantian rocks rest unconformably. However, it is sufficiently marked for the latter to be cut out unconformably by the Lower and Middle Coal Measures to the south-east. Dips are low except in the west where strata dipping at 35° are recorded on the flanks of Maddocks Hill [648 087].

The Lower and Middle Coal Measures are folded to form the Muxton, Stirchley, Hem and Sutton Maddock anticlines and the complementary Donnington, Madeley and Coalport synclines, as well as other minor flexures (Figure 36). These all have a Caledonoid trend; the major structures plunge north-eastwards. Their axes are depicted on Figure 39, which also shows the coal seam incrops into the sub-Hadley Formation unconformity. Three sections across these structures (Figure 37) show the synclines to be stepped down to the south-east. Dips in the Lower and Middle Coal Measures are very largely less than 6°, except in the extreme west and where locally affected by faulting. Dips of up to 45° are recorded adjacent to the Boundary Fault within the Muxton Anticline, and up to 20° beside the Limestone and Warrensway faults in the south-west.

The Donnington Syncline reflects or rejuvenates the syncline in the underlying Dinantian strata, but it is a very gentle and poorly defined structure, apparently dying out both to the north-east and south-west, and is confused by minor folds. The Stirchley Anticline is asymmetrical (Figure 39) and the Hem Anticline probably so.

The crests of these anticlines run close to the lines of the Limestone and Madeley faults and both anticlines decline in amplitude northwards. The Madeley Syncline apparently bifurcates to the south-west (Figure 36) as does the Hem Anticline, resulting in relatively complex folding. Little is known about the Coalport Syncline and Sutton Maddock Anticline, although the latter (as shown on Section 2 of the Telford 1:25 000 map) affects Silurian strata much more strongly than the Lower and Middle Coal Measures.

In the east of the area the Coalport, Keele and Enville strata all dip to between east and north-east, and thus strike nearer to due north than do the underlying productive measures. The Bridgnorth Sandstone and Triassic formations also strike north and dip gently eastwards into the Stafford Syncline, which forms a northern continuation of the Worcester Basin.

North of the Boundary and Wrekin faults, dips are gentle in the Cambrian and all overlying strata, being generally eastwards in the east and south-westwards in the south-west.

FAULTING

Figure 38 shows most of the faults known in the district. These mainly follow three trends: north-easterly (Caledonoid), north-westerly (Charnoid) and northerly (Malvernoid). Most faults were active in the post-Triassic or pre-Triassic/post-Enville periods, but many show clear evidence of previous movement, and several are as old as Precambrian.

Most of the structures are normal faults, at least in terms of their youngest phase of movement, but many faults show reversal of throw during successive tectonic episodes. The inclination of the faults ranges from 45° to vertical, and Prestwich (1840, p.453) refers to 'perpendicular faults' with crush zones up to 46 m wide, which suggest wrench faulting.

Caledonoid faults north-west of the Coalbrookdale Coalfield

This set of parallel faults forms the north-eastward continuation of the Church Stretton fault system, which stretches from New Radnor (Rastall, 1925) to beyond Lilleshall. The faults have been active periodically since the Precambrian, and have included normal, reverse and horizontal displacements (Whittard, 1952). Their latest major movements were evidently post-Permian, uplifting the Uriconian horsts of Wrockwardine and the Wrekin. The lastest main displacement on the Boundary Fault involved downthrow to the north-west, juxtaposing

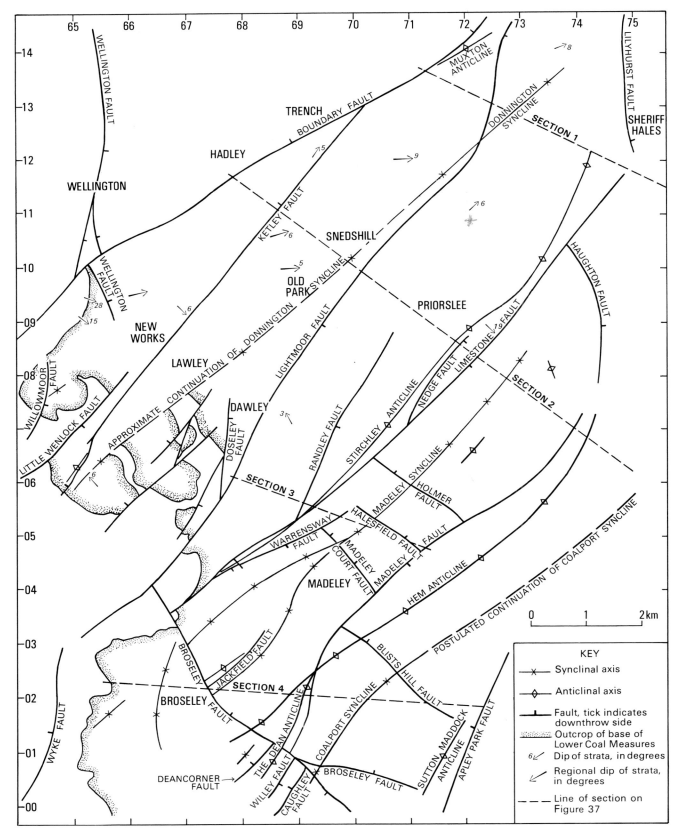

Figure 36 Major structural elements of the Lower and Middle Coal Measures of the Coalbrookdale Coalfield.

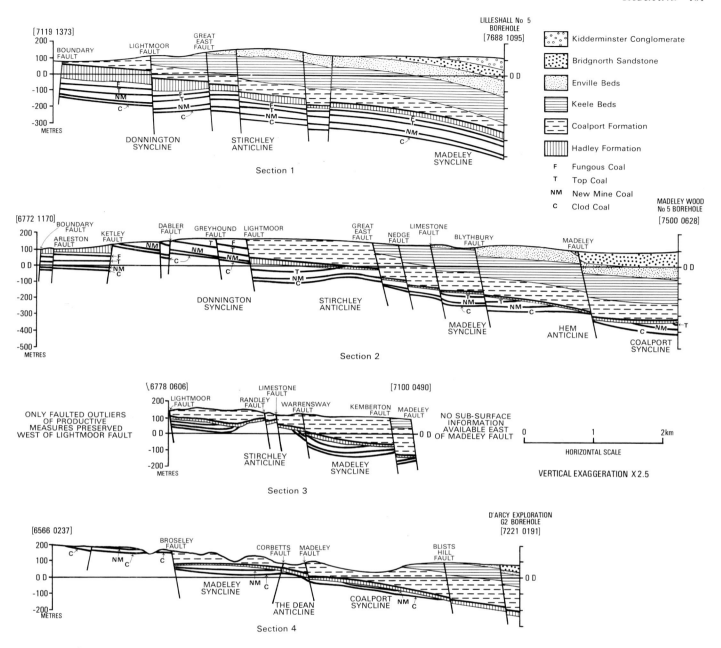

Figure 37 Serial sections across the Coalbrookdale Coalfield, showing the synclines and anticlines affecting the Lower and Middle Coal Measures. Lines of section are shown on Figure 36.

Bridgnorth Sandstone against Lower and Middle Coal Measures. However, this fault had previously moved with a downthrow to the south-east, as the depth to the Uriconian rocks is only 88.5 m at the Lodge Farm, Trench Borehole on the north side of the fault, but around 1600 m on the south side of the fault.

Wrench movement may have occurred along this set of faults; such movement is known at Church Stretton (Whittard, 1952) and is recorded along parallel faults to the north-west in the Wem (Pocock and Wray, 1925) and

Nantwich (Poole and Whiteman, 1966) districts, with sinistral displacements of up to 8 km. The continuation of the Boundary Fault, along the south side of the Wrekin to Neves Castle [612 070] does not appear to have a significant wrench component, and the small displacement of the Dinantian strata across the Boundary Fault at Wellington argues against major wrench movement along this line, at least since the start of the Dinantian, but an apparent displacement of the Wellington Fault by the Boundary Fault may indicate a small dextral wrench movement.

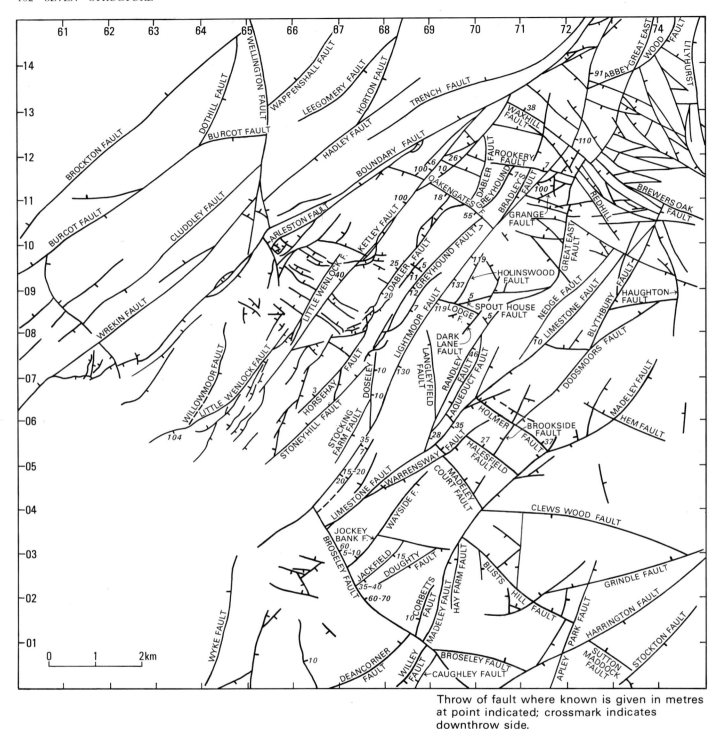

Throp of fault where known is given in metres at point indicated; crossmark indicates downthrow side.

Figure 38 The fault pattern of the Coalbrookdale Coalfield. The important faults are named.

The Wellington Fault itself may be a dextral wrench fault, in which case the Boundary and Wrekin faults could have been continuous. This interpretation is supported by geophysical evidence, the Bouguer gravity contours being displaced dextrally across the Wellington Fault (see Figures 40 and 41). The apparent lack of a wrench component at surface suggests that the lateral movement probably took place mainly within the Precambrian rocks; south of the Boundary Fault these are overlain by largely argillaceous cover rocks, in which numerous small faults, as seen in the Coal Measures at Limekiln Lane, would have been produced.

The Boundary Fault represents a significant growth structure between two distinct areas. To the south (in the Donnington Syncline) the Precambrian is overlain by about 1500 m of Cambro-Ordovician to Duckmantian strata, which are in turn overlain conformably or with gentle unconformity by the Hadley Formation; whereas to the north the equivalent of the Hadley Formation rests directly on the Precambrian. A long period of progressive southward downthrow is envisaged, so that erosion occurred to the north contemporaneously with deposition in the south. Movement probably ceased before the end of the Bolsovian, since the Ruabon and Coed-yr-Allt strata to the north closely resemble the Hadley and Coalport formations to the south.

Caledonoid faults within the Coalbrookdale Coalfield

Within the coalfield the major faults also have a generally north-easterly trend. However, they are orientated more to the north of north-east so that the main Ketley and Lightmoor faults converge with the Boundary Fault towards the north-east (Figure 38). Numerous minor faults run parallel to these two major structures, and there is a clear tendency for the throw on these to decline to the south-west. The major faults are proved by mining data to be normal, at least in their latest phase of movement, but at least one reverse fault with this trend has been noted [7131 0793].

Most of the faults evidently had post-Enville displacements but many had earlier phases of movement. The presence of the Dinantian Upper Limestone north-west of the Little Wenlock Fault and its absence to the south-east (Pocock et al., 1938, p.127) suggests late Dinantian or early Westphalian reverse faulting with a north-westerly downthrow. The Deancorner and possibly the Willey faults show post-Silurian/pre-Lower Coal Measures and post-Middle Coal Measures/pre-Hadley Formation displacements, both in the same direction as their post-Enville movements. The Limestone, Caughley and Jackfield faults all show post-Lower Coal Measures/pre-Hadley Formation movements as well as a post-Enville phase: in the case of the Jacksfield Fault both phases of displacement involved a downthrow in the same direction, but in the other cases the two movements were in opposing directions, the faults acting as reverse faults initially and as normal faults later. Similarly, the Lightmoor Fault operated as a reverse fault in Middle Coal Measures times and as a normal fault later. These faults are significant Caledonoid structures, and are therefore likely to have had earlier movements than those that can be demonstrated.

Charnoid faults

Many small faults have a north-westerly trend, particularly within the exposed coalfield, but the only one of any great length is the Broseley Fault in the south of the coalfield. None can be demonstrated to have moved more than once, but some may have a deep-seated and ancient origin, rather than being merely accommodation fractures perpendicular to the main north-east-trending

structures. Evidence for this lies in the parallel Holmer, Halesfield and Madeley Court faults, which are directly in line with a series of parallel faults around New Works and Lawley, and the Blists Hill Fault which is in line with an important, though short, fault to the north-west [679 046]. All these may represent rejuvenation of deep-seated structures.

Malvernoid faults

North–south faults are few in number. They include the Doseley and Langleyfield faults within the exposed coalfield, and several faults to the east and west of the coalfield. It has been suggested (above) that the Wellington Fault may include an element of wrench movement. The north–south faults may represent rejuvenation of old, deep-seated structures, but evidence is lacking. The Wellington, Willowmoor and Wyke faults in the west may together represent a single major structure at depth, as may the Apley Park, Haughton and Lilyhurst faults in the east. Complex fault zones at New Dale [676 096] and Lawley Common [677 084] are in line with the Doseley Fault and may indicate its deep-seated northward extension to intersect the Ketley and Dabler faults.

TECTONIC SYNTHESIS

Cobbold (1925) and Whittard (1952, p.185) drew attention to the large number of unconformities in the Church Stretton area; these are related to the Church Stretton fault system, which has shown recurrent movement since Precambrian times. The Coalbrookdale Coalfield is adjacent to the north-eastern continuation of this structure and exhibits a similarly disturbed history. Events affecting the rocks of Westphalian and later ages are discussed below.

Upper Carboniferous tectonism (Langsettian to Bolsovian)

During the Namurian Epoch, a period of uplift led to erosion of Dinantian and earlier strata. This was followed by relative subsidence and onlap, which commenced from the north-east in late Namurian or early Westphalian time. Throughout deposition of the Lower and Middle Coal Measures and Hadley Formation, variations in sediment thicknesses imply differential subsidence. The lower part of the Lower Coal Measures thickens north-eastwards, reflecting the differential subsidence which initiated the Coal Measures onlap. However, the Lower Coal Measures from the Clod Coal upwards are thickest in the east, perhaps controlled by Caledonoid structures (Figure 9). The zone of minimum thickness, north-west of the Limestone Fault, may represent a buried continuation of the positive ridge of Wenlock Edge.

The Middle Coal Measures are thickest in the northeast, although the isopachytes (Figure 11) for strata up to the Top Coal do not show a uniform north-eastward thickening; local reversals of the trend suggest control by

Charnoid as well as Caledonoid structures. Isopachytes for the Hadley Formation show a very marked Caledonoid trend (Figure 12), with the thickest sequence (over 90 m) in the north-west, in an elongated trough to the south-east of the Boundary Fault.

Four disconformities are known within strata of Langsettian to Bolsovian age: a washout between the Yard and Double coals; a washout between the Brickmeasure ironstone and the Gur Coal; a washout above the Fungous Coal; and a more prominent, widespread unconformity at the base of the Hadley Formation. The first is evident only in the Madeley Syncline; it resulted in downcutting as low as the Pennystone in the south-west (near Broseley), but simultaneous deposition of up to 30 m of strata in the north-east (Figure 30). The second, northwest of the Stirchley Anticline, resulted in downcutting as low as the Yellowstone near Dawley, but simultaneous deposition of over 30 m of strata towards Sheriff Hales in the north-east (Figure 23). Scott (1861) refers to this disconformity as the Symon Fault at Old Park Colliery. The incrops of coal seams into this disconformity, in the area from Dawley to Priorslee, are shown in Figure 39. The incrops follow a Caledonoid trend, parallel to the incrops of lower seams into the later sub-Hadley Formation unconformity. The Lightmoor Fault appears to have been active during the erosional episode, which cut down more deeply on the south-east side of the fault than on the north-west, causing the incrops of coal seams into the disconformity to terminate against the fault (Figure 39). The fault would then have had a downthrow to the north-west, a reverse movement relative to that of its latest displacement. The third disconformity, above the Fungous Coal, is known only around Old Park and Lawley [67 08 to 69 09], cutting down to below the Gur Coal; it is less well documented, because little of the overlying sequence survives below the sub-Hadley Formation unconformity. However, the incrops of the Fungous, Deep and Gur coals into this washout are evident from drilling in Old Park (Figure 39 and 1:25 000 Telford map).

The intra-Westphalian or Malvernian movements (Moore and Trueman, 1939; Trueman, 1948) reached a peak with the unconformity at the base of the Hadley Formation. By contrast with the washout disconformities, which imply only localised syndepositional tectonic movement along Caledonoid (north-east-trending) lines, the unconformity at the base of the Hadley Formation implies intra-Coal Measures uplift of the southern parts of the coalfield (Figure 13). This unconformity is the one to which the name Symon Fault or Symon Unconformity was originally and most commonly applied.

In the southern part of the coalfield the base of the Hadley Formation is unconformable in all the three main synclines (Coalport, Madeley and Donnington) as well as in the intervening Hem and Stirchley anticlines (Figure 39), and it oversteps on to Silurian rocks. However, the degree of downcutting decreases northeastwards, with Fungous Group coals coming in beneath the unconformity in the Donnington and Madeley synclines. Farther north still the unconformity dies out altogether; the grey measures pass up conformably into the Hadley Formation, with no evidence of a major break below any of the espley sandstones within that formation. In the Madeley Syncline the sub-Hadley unconformity is identifiable in boreholes around Shifnal, but apparently not in Lilleshall No. 5 Borehole in the north-east. In the Donnington Syncline the unconformity is not known in any of the deep coal boreholes in the north-east (except possibly Hollybank Wood), nor in the Hadley and Snedshill areas, but it appears to persist farther north along the Stirchley Anticline than it does in the Donnington Syncline (Figure 39), being influenced by Caledonoid folding. Where the transition from productive measures to Hadley red beds is conformable, it is diachronous and rises stratigraphically north-eastwards. The earliest deposits of red-bed facies are those formed just northeast of the limits of the unconformity, around Hadley in the Donnington Syncline and Hollybank Wood Borehole in the Stirchley Anticline. These pass laterally into grey measures north-eastwards, whereas to the south-west the Middle Coal Measures were subjected to erosion. During the Bolsovian times, later Hadley facies sediments built up north-eastwards and simultaneously overstepped unconformably south-westwards.

Contemporaneous movements on the Caledonoid Limestone, Deancorner, Willey, Caughley and Jacksfield faults can be identified; gentle folding along Caledonoid lines produced the north-eastward plunging synclines and anticlines during this period, as shown by the incrop pattern of coal seams into the base of the Hadley Formation (Figure 39).

Upper Carboniferous and Permian tectonism (Coalport Formation to Bridgnorth Sandstone)

Within the Coalport, Keele and Enville strata there are no major unconformities, and little evidence of significant variations in thickness attributable to contemporaneous earth movements. The decrease in the proportion of sandstone in the upper part of the Keele Beds is interpreted as implying a lowering of relief in the source area rather than any change in the basin of deposition. The return of thick sandstones and the incoming of Lower Carboniferous debris in the Enville Beds do imply uplift in the source area, however.

Major tectonic disturbance occurred after deposition of the Enville Beds and before deposition of the Bridgnorth Sandstone. This would appear to be the period of greatest movement along the north-east and north-west-trending faults that dominate the coalfield. Tilting caused the Upper Coal Measures to dip eastwards, and subsequent erosion removed the Enville Beds in the south, and presumably Enville and lower formations in the west.

The main period of north–south folding in the Malvern Hills also occurred in late- or post- Upper Coal Measures times, and has been attributed to the Asturic phase of the Hercynian orogeny (Mykura, 1951, p.389). Along the northward continuation of the Malverns, thrusting and folding (including overfolding) are recorded along north–south axes, affecting rocks equivalent to the Coalport Formation (Mitchell et al., 1962). Wills (1956, p.85) considered that this period of tecton-

Figure 39 Map showing incrops of coal seams into the sub-Hadley Formation unconformity and Middle Coal Measures washouts, and relationships with major folds and faults.

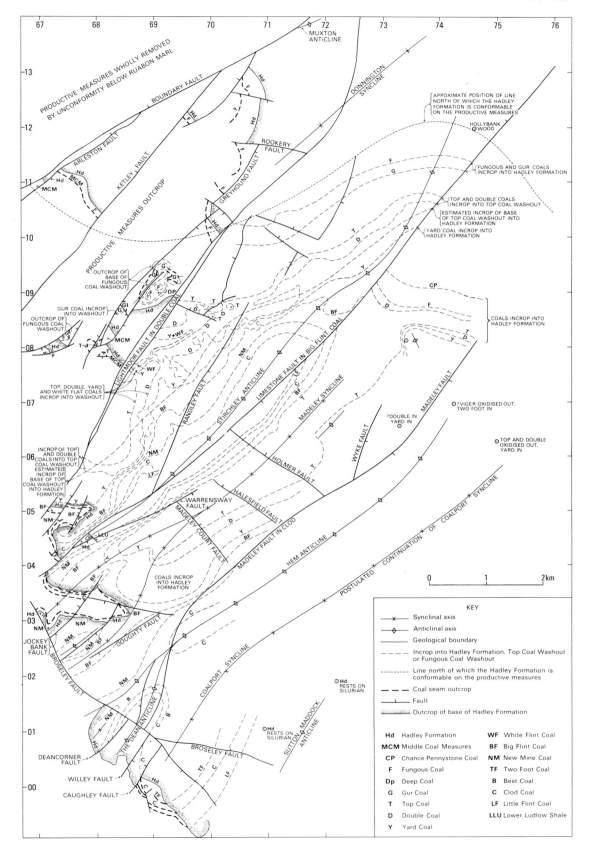

ism was initially compressive (in Enville Conglomerates and Tile Hill Group times), but later tensional (in Clent–Kenilworth Breccia and Bridgnorth Sandstone times). In the Telford area a post-Enville phase of east–west compression would account for the eastward tilting and possibly for some dextral movement on the Wrekin and Boundary faults; a succeeding period of tension would account for the widespread normal faulting.

Erosion occurred before deposition of the Bridgnorth Sandstone; this formation rests upon Enville Beds in the north-east and on Keele Beds in the south-east, and upon Keele Beds and Precambrian rocks north-west of the Boundary Fault. Triassic formations up to the Wildmoor Sandstone follow conformably in the east of the area and are the youngest solid strata preserved in the Telford district.

Post-Permian movements

Minor post-Permian tectonism slightly increased the eastward tilt of the strata on the eastern flank of the coalfield, and gently folded the area north-west of the Boundary and Wrekin faults. These show a late phase of displacement with downthrow to the north-west, resulting in erosion of Permo-Triassic strata from the exposed Coalbrookdale Coalfield. Some of the north-east- and north-west-trending faults were rejuvenated, especially in the north-west. Seismic data (see Chapter 8) show that across the Wappenshall and Leegomery faults the thickness of Keele Beds remains constant, but the thickness of Bridgnorth Sandstone varies; hence these faults were active post-Permian, but not earlier. Around the periphery of the coalfield, north–south faults, such as the Wellington Fault, were also active. The age of this phase of faulting and folding cannot be deduced within the local area alone, but Taylor et al. (1963) suggest a Tertiary age for similar movements in Cheshire, where the Lias is affected.

DETAILS

Area between the Boundary and Ketley faults

Opencast coal workings at Willowmoor Farm [645 078] (see Figure 18) revealed several small faults trending roughly north–south but deviating westwards in the south. Of these, the Willowmoor Fault (Figure 36) displaces the feature formed by the Dinantian Lower Limestone [643 070], and a valley to the south-west [638 062] may indicate an extension that joins the Little Wenlock Fault. The Coal Measures outcrop of Willowmoor is preserved in a shallow, asymmetrical north-east-trending syncline (Figure 36). Maddocks Hill [651 085] and Huntington Heath [655 083] opencast sites (Figure 18) revealed a suite of small faults trending north or north-west. Their throws rarely exceed a few metres and they never exceed 100 m or so in length.

The Little Wenlock Fault throws down to the south-east and extends at least to Saplins Farm [6330 0575], where it throws Lydebrook Sandstone and Little Wenlock Basalt against Pentamerus Beds with a displacement in excess of 10 m. It may continue as a zone of disturbance to the confluence of two

small streams [6285 0552] in Saplins Wood, where the Pentamerus Beds form a monocline with a similar axial trend. The Little Wenlock Fault was seen along abandoned faces of the former Coalmoor Opencast [654 072], complemented on its downthrow side by a series of more gently-inclined parallel faults throwing down north-west. North-west of the Little Wenlock Fault, Coal Measures rest on the Dinantian Upper Limestone, which in turn rests on Little Wenlock Basalt; on the downthrow side, however, the Coal Measures rest directly on the basalt, indicating two periods of fault movement with opposing throws. Coal seams dipping gently towards the fault are upturned almost to vertical against and parallel to the fault plane. To the north-east the fault divides [6551 0758]; the western branch terminates 600 m farther to the north-east, but the eastern branch continues at least as far as Newdale [6704 0977] (see Figure 18).

A fault parallel to the Little Wenlock Fault starts within the Swann Farm Opencast [6483 0660], increasing in throw southwards to 5 m within the site and continuing along the western side of Harris's Coppice [644 058] and along the eastern tributary of Devils Dingle. Between the Ketley and Little Wenlock faults, several faults extend beyond the coalfield, cutting the scarp along Braggers Hill [as at 6460 0590]. The Coal Measures there dip consistently north-west at about 6°. At New Works [663 084] and Limekiln Lane [660 095] the dip is east or north-east, but the outcrops are disrupted by a suite of north-west-trending faults. These have small throws, but are persistent structures, sufficient to curtail mining of many thin seams in the Lower and Middle Coal Measures.

Around Limekiln Lane the structure is complex. The major north–south Wellington Fault is displaced by the Boundary Fault and interacts with its subparallel faults (such as the Arleston Fault). The Arleston Fault (see Figure 39) is believed to divide south-west of Arleston [665 105], with both branches throwing down to the north-west. Between the two branches the north-west-trending normal faults appear to have a shallower hade than around New Works and Lawley, and may in some cases become reverse faults. The Arleston Fault parallels the Boundary Fault through Ketley and Hadley but joins it [6888 1235] by Trench Pool. A fault parallel to the Ketley Fault at Wombridge is known from mine plans, and boreholes indicate a throw of about 6 m. Mine plans also show small northwesterly faults between this and the Boundary Fault; in this area a northerly dip of 15° was measured in the Coalport Formation [690 122], but a north-easterly dip of only 5° is evident in the productive measures underground [694 122].

The Ketley Fault

The Ketley Fault cuts the Lydebrook Sandstone scarp [6480 0570], with a north-westerly downthrow of 5 m to 7 m. It continues as a slightly sinuous fault following the course of a gentle anticline, with a variable throw often as low as 2 m to 3 m. The Coal Measures have been extensively worked opencast on both sides of the fault. In the Smalleyhill Opencast [663 083] it was seen to be a single, clean, high-angle fault; old mine workings extended to within a short distance of the fault and its underground position was therefore recorded accurately. At the southern limit of the Trough Opencast [6705 0920] the Top and Yard Coals (dipping 6° east-south-east) are faulted against the Clod and Little Flint Coal, a throw to the north-west of about 40 m. Towards the north-east, the throw continues to increase, so that at Newdale [674 096] the Top Coal is faulted against the lowest strata of the Coal Measures. The Ketley Fault here is disturbed by east–west faulting and by arcuate splay-faults which swing into an east–west direction. North-east of this complex, two faults 60 m to 70 m apart, which probably combine at depth, throw the Fungous Group against the Best Coal Group, a combined throw to the north-west of 70 m. At Redlake [6824 1062] the faults recombine and from there a single fault can be traced with certainty at surface. Around Petershill [684 108] the Big Flint Rock is juxtaposed against the Hadley Formation, implying a throw of 110 m on the Ketley Fault. This must further increase to the north-east, as shallow mining of the New Mine Coal from Wombridge Hill Pits [6880 1130] comes to within 100 m distance of surface quarrying [6870 1125] for Hadley mudstones. The fault is well documented from mine plans, boreholes and surface features from Wombridge Church to [697 125] near Teague's Bridge, beyond which it continues to join the Boundary Fault. The throw by the church must be about 140 m, because the Main Sulphur and Little Flint coals are juxtaposed. To the north-east the throw on the main fault is reduced as two arcuate faults diverge eastwards and throw down to the north.

Area between the Ketley and Lightmoor faults

In the south-west of this area the numerous faults all have small throws. The Stoneyhill Fault extends from Timber Wood [655 051] to Lydebrook Dingle and then along Wellington Road [6665 0620], separating the Stoneyhill and Clay Colliery opencast sites; its throw is no more than a few metres and it evidently terminates beyond Horsehay quarries [675 068].

The Horsehay Fault parallels the Stoneyhill Fault some 400 m to the north-west. In the north-western part of the Clay Colliery Opencast [665 066] its throw is known to be about 3 m. This clearly increases as it follows the disused railway line [6765 0800] east of Horsehay Common, throwing the Big Flint Rock against the Hadley Formation. However, farther to the north-east the throw decreases as it approaches a complex structure associated with the Dabler Fault. The Stocking Farm Fault [6720 0555] lies 200 m to 300 m north-west of the Lightmoor Fault, and for much of its length throws Lydebrook Sandstone against the Best Coal to Little Flint Coal sequence.

The Stocking Farm Fault is truncated by the Doseley Fault, a north–south structure which influences the course of Horsehay Brook and its buried channel. To the south the Doseley Fault joins the Lightmoor Fault [6768 0580]. It is closely defined south-west of Doseley Church, where basal conglomeratic sandstones of the Coal Measures are seen [6772 0652] a few metres from deeply weathered basalt at the quarry entrance [6766 0655]. The throw here is at least 10 m to the east, and this order of throw is maintained northwards to a point adjacent to Brandlee No. 3 Shaft [6781 0764] where the fault apparently terminates against a sinuous cross fault.

The Dabler Fault, 800 m to the north, has a general north-east trend, although south and west from Lawley Common [678 085] it divides into several faults which swing into an almost east–west orientation. The interpretation of the complex structure around Lawley Common is based on extensive drilling and the surface fault pattern is best explained by deep-seated north–south movement along a continuation of the Doseley Fault. The structure is further complicated by a set of north-west-trending faults which have small throws, but persist for more than 1 km between the Dabler complex at Lawley and the Ketley Fault.

The Dabler Fault is recorded in Princes End Opencast with a throw of about 20 m to the south-east, and around The Rock with an underground throw of 25 m to 30 m to the north-west, but farther to the north-east its throw must increase since, at Mannerley Lane Opencast [691 102], crop workings of the Clunch Coal are faulted against the Big Flint Rock. North of Mosseygreen the Dabler Fault splits into two branches, but only one persists north of the Oakengates Fault.

The Greyhound Fault commences at Heath Hill [680 080] and may be a continuation of the Doseley or Stoneyhill faults. It is proved through Old Park by mine workings and drilling; the former quotes a throw of forty yards (36.6 m), the latter indicates about a third of this figure, and drilling for the Eastern Central Primary Road indicates a throw of only 6.3 m [700 104].

The Oakengates Fault is well known in mine workings, and a throw of 18 m in the Two Feet Coal is documented at Wombridge Colliery [695 110], but drilling shows that it may be as much as 55 m. At its west end the Oakengates Fault is shown in mine plans to abut against an unnamed north-east-trending fault which joins the Ketley Fault to the south-west, near Wombridge Hill Pits. The throw of the fault is about 10 m where it crosses the line of the North Eastern Primary Road boreholes [694 116], and at least 26 m, throwing the Fungous Coal against the Three Quarter Coal, where it crosses the Dawley–Donnington Distributor Road boreholes [700 122]. This fault limits the Top Coal workings from Donnington Colliery [704 126] and is assumed to join the Boundary Fault to the north-east [708 134]. Further faults run between this fault and the Ketley Fault, two trending north-west and one east-north-east. The latter also throws the Fungous Coal against the Three Quarter Coal.

The Dabler and Greyhound faults both continue north of the Oakengates Fault; a throw of 12 m on the Dabler is proved by boreholes [698 108] and it evidently joins the unnamed fault described in the preceding paragraph. The Greyhound Fault is offset by the Oakengates Fault; it was exposed behind a row of houses [7007 1065], with Hadley mudstones dipping at 30° to the south-east faulted against horizontal Middle Coal Measures believed to be of the Top Coal Group. It continues at least to the Rookery Fault [709 117], with a throw of 7.3 m in the Clod Coal. The Rookery Fault also has a throw of around 7.3 m, and this fault can be readily detected at surface [715 116], but it is uncertain if it continues west beyond Wrockwardine Wood [698 120].

Between St Georges and Muxton the faults between the Lightmoor and Boundary faults are detailed in mine plans. Bradley's Fault joins the Lightmoor in the south and runs parallel to the Greyhound, but continues north almost to Freehold Pit; throws of around 6.2 m are quoted for the Fungous, Top and Double coals, but 15.9 m in the Clod Coal near Waxhill Barracks. Other major faults in this area have a north-westerly trend; most throw less than 10 m but the Waxhill Fault, which is the only fault in the coalfield to affect the Lightmoor Fault, has a maximum north-eastward throw of 38.4 m.

From Snedshill to Freehold Pit the Coal Measures dip at about 10° to the east, but farther north between the Boundary and Lightmoor faults the dip changes to south-east and increases rapidly northwards, workings from Freehold Colliery being abandoned when the dip reached about 33°. Investigations in the area east of Muxton indicated a north-east-trending anticline (pitching slightly to the south-west), with dips of 20° to 25° to the north-west and 20° to 45° to the south-east. Farther to the north BGS drilling proved a fault trending east-north-east at the south end of the Lilleshall inlier, throwing grey Coal Measures against Upper Cambrian shales and Comley Sandstone.

The Lightmoor Fault

North of the River Severn, the Lightmoor Fault preserves an outlier of Lower Coal Measures sandstones at Captains Coppice [6660 0430]. Its throw there must exceed the 6 m to 8 m thickness of exposed sandstone. To the north-east the fault crosses the Coalbrookdale Valley to flank the wooded slopes of Woodside [6700 0482], where the Clod and higher coals are faulted against Wenlock Shale; north of the Lightmoor Valley the throw is about 35 m. It is clearly evident along the lower parts of a prominent feature [6803 0660], where the Thick Rock of the Coalport Formation abuts against the Lower and Middle Coal Measures proved by boreholes around Sandy Bank [6790 0666]; the throw there is about 130 m.

Prestwich (1840) recorded throws of 90 m at Lightmoor, 150 m at Great Dawley, 107 m at New Dawley, 210 m at Dark Lane and Malinslee, and 90 m at Snedshill. From Pool Hill to Pudley Hill the fault is recorded in the workings of Dawley Colliery and Old Park Colliery; the latter had workings on both sides of the fault with quoted throws of 137 m [695 089] and 119 m [699 096]. The fault crosses the line of the Eastern Central Primary Road [699 097], where boreholes indicate the Three Quarter Coal cropping out to the north-west, and Coalport Formation to the south-east. The incrops of the Top, Double and Yard coals and White Flat ironstone into the post-Top Coal washout in the Old Park area can be mapped into the south-east side of the fault; but on the north-west side the seams are not cut out by the washout at all, so the degree of downcutting there is considerably less. This suggests that the Lightmoor Fault was active at the time of the formation of the washout, but with a downthrow to the north-west, in the opposite direction to its later throw.

From St George's to Muxtonbridge the surface position of the fault is readily apparent; it is a clean fracture, and in places its position can be fixed to within a couple of metres by augering. Donnington Colliery workings extended up to the west side of the fault, with throws quoted as 110 m and 91 m [716 114], 110 m [723 123] and 91 m [725 138]. The throw may vary as a result of cross-faulting; apart from the Waxhill Fault, which clearly offsets the Lightmoor, there is very little correspondence between the faults abutting from either side. The Muxton Bridge Fault of Whitehead et al. (1928, p.155) is in fact the Lightmoor. At Lilyhurst Road [727 145] the Lightmoor Fault splits; the western branch continues almost due north along the east side of the Lilleshall inlier, throwing Cambrian rocks against Carboniferous and joining the Boundary Fault north of the Telford district [731 161], and the eastern branch runs east of north to join the Great East Fault, also north of the district boundary.

Area between the Lightmoor, Broseley and Limestone faults

Two faults run subparallel to the Lightmoor Fault near Castle Green. The more north-westerly [6720 0470] throws down to the north-west by about 20 m and extends beyond the Coal Measures into Wenlock Shale; it may in fact extend farther south-west, paralleling the Coalbrookdale Valley sides to meet the Broseley Fault [6660 0390]. Northwards across the Lightmoor Valley its throw decreases to between 6 m and 8 m before it terminates. The second fault does not extend beyond the Coal Measures, but ends in the opencast workings at Castle Green [6733 0438]. Its throw is only a few metres, and is apparently even less in the overlying Hadley Formation.

The Dawley Colliery area, from Dawley Parva to Malins Lee, is unfaulted apart from the northerly trending Langleyfield Fault. Middle Coal Measures dip north-north-west at 3° at Portley Pit, and the Coalport Formation at surface dips gently north-north-east in the Randley Valley. The fault recorded by Whitehead et al. (1928, p.94) in a heading 46.6 m from New Track Pits [689 056] is now believed to be the Randley Fault (a branch of the Limestone Fault), which can be traced at surface from near Aqueduct to the north end of the Randley Valley, and which cuts the shafts of Hinkshay and Forge Meadow pits. Throws recorded are 28 m at New Track Pits and 46 m in the Randley Valley.

The Aqueduct Fault is a branch of the Randley Fault, not known in the mine workings and possibly joining the Randley Fault at relatively shallow depth. It is clear at the surface from Aqueduct to Stirchley, and was seen cutting the Top Rock in the Randley Sewer [701 075] as a normal fault dipping at about 70°. The north-west-trending fault at Aqueduct may be related to the Halesfield Fault, although it may not continue between the Limestone and Warrensway faults. The Coalport Formation between Aqueduct and Stirchley Grange dips gently north-east, while drilling for the Randley Sewer revealed an asymmetrical syncline [701 076 to 705 080] (Figure 34), with dips of 6° north-east on the southern limb and 2° south-west on the northern; this structure is not seen in the Randley brick pit and is related to the Aqueduct Fault.

To the east and north-east the strike in the Coalport, Keele and Enville strata is north–south. Two further branches of the Limestone Fault are known, paralleling the Randley Fault. The Nedge Fault accounts for a 20° dip in the Priorslee Rock in the Nedge Valley, and in a sewer trench [7131 0793] two branches were seen — a normal fault on the east face throwing down 4 m to the south, and a reverse fault on the west face throwing down about 7 m to the south. North of there the fault is fixed by boreholes for the Nedge–Stafford Park sewer and the Stafford Park industrial estate, and is obvious at surface from Castle Farm to Wards Rough.

Most of the faults in the productive measures around Malins Lee and Dark Lane trend north-north-east, particularly those near the Lightmoor Fault at Malins Lee and Pudley Hill, and most of those throw west-north-west, against the Lightmoor. One is known to reach the surface at Pudley Hill Pits and Malins Lee Hall, and more may in fact do so. The Dark Lane Fault also follows this trend, a throw of 10 m to the east being quoted in the Big Flint Coal near Wharf Pits. This fault was seen in borehole TC34 [7035 0878] and in the Town Centre sewer trench [7036 0883] to hade west; at surface it appears to throw down to the west, south of the Spout House Fault, but to the east on the north side of it. It was also seen in the Hollinswood sewer trench [7052 0920]. A branch fault trending north-north-west was seen in the same trench [7043 0927], throwing down to the north-east. The Lodge Fault also throws down to the north-east at surface along its whole length, and was seen in the Town Centre sewer trench [7023 0825] with a throw of 5 m. Underground a throw of 8.2 m to the north-east is recorded in the White Flat [697 087] and 11 m in the Double Coal. However, south-east of the Dark Lane Fault two close parallel faults are known, the southern one throwing down to the south-west and the major northern one to the north-east (by 9 m in the White Flat). Several more faults trending north-west are known underground east of there, throwing northwards by up to 16.5 m. The almost east–west Spout House Fault is known both underground and at surface; in a trench [6984 0869] it was seen to throw down 5 m to the north. Dips in the Coalport Formation throughout this area are low and variable, but the overall dip is easterly.

At Priorslee Colliery faults mainly trend west-north-west, the largest having a throw of 41 m to the north [708 103 to 719 099] and reaching the surface just south of Woodhouse Pits. Faults shown on the map are surveyed largely from outcrops of the Priorslee Rock, but their throws are not known. Three faults throwing down to the south-west in the Double Coal are shown beneath Redhill; one throwing 6.4 m [728 107] may be the Redhill Fault, with its throw reversing at surface. Another fault, throwing 64 m to the north-east [735 108] in the Double Coal, is larger than any located at the surface in this area. The Double Coal has an overall easterly dip of 2° to 3°, increasing eastwards, comparable to that in the Coalport Formation at surface.

North-west of Woodhouse Pits several north-north-east-trending faults, documented underground, throw down about 7 m against the Lightmoor. The Great East Fault also trends in this direction [719 099] and throws down 41 m to the east, in the Top and Double coals. To the south it swings south-westwards to join the Randley Fault and its throw decreases. Workings from Granville Colliery have proved its north-eastward extension to at least Hugh's Bridge [739 148], and a throw of 76 m is quoted in the Double Coal [738 132]. From Woodhouse to New Lodge [720 106 to 731 128] it can readily be traced at surface; beyond there it cannot be discerned across the Keele Beds outcrop, but to the north it causes dips up to 60° in the Hugh's Bridge Borehole, and it cuts Crow Hayes Shaft [7402 1568].

The Abbey Wood Fault is readily mapped at surface where it separates Keele and Enville beds; farther north this fault limits the limestone workings at Pitchcroft. Westward workings from Granville Colliery cease at the Grange Fault (Whitehead et al., 1928, p.156), which runs parallel to the Lightmoor [718 111 to 728 132] with quoted throws up to 38 m to the west. Workings from Grange Pit prove a further parallel fault [714 112] which, in the Big Flint Coal, throws down 23 m against the Lightmoor. The absence of workings west of the Grange Fault farther north suggests a wide zone of fracturing adjacent to the Lightmoor Fault.

Faults trending approximately north-west are also proved, both at surface and underground, between the Grange and Great East faults, the largest throwing down 21 m to the north in the Double Coal [728 128]. Contours on the Double Coal indicate a 6° dip to the north-east around Watling Street Grange and 8° to the east-north-east near Lilleshall Abbey; a southerly dip of 27° in the Top Coal [719 115] probably reflects the proximity of the Lightmoor Fault.

East of the Great East Fault the major surface structure is the Redhill Fault, which trends north-north-west. To the north and east the alternation of sandstones and mudstones in the Enville Beds, and the limited drift cover, allowed identification of a remarkable number of north-west-trending faults. Some continue through the Bridgnorth Sandstone. Granville Colliery workings indicate a comparable north-westerly trend for the majority of the faults, but a higher proportion trend north-north-east; the underground faults are fewer in number but evidently have greater throws (up to 37 m). Contours on the Double Coal indicate a gentle north-easterly dip at Redhill, swinging to an easterly dip in the north-east.

The Limestone Fault

This structure was originally identified in the Lincoln Hill limestone mines at the entrance to Ironbridge Gorge [6696 0375], although the fault there is not a simple dislocation. The shaft sunk on the downthrow side passes through Lower Coal Measures sandstones and reaches workable Wenlock limestones at about 30 m depth. The limestones dip at 45° to the south-east. Up-dip from the base of the shaft the workings pass through a fault hading to the north-west and enter Coal Measures sandstones for a short distance, so more than one fault plane exists, at least at depth. At the surface the fault branches where it meets the Broseley Fault.

Reference to the Limestone Fault in Madeley Meadow Pit workings must refer to the Warrensway Fault, and the fault recorded at New Track Pit and referred to as the Limestone Fault by Whitehead et al. (1928, pp.94 and 157) is likely to be the Randley Fault. However the Limestone Fault itself can be traced at surface through Roughpark, Aqueduct and Stirchley, and across the northern end of Nedge Hill. At Aqueduct, juxtaposition of the Thick Rock and Top Rock (Coalport Forma-

tion) implies a throw of around 35 m, while the underground position of the Limestone Fault was proved in a heading [7257 0877] from Stafford Pits. Beyond there it can be traced through Enville Beds as far as the Brewer's Oak Fault [741 109], but it becomes steadily less important.

From Lincoln Hill north-eastwards to near Stirchley [709 070], the fault closely follows the north-east-trending Stirchley Anticline in the Lower and Middle Coal Measures (Figure 39). As coal seam incrops into the basal Hadley unconformity are displaced across the fault, there must have been fault movement before deposition of the Upper Coal Measures as well as after.

Area between the Limestone, Broseley and Madeley faults

The productive measures in the asymmetrical Madeley Syncline have steeper dips on its north-western side than on the south-eastern; but this folding does not affect the Upper Coal Measures, which dip uniformly eastwards. Successive coals crop into the basal Hadley unconformity on both sides of the syncline (Figure 39). The syncline plunges north-eastwards, and higher seams are preserved in the north-east.

South-west of Madeley the subparallel Jockey Bank, Wayside, Jackfield, Doughty and Corbett's faults (Figure 38) lie between the Limestone and Madeley faults. Cross-faults occur at the base of Lloyds Coppice and at the Tuckies between the Doughty and Madeley Faults. The Jockey Bank Fault [6714 0270] has a downthrow of about 5 m to 10 m to the north-west, in the Hadley Formation. Its throw in the Severn Gorge is smaller, since the Best Coal Group and Little Flint Coal are in juxtaposition [6783 0342]. At Jockey Bank it may join the Wayside Fault, although the throws are in opposite directions. The Wayside Fault juxtaposes Thick Rock to the south-east against probable Sulphur Rock to the north-west.

The Jackfield Fault commences just north of Broseley [6733 0225]; the Main Sulphur Coal has been mined at 42 m depth on the downthrow side, and is at outcrop on the upthrow side. The throw must reduce north-eastwards to about 15 m in the Hadley Formation around Jackfield. The base of the Hadley Formation there rests on the Pennystone Measures on the upthrow side, and on the Big Flint Coal and higher measures on the downthrow side, indicating pre-Hadley Formation fault movements. The Doughty Fault [6911 0311] throws down to the south-east, but unlike the Jackfield Fault appears not to reach the Broseley Fault. In the south-west it is inferred from the abrupt termination of sandstone outcrops in the Coalport Formation, and it is recorded in the workings from Doughty's Mine. Corbett's Fault parallels the Madeley Fault; the displacement of sandstones and breccia beds in the Coalport Formation in Corbett's Dingle indicates a throw of the order of 10 m to the west. This is consistent with Main Sulphur Coal depths of 71 m in Deep Pit and 87 m in Amies Field Pit. Exposures in the eastern tributary to Corbett's Dingle [6900 0202] show high dips adjacent to the fault, which cannot be traced farther north beneath the slipped ground around Tuckies, but may continue to Lloyds Coppice.

The Warrensway Fault is known in workings for the Little Flint Coal [688 049] and the Best Coal [697 054]; it was exposed at Brookside Middle School [701 059], and it can be traced as far as the Holmer Fault. A parallel fault [698 063 to 707 067] is inferred from site investigation boreholes. Three faults throwing down to the north-east are known between Madeley and Holmer. The Madeley Court Fault is known underground north-east of Madeley Court, and was seen in a sewer tunnel [7005 0414] dipping north-east at about 45°. The Halesfield and Holmer faults are both clear at surface and underground, with throws in the Top Coal of 27 m and 37 m respectively. The former is not present between the Warrensway and Limestone faults, although beyond the Limestone Fault a fault is known in line with it. East of Holmer, eleven small closely spaced faults trending north-west are shown on mine plans, and either side of these, two faults were proved at surface throwing down to the south-west. One of these [710 061] may continue to the south-east and north-west, where it apparently controls the course of the Mad Brook; the other [7121 0645] was seen in bridge excavations to be mineralised with calcite, hematite and malachite. Faults with this trend in the Enville Beds include an extension of the Hem Fault at Spring Bower [726 063], a major fault with a south-westerly throw north of Shifnal, and the Brewers Oak Fault.

The Brookside Fault was exposed in the Keele Beds [7054 0546], with malachite mineralisation in the Brookside Rock. A north-east-trending fault, proved by drilling to cross Madeley High Street [7001 0447], may be a continuation of the Brookside Fault. At Holmer Farm [709 060] two faults are known with this trend: the more westerly is considered to be the Brookside Fault as it has a throw to the north-west, which was visible in the harbour [709 061]. The Dodmoors Fault, which has a throw to the east-south-east, is known from drilling at Holmer Farm and can be seen cutting the Enville scarp north of the Dodmoors. North of Shaw Farm it splits; the eastern branch has a small throw to the north-west and can be clearly seen where it cuts the conglomerate band beyond Haughton Farm. It is proved by drilling to cross the Wesley Brook and join an almost east–west fault. The Blythbury Fault is probably the major branch of the Dodmoors Fault, but is less well known as it follows low drift-covered ground until it joins the Limestone Fault [739 104].

The Madeley Fault

From its junction with the Broseley Fault [6881 0102], the Madeley Fault can be mapped at the abrupt termination of sandstone features within the Coalport Formation and by seepage lines. The fault was exposed in a drain cutting [6917 0194] 600 m north-east of Handleyshitch. It is known in Clod Coal workings from Hills Lane Pits [698 035 to 711 046], but not in mine workings farther to the north-east, as the seams are cut out by the sub-Hadley unconformity to the west of the fault (Figure 39). The fault was intersected by a sewer tunnel [7040 0430], and seen in foundation excavations for the Alycast plant [712 050], where the fault zone comprises about a metre of structureless red mudstone. Keele mudstone dips at about 50° to the south-east on the north side of the fault, and at about 35° on the south side. Beyond there the fault cuts diagonally through the hill to The Hem and then forms the boundary between the Enville Beds and Bridgnorth Sandstone east of The Wyke, where it was proved [736 067] by BGS power-auger holes. Farther north the line of the fault and of the Enville/Bridgnorth boundary are conjectural. North of the railway the boundary is formed by the Haughton Fault, which may be a northward continuation of the Madeley Fault.

Area east of the Madeley Fault

South of the River Severn, the Lower Coal Measures are preserved in the north-east-trending Coalport Syncline (Figure 39). This is smaller than the Madeley Syncline and its north-eastward continuation is unproven, but Madeley Wood Borehole No. 5 [7500 0628] preserves higher coals than No. 6 [7427 0698], which places it on the eastern flank of the Hem Anticline and in turn implies a continuation of the Coalport Syncline. Both the Upper Coal Measures and Bridgnorth Sandstone dip eastwards; however, there must be a slight difference in strike to account for the southward disappearance of the Enville Beds below the Bridgnorth Sandstone unconformity.

The faulting in this area does not follow such a clear pattern as in the worked coalfield, and faults with approximate north–south and east–west trends are more important. The former include a branch of the Madeley Fault at Hay Farm and The Werps, other faults with westward downthrows at Sutton Wood and Lodge Hill, the Apley Park Fault with an eastward throw at Sutton Maddock, and a structure at Kemberton which apparently does not cut the Bridgnorth Sandstone. Faults that do cut the Bridgnorth Sandstone mainly trend east-north-east and west-north-west, including the Hem, Clews Wood, Grindle, Harrington and Stockton faults, although the last-named is more nearly parallel to the north-east-trending faults in the coalfield. The Blists Hill Fault parallels the north-west-trending faults of the coalfield, and to the east it may continue as the Sutton Maddock Fault, with a similar trend; however, south of the Stockton Fault the trend swings to north-north-west.

The Broseley Fault

The Broseley Fault apparently terminates [6641 0406] at the Lightmoor Fault south-west of Captains Coppice. South of the River Severn the fault is clearly marked where Silurian strata and basal Coal Measures sandstones are faulted against extensively mined Lower Coal Measures, a strong seepage line indicating the course of the fault. The throw here is about 60 m to the north-east, increasing to 70 m around Broseley itself. Coal seams are known in public house cellars in Broseley High Street, and the same seams have been mined at 80 m depth 400 m to the north of Fishouse Colliery. North of All Saints Church [6788 0153] a strong seepage line and the termination of Coalport Formation sandstone features indicate the course of the fault towards the former Broseley Tileries, where it is recorded in workings from the upthrow side in the Main Sulphur Coal; a mine plan for the Dunge No. 7 Pit records a throw of 60 m. At Upper Riddings Farm [6904 0085] the fault splits, the northerly branch being the main continuation of the Broseley Fault.

Area west of the Broseley Fault and north of the Deancorner Fault

This area is comparatively sparsely faulted. Two trends dominate: north–south in the south around Willey and Barrow, and west-north-west in the north around Benthall. A syncline is present beneath Posenhall [657 017], but its north-western limb is largely cut out by an axial fault. The north–south fault east of Barrow joins the Deancorner Fault beyond the southern margin of the area, and is readily detectable on the Willey Estate [664 002] where early mining of the Little Flint Coal occurred alongside Silurian mudstones. North of the road from Barrow to Broseley a distinction is clearly seen in the field brash between the basal Coal Measures sandstones and fossiliferous Upper Ludlow Shales. The throw of the fault is probably no more than 10 m to the east. In the Benthall area west-north-west-trending faults have throws of 2 m to 5 m. These do not extend far beyond the outcrop of the lowest coal seam. From Benthall to Deerleap the Coal Measures dip to the south-east in the north, to the east in the west, and generally to the north-east in the south, indicating the presence of a syncline.

The Deancorner, Willey and Caughley faults

These may be considered as continuations of the Corbett's, Madeley and Hay Farm faults, south of the Broseley Fault. The

Deancorner Fault is defined in field brash [6700 0006] and by the evidence of coal mining around Deancorner, where the throw is about 60 m. To the north-east the fault crosses the Dean Brook [6784 0048] and the Broseley–Bridgnorth Road. On the north-western (downthrow) side, the Hadley Formation rests on Pennystone Measures (Middle Coal Measures), while the Lower Coal Measures first rest on Downtonian rocks [6760 0040] and then overstep on to Upper Ludlow Shales. On the upthrow side the Hadley Formation rests on lowermost Lower Coal Measures, which in turn rest on Silurian strata a few metres above the Aymestry Group. Estimated displacements are therefore: base of Hadley Formation 7 m to 8 m, base of Lower Coal Measures 20 m, Aymestry Group about 35 m; these indi-cate a lengthy period of activity along the fault, with post-Silurian/pre-Lower Coal Measures movement, post-Middle Coal Measures/pre-Hadley Formation movement, and post-Hadley Formation movement.

A similar sequence of events may have taken place along the Willey Fault, which throws down to the south-east. Between the two faults strong Caledonian folding in the Ludlow rocks extends beneath, but does not affect, the Coal Measures. South-east of the Caughley Fault, the Little Flint to Ganey coals of the Lower Coal Measures survive beneath the Hadley Formation, and their apparent absence north-west of the fault can be attributed to faulting and uplift prior to deposition of the Hadley Formation.

EIGHT

Geophysical surveys

Several geophysical surveys have covered the area, in whole or in part. BGS regional gravity surveys in 1951 and 1966 covered most of the district with a station density of one per square mile. A gravity survey of the Welsh Borders by Cook and Thirlaway (1955) extended as far north as Wellington and Lilleshall, but their station density was low and only large anomalies were discussed.

Aeromagnetic surveys in 1955 and 1958 together covered the area. The 1955 survey was flown at a barometric height of 305 m and covered the eastern part of the district with east-west flight lines at intervals of 1.6 km, and north–south tie-lines at intervals of 9.6 km. The 1958 survey was flown at a mean terrain clearance of 305 m with east-west flight lines spaced at 2 km intervals and north-south tie-lines at intervals of 10 km.

During the resurvey, detailed Bouguer gravity anomaly profiles were observed over 40 line-km in eight traverses (Figure 40, 1–8) in the area between Rushton and Lilleshall, and three traverses (Figure 41, 9–11) over concealed structures in the eastern half of the district. An additional 5 line-km of detailed survey were completed in two traverses (Figure 41, 12–13) north of the Wrekin, to improve the definition of regional contours in this area of steep gradients. Station spacing was 50 m for all traverses; 350 regional stations were also added to the previous observations, increasing the regional gravity stations to two per square kilometre. Magnetometer readings were taken on the Wrekin and Ercall hills to locate shallow dolerite dykes in the Precambrian rocks. Locally, resistivity surveys were carried out to supplement the gravity data.

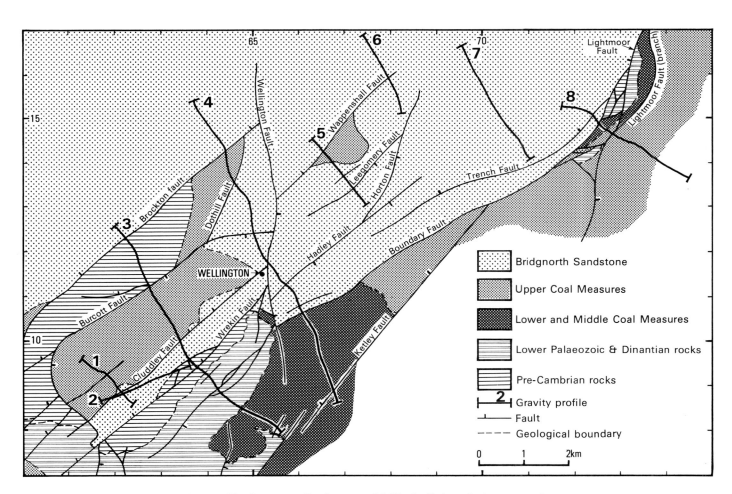

Figure 40   Location of gravity profiles between Rushton and Lilleshall, in relation to geology.

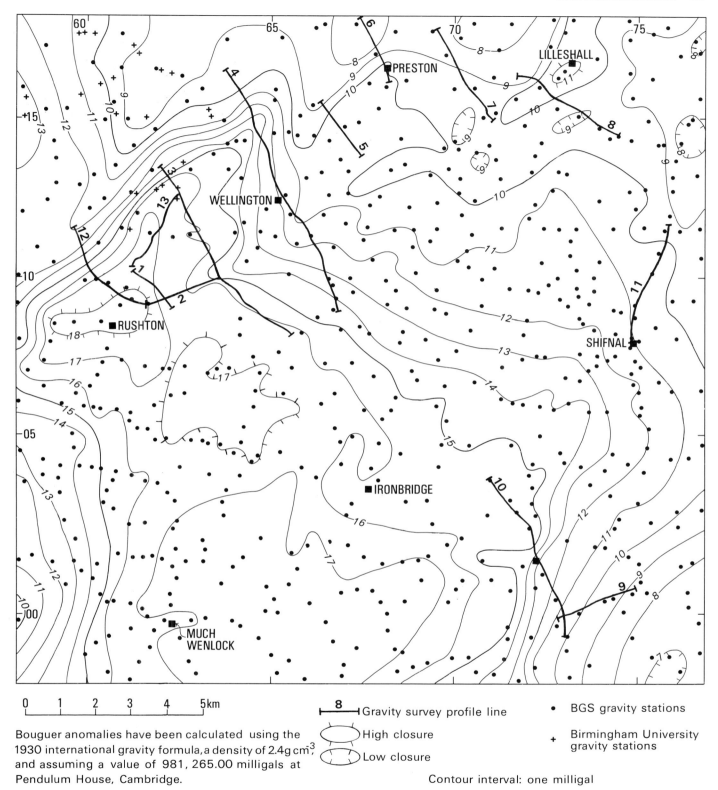

0   1   2   3   4   5km

8⊢ Gravity survey profile line

⬭ High closure

⬭ Low closure

• BGS gravity stations

+ Birmingham University gravity stations

Bouguer anomalies have been calculated using the 1930 international gravity formula, a density of 2.4 g cm^{-3}, and assuming a value of 981, 265.00 milligals at Pendulum House, Cambridge.

Contour interval: one milligal

Figure 41 Bouguer anomaly map, with location of gravity profiles.

GRAVITY SURVEYS

The surveys covered two principal areas; north and east of the Wrekin, between Rushton and Lilleshall, to identify the structures beneath the Bridgnorth Sandstone; and around Sutton Maddock and Shifnal to investigate particular structures.

Three local gravity base stations were established at Wrockwardine, Kynnersley and Buildwas, and linked to the base station at Church Stretton. Gravity values were based on an assumed value of 981 265.00 mgal at Pendulum House, Cambridge by using a value of − 12.04 mgal at Church Stretton. The data were reduced to Bouguer anomalies at mean sea level using a density of 2.4 g cm^{-3} and the 1930 International Gravity Formula.

The results of the survey are presented here as a regional Bouguer anomaly map (Figure 41), Residual Bouguer anomaly map (Figure 42) and examples of detailed profiles (Figures 43 to 45). The Bouguer anomaly map includes some gravity observations made by Birmingham University. The national gravity datum and 1930 International Gravity Formula have since been revised; 2.53 mgal should be subtracted from the Bouguer anomalies to convert them to the modern system.

Mean saturated rock densities for the main contrasting stratigraphic groupings, derived from measurements made on rocks from the English Midlands and Welsh Borders by Parasnis (1952), Cook and Thirlaway (1955), Brooks (1966) and BGS laboratory measurements are:

	g cm^{-3}
Permo-Triassic sandstones	2.22
Upper Carboniferous rocks	2.48
Lower Carboniferous rocks	2.60
Lower Palaeozoic rocks	2.66

Single specimen samples from BGS boreholes in the area gave the following saturated density values (Forster, 1972).

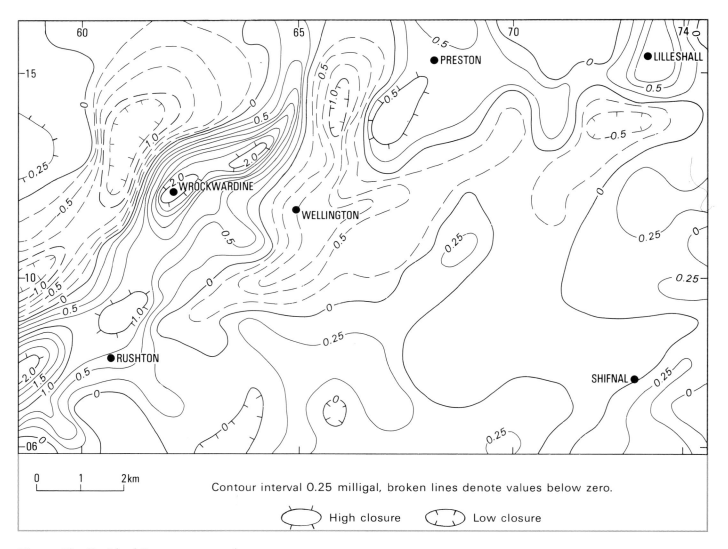

Contour interval 0.25 milligal, broken lines denote values below zero.

High closure   Low closure

Figure 42   Residual Bouguer anomaly map.

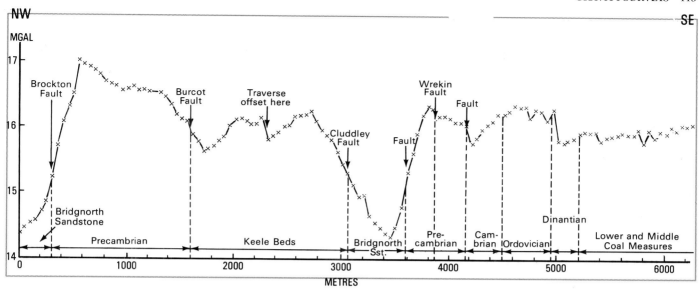

Figure 43 Bouguer anomaly profile 3.

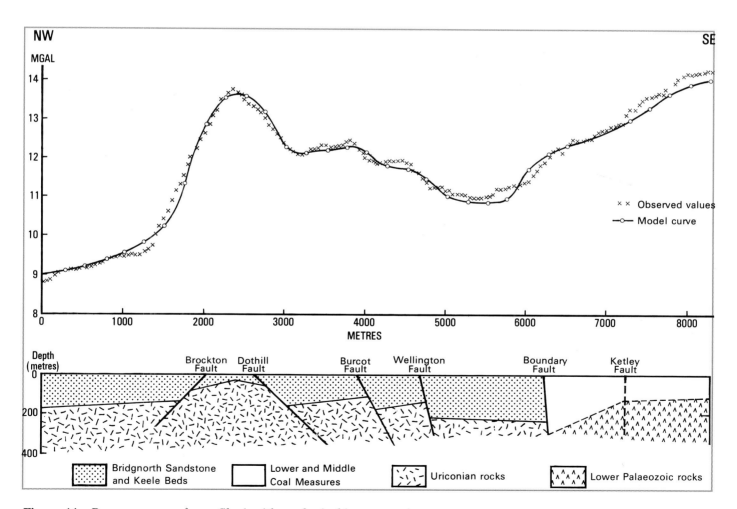

Figure 44 Bouguer anomaly profile 4, with geological interpretation.

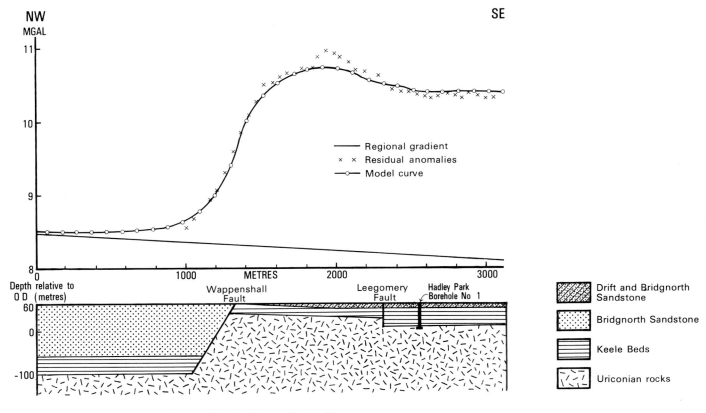

Figure 45 Bouguer anomaly profile 5, with geological interpretation.

	g cm^{-3}
Bridgnorth Sandstone	2.13
Keele Beds (sandstone)	2.41
Keele Beds (mudstone)	2.46
Uriconian (agglomeratic tuff)	2.58

The composition of the Keele Beds is taken as 60 per cent sandstone and 40 per cent mudstone, giving an overall density of 2.43 g cm^{-3}.

The Bouguer anomaly map (Figure 41) shows values between 7.3 mgal and 18.7 mgal, with strong gradients associated with major faults. In the area between Rushton and Lilleshall, the principal features (Figure 40) are:

i) The steep gradient lying north-west of Rushton and Wellington; this corresponds to the Brockton Fault, which throws Bridgnorth Sandstone on the north-west, against Precambrian rocks and Keele Beds to the south-west.

ii) The abrupt change in the trends of the contours from north-easterly to northerly, to the north of Wellington, reflecting the Wellington Fault.

iii) A Bouguer gravity anomaly low extending east-north-east from north-east of Rushton to south-west of Lilleshall, which corresponds to the thick Bridgnorth Sandstone succession in the basin (or graben) north of the Wrekin and Boundary faults.

iv) A positive anomaly closure of 18 mgal surrounding Rushton, corresponding to the outcrop of the Rushton

Schists, suggesting that they are denser than the surrounding Uriconian and Cambro-Ordovician rocks.

v) An elongated positive anomaly closure surrounding Lilleshall, corresponding to outcrops of Uriconian, Cambrian and Dinantian rocks.

In the south of the area (Figure 41) there is a broad 'high' corresponding to the Silurian outcrop, with a closure of 17 mgal between Ironbridge and Much Wenlock. Contours show the anomaly declining gradually towards Shifnal as the Silurian strata dip below Coal Measures. The elongate Bouguer anomaly high extending south-west from Shifnal corresponds to the Hem Anticline, along which Silurian strata come closer to the surface.

The residual Bouguer anomaly map (Figure 42) removes regional effects, and highlights local, or shallow, structures. It appears to reflect the changes in level of the basement surface quite accurately. There are two positive closures of 2 mgal along the north-east-trending Uriconian axis on the south side of the Brockton Fault. The closure west of Rushton corresponds to the Uriconian outcrop of Charlton Hill; the other at Wrockwardine corresponds to the outcrop of Wrockwardine Hill. This Uriconian axis is truncated by a north–south Bouguer anomaly trough with residual values of −1 mgal between Wellington and Preston, and extending southwards into the east-north-east-trending gravity 'low' (Figure 42) that corresponds with the Bridgnorth Sandstone basin (see above). The north–south zone of steep gradient is interpreted as reflecting the Wellington Fault, throwing down to the east and displacing the basin of Bridgnorth Sandstone and Keele Beds which lies to the north-west of the Wrekin (see Figure 40, profiles 3 and 4; and Figures 43, 44).

To the east of the −1 mgal closure (Figure 42) there is a positive anomaly closure of 0.5 mgal corresponding to an area of shallow Precambrian basement, at about 60 m depth, as seen in Hadley Park and Kinley Farm boreholes.

Detailed gravity profiles

Profile 1 runs southwards from Aston to the base of the Wrekin, where it was stopped because of severe terrain effects. It is intersected by **profile 2** which runs along the Wrekin. Since there is some uncertainty in the effect of terrain on the Bouguer anomaly profile, constant separation resistivity traverses were made alongside the Bouguer anomaly profiles. Where profile 2 is at an acute angle to the Cluddley Fault (Figure 40) resistivity data reflected the fault more precisely than the gravity results. On profile 1 a second fault some 600 m north of the Cluddley Fault is shown. A maximum observed anomaly of 18 mgal corresponds to the area where the basement is at shallow depth.

Profile 3 (Figure 43) defines the intersection of various faults and geological boundaries. The 2 mgal trough over the outcrop of the Bridgnorth Sandstone, south-east of the Cluddley Fault, is a cross-section of the residual 'low' which trends north-eastwards between Rushton and Wellington. The Bridgnorth Sandstone succession is thrown down between the Cluddley and Wrekin faults; if this anomaly is entirely due to Bridgnorth Sandstone its thickness would be about 100 m.

On **profile 4** (Figure 44) the gravity contours run almost parallel to the profile, so no accurate interpretation is feasible. The intersections of the Brockton and Boundary faults with the traverse were previously known; the Dothill, Burcot and Wellington faults are inferred from the Bouguer anomalies. The Brockton Fault throws 60 m to the north-west and the Bridgnorth Sandstone thickens northwards, away from the fault, from 150 m to 180 m. Between the Brockton and Dothill faults the Uriconian is faulted up as a horst, which lies beneath 30 m to 60 m of Keele Beds. South-east of the Dothill Fault, which throws 100 m to the south-east, the Bridgnorth Sandstone reaches a thickness of 150 m. The Burcot Fault throws the Bridgnorth Sandstone down to the south-east by 60 m, and south of the fault the sandstone has a thickness of 170 m. The Wellington Fault, at least partly a dextral wrench fault, has a normal component with an easterly downthrow of 80 m in this area. Between the Wellington and Boundary faults the Bridgnorth Sandstone has a thickness of about 220 m to 240 m, thickening towards the Boundary Fault. The Boundary Fault, also partly a dextral wrench fault, has major normal and reverse components. South of the fault Coal Measures overlie Lower Palaeozoic rocks.

Profile 5 (Figure 45) shows the Wappenshall Fault, which throws Bridgnorth Sandstone and Keele Beds down about 160 m to the north-west against Precambrian rocks; and the Leegomery Fault, which throws the Keele down about 25 m to the south-east. North of the Wappenshall Fault the Keele Beds have an estimated thickness of 40 m and the Bridgnorth Sandstone is 120 m thick; by contrast, between the Wappenshall and Leegomery faults, only about 25 m of Keele Beds lie on the Precambrian. South of the Leegomery Fault the thicknesses are known from Hadley Park No. 1 Borehole: the Drift and Bridgnorth Sandstone together are 11.9 m thick and the Keele Beds 45.7 m.

Profile 6 shows a marked gradient over the Wappenshall Fault, which here has an overall throw to the north-west of 190 m. Two normal fault planes are identified, throwing down the Bridgnorth Sandstone and Keele Beds. The major fault throws 110 m to the north-west, where 210 m of Bridgnorth Sandstone on 60 m of Keele Beds overlie Uriconian rocks; 200 m to the south-east the minor fault throws down 80 m to the north-west. Between the faults only 100 m of Bridgnorth Sandstone overlie 60 m of Keele Beds on Uriconian rocks. The southern end of the traverse is 500 m west of Hoo Hall Borehole, which proved 46 m of Drift and Bridgnorth Sandstone and 45 m of Keele Beds, without reaching Uriconian basement.

Along **profile 7** the small gravity variations are probably due to changes in drift thickness. At the southern end of the profile the approach to the Trench Fault is indicated by a steep gradient but it is not possible to give an estimate of the throw.

Profile 8 crosses the area of shallow Precambrian and Lower Palaeozoic rocks south of Lilleshall. The Bridgnorth Sandstone overlying Lower Palaeozoic and Uriconian rocks is thrown down to the north by three faults: the Boundary Fault, the Trench Fault, and another 320 m north of the Trench Fault. The latter two faults each throw down to the north by about 60 m. The Bridgnorth Sandstone decreases in thickness from 140 m over the northern part of the traverse, to 80 m between the unnamed fault and the Trench Fault, and to only 15 m between the Trench and Boundary faults. There is no significant gradient, here, associated with the Boundary Fault. However, the Lightmoor Fault throws down about 335 m to the south-east; Coal Measures between the Boundary and Lightmoor faults are about 30 m thick, whereas south-east of the Lightmoor Fault they attain 450 m.

Three traverses (Profiles 9 to 11, Figure 41) were made in the eastern part of the area to elucidate specific structures.

Profile 9 was sited across an infilled glacial channel east of Stockton. The traverse shows an irregular anomaly trough with a number of shoulders developed in the profile. A resistivity (expanding probe) survey at the centre of the anomaly gave a depth of 36 m to the contact between the Drift and the Wildmoor Sandstone, with resistivities of 330 ohm m and 725 ohm m respectively. These results suggest an overdeepened channel, with an estimated maximum depth of 44 m below ground level at its deepest point, and filled with sand and gravel.

Profile 10 detected the Apley Park Fault, which runs north-north-eastwards along the line of the steep gradient shown on the Bouguer anomaly map (Figure 41). The fault has a throw of about 170 m to the east, letting Bridgnorth Sandstone down against Enville, Keele and Coal Measures strata.

Profile 11 was made to confirm the positions of the unnamed fault north of Shifnal and of the Brewers' Oak Fault. The unnamed fault throws about 65 m down to the south; 40 m of Bridgnorth Sandstone on Coal Measures are present to the south of it. Between this fault and the Brewers' Oak Fault the Bridgnorth Sandstone varies from 0 m to 35 m in thickness, overlying about 200 m of Coal Measures. The Brewers' Oak Fault throws down 160 m to the north, letting down 50 m to 80 m of Bridgnorth Sandstone on Coal Measures, which are about 300 m thick.

Profiles 12 and 13 were observed for better definition of regional contours where gradients are steep. No interpretation is attempted because they are not straight lines, and they cover areas where the subsurface geology was already known.

MAGNETIC SURVEY

Reconnaissance magnetometer traverses were made over the Wrekin and Ercall using an Elsec proton magnetometer with a station spacing of 10 m, reducing to 1 m in anomalous areas.

The traverses show anomalies produced by shallow dolerite dykes in the Precambrian rocks beneath the drift cover. On the Wrekin, in particular, many more anomalies are recorded than dykes could be mapped.

NINE

Quaternary drift deposits

Superficial (Drift) deposits of Pleistocene and Recent age comprise glacial deposits of various kinds, plus river terrace deposits, alluvium, peat and landslip material.

GLACIAL DEPOSITS

More than half of the Telford district is covered by glacial drift, which ranges up to 36 m in thickness. The Telford area lies astride a preglacial watershed (Figure 46) which ran from Wenlock Edge to the Wrekin and then along the Coal Measures escarpment to Lilleshall. The ice sheet entered the area from the north and north-west and crossed the watershed; distinctive sequences were laid down north-west and south-east of the watershed, and glacial meltwater channels were cut through it. Such channels at Oakengates and Lightmoor (Figure 46), and a possible third from near Ketley to the Horsehay Brook, are now buried beneath glacial deposits, whereas the Ironbridge Gorge remains almost clear of drift. The River Severn now crosses the old watershed via this gorge; before the gorge was cut, the headwaters of the Severn (draining the area west of the

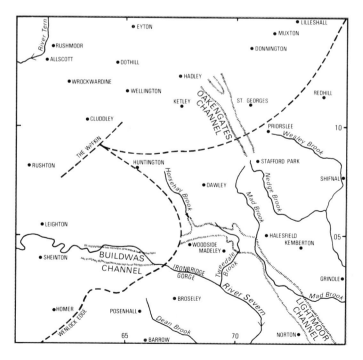

Figure 46 The preglacial watershed (dashed line) and the Oakengates, Lightmoor and Buildwas buried glacial channels in relation to present drainage systems.

Wrekin) flowed out northwards to the Irish Sea, and the Dean Brook (Figure 46) formed the headwaters of that part of the Severn which now flows through Bridgnorth to Stourport.

The glacial drift is believed to be all of late Devensian age (Mitchell et al., 1973). However, the detailed stratigraphy of these deposits is complex; the glacial history of the area and the derivation of the various drift lithologies have been discussed by Hamblin (1986).

Till (Boulder clay)

Till is a deposit of unsorted rock and sediment debris formed by direct action of glacier ice and not subsequently disaggregated. The maximum thickness recorded is 17 m at Lees Farm near Madeley. The till in this area is a stiff sandy clay, generally overconsolidated, with a variable content of sand and rock fragments. It is most commonly brick red, chocolate or purple-brown in colour, through locally pale grey, yellowish or green. The rock fragments are mostly of local origin: blocks of Coal Measures sandstone up to 1.3 m across, shale, coal and sideritic ironstone nodules, Lower Carboniferous chert (possibly rederived from the Enville Beds), Wrekin Quartzite, Comley Sandstone and Uriconian volcanic rocks. Erratics include Bunter quartzite pebbles; igneous and metamorphic material from the Southern Uplands of Scotland, the Lake District and North Wales; and marine shells from the Irish Sea. Granite boulders up to 0.8 m across are recorded at Kemberton Colliery, and a Liassic ammonite is recorded near Holmer. In parts of the area two tills are identified, separated by waterlaid deposits. However, the lower till is not significantly different from the upper; both contain Lake District and Southern Upland erratics as well as Welsh and local rocks. Pods and beds of sand and gravel are common within the upper till, reaching 20 m in length and 0.7 m in thickness in the Nedge Valley; their bedding is highly disturbed and they commonly have sheared upper surfaces.

Waterlaid glacial deposits

Gravels, sands and laminated clays deposited mainly by meltwater from the ice sheet occur between and above the two tills, and there is a laminated clay below the lower till at Hoo Hall. Most of these deposits occur stratigraphically between the two tills. They are found over a wide area north-west of the main Wenlock Edge–Wrekin–Lilleshall watershed, and also in major valleys which cut through the watershed and drain to the southeast: the Buildwas and the Lightmoor channels, the Oakengates channel and the valleys of the Mad Brook and

Wesley Brook. Waterlaid deposits postdating both tills are widespread north of the watershed and are also well developed in the Mad Brook Valley, but are not important in the Lightmoor Channel and the Wesley Brook. Some of the waterlaid sediments, particularly certain laminated clays, are believed to have formed after the retreat of the ice from the area, but they are lithologically similar to the meltwater deposits.

Most of the gravels recorded are of glaciofluvial origin, and occur within the major river valleys in situations indicating both subglacial and subaerial deposition. Those that lie between the tills are poorly sorted, fine to coarse grained, with sand and clay matrices. Clasts up to 1.3 m in diameter are of rock types comparable to those in the tills. Glaciofluvial gravels postdating the upper till are important only in the Mad Brook Valley; they are cleaner and better sorted than the earlier gravels, although they still vary from fine to coarse in grain size: they were subject to a greater degree of fluvial sorting and washing out of the sand and clay fractions, but clasts of coal up to a metre across occur in the gravels at Woodside. Sands occurring between the two tills are pink or red in colour, and generally rich in clean sand derived from the Permo-Triassic rocks.

The **Buildwas Sands** were deposited in thin cross-stratified units with numerous cut-and-fill structures and are interpreted as having formed in braided streams of low sinuosity (Shaw, 1972; Coope, in Shotton, 1977). The **Cuckoo Oak Sands** are their downstream equivalents in the Lightmoor Channel; these show no cross-stratification but are finely laminated with scattered seams of laminated clay. Rock fragments are rare except for coal, which occurs as scattered individual clasts up to 20 cm across and in beds of comminuted coal up to 15 cm thick. At least between Lightmoor and Springhill a definite succession is present within the Lightmoor Channel; thick sandy gravels are overlain by Cuckoo Oak Sands and laminated clays and by further sands and gravels. The latter are unconformable on the underlying sands and, although only about 3 m thick, are very persistent laterally. Sands resembling the Cuckoo Oak Sands are also present in the Mad Brook and Nedge valleys.

Laminated clays are known throughout the district at stratigraphic levels below, between and above the tills. They are purple-brown, brick-red, pale grey or yellow in colour, vary from smooth to silty and from poorly to well laminated, and may contain sand laminae and scattered pebbles. They are characteristically plastic, as a result of parallel orientation of the clay particles; they are thus distinguishable from the tills, in which the constituents have a random orientation. Rhythmites occur, with alternating clay and sand laminae. Laminated clays are most widespread north of the Wrekin–Lilleshall watershed, where they occur as large sheets.

Head, scree and hillwash

Head is thickest and most widespread in the Nedge and Mad Brook valleys, where up to 4.3 m are recorded. It is produced by solifluction, the downhill mass-movement of earlier drift or weathered bedrock material in peri-glacial conditions of alternate seasonal freeze and thaw. During this process the finer fractions of the original material tend to be washed out, leaving it coarser and looser; the result is generally a soft sandy clay or clayey sand, depending on the original up-slope source material. Probably all the head preserved is later than the upper till. In the Mad Brook Valley, head has flowed over the earlier glacial deposits and has diverted the stream to its present position. At Stirchley, solifluction of material derived from the Coalport Formation has resulted in tabular masses of coal being preserved in pale grey clay.

Scree and hillwash formed largely of Silurian limestone and Precambrian igneous rocks are found on the north-west flanks of Wenlock Edge and the Wrekin respectively. These deposits formed partly under periglacial conditions and partly in more recent times.

DETAILS OF GLACIAL DEPOSITS

Areas south-east of the preglacial watershed are described first; then the buried channels which cut through that watershed (Oakengates and the Mad Brook, Lightmoor); then the Buildwas area; and finally areas north of the Wrekin–Lilleshall watershed. Figure 47 is a simplified map of the surface distribution of the drift deposits, and shows the location of places mentioned in the text.

Posenhall, Barrow and Broseley

Patchy till of no great thickness occurs between Benthall, Much Wenlock and The Dunge. This is locally overlain by knolls and patches of sand and gravel, of which the major deposits form a line from the Vineyards [651 025] to near Deancorner [672 003], following the line of the Dean Brook. The Dean Brook joins the Severn opposite the Main Terrace deposits of Apley Lawn, which are the furthest upstream Main Terrace deposits on the Severn; it is probable that before the cutting of the Ironbridge Gorge, the Dean Brook formed the headwaters of the Severn.

Roughpark, Madeley, Norton

From Roughpark [681 048] to Madeley [696 044] up to at least 7 m of till, red-brown or purple and mottled yellow, red and black, rests largely on bedrock, but overlaps the Lightmoor Channel deposits to the north and east. Poorly sorted, clayey grey-brown sand underlies this till at Coalport Road [695 040] and was proved in boreholes nearby [696 043]. From Madeley to Ironbridge, the till varies rapidly in thickness; for example, it was 5.5 m in Lees Farm Borehole No. 1 [6873 0372] and 17.0 m in No. 2 [6868 0367]. A little till is found at the bottom of the Ironbridge Gorge [677 033], and 6.0 m of hard red-brown till with mostly local sandstone clasts [6930 0286] are present at the bottom of the Tweedale valley; till is continuous across the floor of this valley, which contains no buried channel.

Till up to 6.1 m thick mantles the south-east slopes of the Tweedale Valley and is continuous through Springhill and Sutton Maddock to Norton, overlain locally by laminated clays and brown sandy head, and by a patch of gravelly sand at Blists Hill [696 033]. The till overlaps the sands of the Lightmoor Channel at Hills Lane and from Brockton to Astol, but passes beneath the channel sands at Springhill Farm [706 042], suggesting the presence of two tills there. The valley between Sutton Common [715 021] and Sutton Hall [719 014] contains

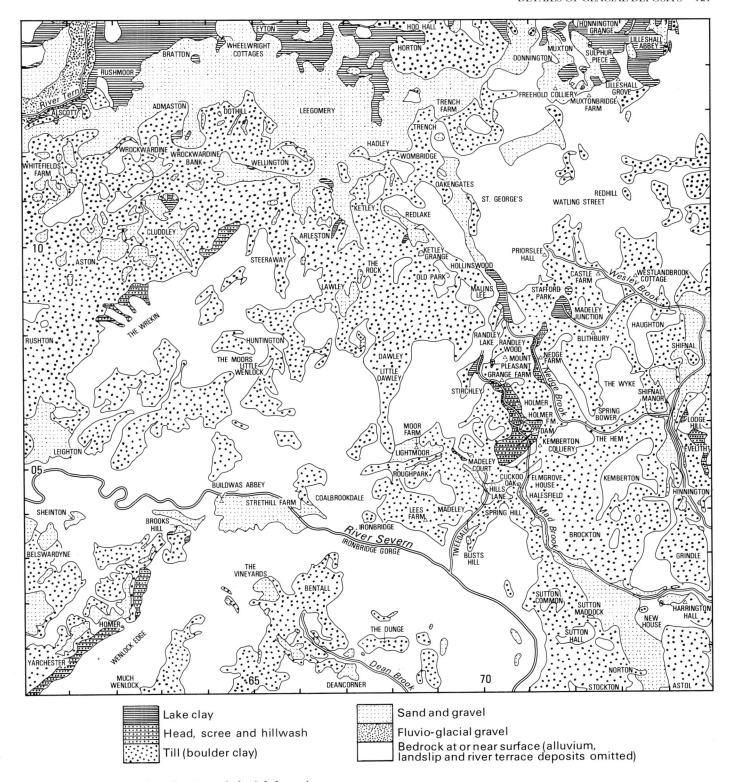

Figure 47   Surface distribution of glacial deposits.

a buried channel with running sand, which falls eastwards to join the Lightmoor Channel deposits [722 019].

Huntington, Dawley, Ketley

Patches of till occur on the high ground around The Moors, Little Wenlock and Huntington, whilst farther north till infills the valley above Steeraway [655 096], overlain and underlain by patches of sand [661 097, 659 101]. The till cover is more continuous around The Rock, Lawley and Dawley, up to 10 m thick and overlain by an extensive spread of sand at Lawley [670 087]. The ridge from Redlake [684 105] to Ketley Grange [690 101] is capped by sand and gravel, locally underlain and overlain by till; the section at Ketley Grange opencast coal site [690 100] can be generalised as follows:

	Thickness m
Till; dark grey above, with angular Coal Measures fragments; reddish brown and sandy below with Bunter quartzite pebbles and igneous erratics; unconformable on	5
Sand, pale red, coarse-grained, cross-bedded, coal-rich, thin (to 10 cm) beds of laminated clay	1.5
Finely laminated clays, silts and sands; plastic, pebble free	3
Till; Coal Measures blocks in stiff grey clay	2

Till, up to 6.4 m thick, mantles the upper slopes between Ketley Grange and Malins Lee [700 088], and at its southern edge this overlies at least 3 m of red-brown well-bedded sand in a north-north-west-trending buried channel. These sands vary from clean and well sorted to very clayey or gravelly and poorly sorted, and include layers of coal and beds of olive-brown laminated clay or silt. One borehole [6984 0894] records a lower till beneath the sands.

South of Malins Lee the till is overlain [698 086] by crudely bedded clayey sandy gravel, interbedded with clean but poorly sorted sand; these sands and the till are locally underlain [697 087] by pale grey, deep red and yellowish highly laminated smooth to silty clay. Till is almost continuous across the high ground of Old Park and Dawley, thickest (10 m) in the north-west, and a tongue extends down the valley from Little Dawley to Lightmoor, overlying sand and gravel in a tributary of the Lightmoor Channel. Till and head mantle the interfluve between the Tweedale and Mad brooks (between Holmer and Madeley Court), the former overlapping the Lightmoor Channel deposits to the south-west but passing below the channel deposits of the Mad Brook to the north-east. The till at Madeley Court [698 055] appears to be a lodgement till, with characteristic basal boulder bed and vertical discontinuities. Near Stirchley, till rests on solifucted material from the Coalport Formation [7020 0620], pale grey clay containing tabular masses of coal up to 2 m long and 0.3 m thick. Head is particularly widespread in this area, overlying till, bedrock and the channel deposits of the Mad Brook; it comprises up to 4.3 m of red-brown sandy clay and silty clayey sand, derived from the Keele Beds.

Stafford Park, Halesfield, Kemberton, Grindle

The laminated clay around Madeley Junction [718 085] is up to 4.3 m thick, brown, purple or brick red, soft and plastic, smooth to silty and sparsely pebbly. It is underlain by clean brown sands, which are well bedded, coarse grained and poorly sorted with gravel layers and coal clasts to 75 mm across. Till surrounding the clays and sands is also continuous beneath it.

This is up to 7.7 m thick [7166 0871], brown, purplish or reddish sandy or silty unbedded clay with clasts up to 0.2 m across of coal, sandstone and quartzite; it contains lenticles of well-bedded clayey brown sand and fine to medium gravel. Small outliers of laminated clays and silts were exposed [7163 0879, 7123 0836 and 7135 0887], and up to 2.3 m of head (pale brown clayey pebbly sand) overlie the till [719 090]. Sand and gravel flank the stream that flows from Stafford Park past Blythbury [725 081] but there is no buried channel.

The Nedge Brook north of Randley Wood [707 079] flows through a deep steep-sided valley containing at least 15 m of till but no buried channel. The brook turns sharply southwards into a more mature valley which does contain a buried channel. This was proved east of the stream [7131 0757 to 7130 0767] and the deposits resemble those at Cuckoo Oak, with clean well-sorted brown sand overlain unconformably by sands and gravels that pass up into till. A boulder bed [7127 0798] included erratics of granite, granodiorite, diorite, adamellite, andesite tuff, agglomerate, quartz porphyry, limestone and siltstone, from southern Scotland, the Lake District, Montgomeryshire and Clwyd. The till that overlies the buried channel is continuous across the valley floor, but is overlain within the valley by up to 2.6 m of head comprising brown or yellow clayey sand, sandy clay and clayey sandy silt, with pebbles and cobbles. The till is hard chocolate-brown pebbly sandy clay, and incorporates highly disturbed lenticles of sand and gravel.

North of Holmer [708 063] till mantles most of the high ground of the Keele Beds outcrop, but does not extend down into the Randley Valley north of Grange Farm; it is overlain by clayey sandy head [7021 0735] near Mount Pleasant. East of Holmer the extensive spread of till in the Nedge Valley is continuous through the col to Kemberton Colliery [713 056] and through the gorge of the Nedge Brook to The Hem [727 057], where it joins the wide drift-filled valley running from Shifnal Manor [739 064] to Brockton [721 035]. South of Haughton and east of the Wyke and Kemberton, till overlaps sands to the east, and south of Kemberton a wide spread of till overlaps the channel deposits of the Mad Brook, but it is probably thin as several inliers of Bridgnorth Sandstone occur.

Redhill, Priorslee, Shifnal

Scattered areas of till occur on the low ground on either side of the A5 road, east of Redhill. Till fills the Westlandbrook valley; boreholes [733 098] showed up to 5.9 m of till on 3.8 m of red-brown sand, gravel, silt and clay, possibly indicating a minor buried channel. The Wesley Brook rises in a till-filled valley east of Priorslee Hall [714 097], and below Castle Farm [725 093] a buried channel closely follows the present-day stream, with up to 6.4 m of sand and gravel overlain by up to at least 6 m of till. Shifnal is built on glacial sand; excavations revealed 2 m of clean brown well-laminated sand, locally cross-bedded, overlain by till. Farther north, brown and pale green laminated clays were interbedded with the sand. The wide expanse of glacial sands at and around Shifnal is clearly overlain by till to the north, west and south-east.

South of Shifnal, the Wesley Brook cuts through the drift into Bridgnorth Sandstone from near Shifnal Manor [742 066]. The latter is sited on sandstone and the Wesley Brook passes east of it with glacial sands flanking its eastern bank, but BGS power auger holes (Figure 48a) proved that the main buried channel passes west of the Manor, with up to 7.8 m of sand overlain by up to 6.7 m of till and underlain at one point by a possible lower till, soft dark purple-brown sandy clay. It is not known whether there is a buried channel in the valley between Spring Bower [727 062] and Kemberton, but excavations [739 061] revealed till overlying sand largely reworked from the Bridgnorth Sand-

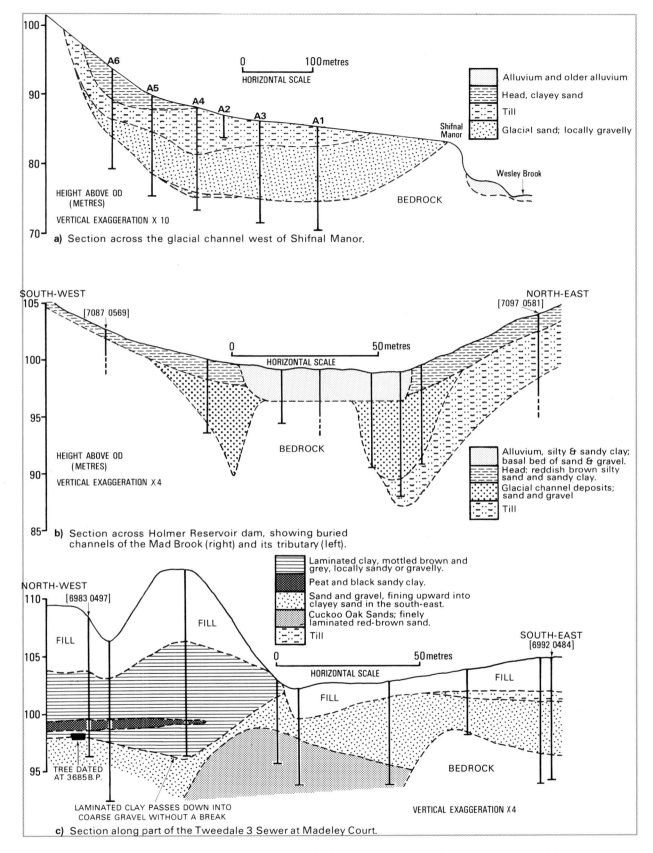

a) Section across the glacial channel west of Shifnal Manor.

b) Section across Holmer Reservoir dam, showing buried channels of the Mad Brook (right) and its tributary (left).

c) Section along part of the Tweedale 3 Sewer at Madeley Court.

Figure 48 Sections though glacial channels and drift deposits. Boreholes shown as vertical lines.

stone. Between Lodge Hill and Kemberton, the Wesley Brook passes through a narrow valley, flanked on either side by glacial sands overlain by till. As the valley widens, the river again flows along the eastern side of the buried channel, and downstream the sand outcrops become more scattered and are largely obscured below till. Beyond the limits of the Telford district these patches of sand run out into the third or Main Terrace of the River Worfe. East of the Wesley Brook, from Shifnal to Hinnington, till rests on bedrock behind Evelith [744 051], while locally derived loose pebbly clayey or sandy head rests at the base of the Kidderminster Conglomerate scarp.

The Oakengates Channel and Mad Brook Valley

The buried channel from Wombridge through Oakengates (Figure 46) is well known from coal mining records; Prestwich (1840, p.462) records over 30 m of sands and gravels. By Wombridge Church [691 116] there is a double channel; workings from St Leonards Colliery encountered sands to the south-west, while boreholes proved drift (not bottomed) at 78 m above OD to the north-east. Southwards from there, site investigation proved a single channel, with its base rising steadily from 84.7 m [6936 1165] to 104 m above OD [697 108]. This channel was largely filled with sands and soft clays, locally over- and underlain by tills. Boreholes for new road schemes [6990 0996 to 7020 0947] show a steep-sided, deep channel (down to 112 m above OD) with up to 17.5 m of sand and gravel, locally overlain and underlain by up to 5 m of till. The sands contain broken shell fragments and the gravel includes Bunter quartzite pebbles, northern erratics and local Carboniferous sandstones and Uriconian volcanic rocks. Beds of laminated clay are included.

A complex of laminated clays, silts, sands and gravels extends from near Hollinswood [701 095] to the ends of the Nedge Valley [706 083] and the Randley Valley [703 086]. The channel deposits include late-glacial laminated clays, silts and sands overlying channel sands, gravels and laminated clays. Opposite Malins Lee [7034 0938] 2 m of lilac and brick red ?lacustrine clay, poorly laminated and containing much coal and a few pebbles, overlies 2.5 m of coarse gravel with boulders up to 0.6 m in diameter of local Carboniferous sandstones. Farther south the laminated clay included cryoturbated beds, and enclosed pods of Permo-Triassic sand and fine gravel with coal; cross-bedding indicated transport towards the south. Boreholes show the channel to be notably steep-sided, and the deepest drift recorded in this area was in a borehole [7043 0912] which penetrated 1.5 m of alluvium, 6.1 m of sand and gravel and 10.7 m of laminated clay and sand not bottomed at 112 m above OD.

The lacustrine complex clearly overlies till in the mouth of the Nedge Valley, where dark grey, green, brick red and yellow laminated clays and silts are interbedded with yellow, brown and olive-grey bedded and unbedded sands, but a sand and gravel-filled channel emerges from beneath it to run into the Randley Valley. At the southern end of this channel, a borehole [7037 0819] failed to bottom 12.6 m of sand, while nearby boreholes recorded 0.9 m of till on 10.9 m of sand and 0.5 m of till on 4.9 m of pale yellow and grey sandy laminated clay. The sands are clean, well sorted, and cross-bedded, while the till crops out widely west of the channel, reaching at least 4.5 m in thickness [7024 0807]. At the south end of Randley Lake a further glacial ?lacustrine complex forms the valley floor almost as far as Grange Farm [702 070] and also partly occupies a tributary valley that joins from the south-west [697 071]. The deposits are variously coloured soft laminated clays, smooth to silty or sandy and micaceous, with fine silt and sand seams and scattered pebbles and boulders. The greatest thickness measured in a borehole [6997 0707] was 6.0 m, but the deposits lie between 126.3 m and 112.0 m above OD, giving a height range of over 14 m. In the tributary valley, till underlies the ?lacustrine clays, but in the main valley the till does not descend the valley sides to reach the clays, and they are locally overlain by loose brown sand and gravel head [as at 7001 0703].

The lacustrine deposits end in the narrow valley between Grange Farm and Stirchley, through which the Mad Brook crosses the Top Rock Sandstone outcrop. Downstream the valley widens and the Mad Brook flows along the east side of a deposit of coarse gravel and sand 200 m wide. A borehole [7046 0675] near the centre of this channel records alluvium to 1.8 m, sand and gravel to 7.0 m, then till resting on Keele Beds. A borehole in a tributary sand and gravel channel [7060 0645] records 5.3 m of head and sand and gravel on 0.8 m of till. A tributary which joins the Mad Brook [7080 0590] has its own buried channel which runs parallel to that of the Mad Brook [7093 0572] (Figure 48b). The Mad Brook buried channel is the deeper of the two; a borehole [7095 0578] recorded 3.4 m of alluvium, 5.9 m of sand and gravel and 1.4 m + of till. The tributary channel contains no undoubted till but is overlain by head.

East and south-east of Holmer Farm, head overlies till in a valley which may represent an earlier course of the Mad Brook. One borehole in this valley [7108 0604] records sand and gravel beneath till (4.1 m thick) and head (0.9 m); temporary sections revealed pale brown sandy head, locally pebbly and clayey, on stiff chocolate-brown till. South of the railway the late-glacial course of the Mad Brook continues as a single narrow channel, closely following the present-day stream and bounded by till and head to the east and west; a borehole in the channel [7093 0511] records alluvium to 1.9 m, sand and gravel to 5.6 m, and till to 7.1 m. These channel gravels disgorge into the Cuckoo Oak complex [7090 0493] where they overlie a glacial sequence that includes two tills.

The Lightmoor Channel

A major development of sands and gravels infills this buried channel (Figure 46), which is widely overlain by till and locally by later sands and gravels. Buried sands are known as far upstream as 150 m west of Lightmoor Station [6778 0503]; beyond there, till continues in the Lightmoor Valley [672 049] but does not drop down into Coalbrookdale. A north–south tributary valley which joins the main valley [681 054] is known from shafts and mine workings to contain sand below the till, while a southerly tributary which falls northwards from [6816 0454] near Hilltop Farm contains up to 5.5 m of till on over 2.4 m of gravel and coarse-grained sand. The main channel is 750 m wide near Moor Farm and boreholes prove 15.2 m of silty clayey sand with some gravel, down to 93 m above OD. This is overlain by a tongue of till along the valley floor, thickening from 2.0 m [691 053] to 4.6 m [6805 0502], and by till at a much higher level on the valley sides, up to 7.6 m thick in the north-east [6919 0552] and 2.1 m in the south [6897 0520]. Erratics include metamorphosed porphyritic andesite and adamellite, both probably from the Lake District. Exposures [691 050] show the till overlain and underlain by coarse-grained loose sands and gravels and laminated clays.

North-west of Madeley Court [6954 0512] alluvium obscures till overlying sands, gravels, silts and clays. Excavations along the western side of the alluvium revealed the following succession:

	Thickness m
Head; soft grey clay and loose brown sand, pebbly	up to 1.7
Till, chocolate brown, sandy, pebbly, with pods of clayey brown sand; base clear-cut or interbedded with	up to 3.0

	Thickness m
Sand and gravel; red Permo-Trias-derived sand, with beds of coal debris, cross-bedded, interbedded with fine to coarse gravel; clasts to 0.7 m of local and erratic sandstone, quartz, quartzite and igneous rocks; clear-cut erosive base	0–2.0
Cuckoo Oak Sands (?lacustrine), pink, grey and brown; clean, well-rounded Permo- Trias-derived grains, finely laminated but not cross-bedded, with beds up to 15 cm thick of pure coal debris with clasts up to 20 cm; a few thin clay seams and pebbly layers	up to 4.0
Gravel	—

The Cuckoo Oak Sands are individually named here because they form a widespread and readily recognised unit known all along the Lightmoor Channel and best exposed at Cuckoo Oak (Figure 49a). At Madeley Court the channel narrows to 200 m, but beyond there it widens and is joined from the north by a tributary buried channel; within the latter, Cuckoo Oak Sands were exposed by the old windmill [697 053], and a borehole [6977 0536] recorded 9.1 m of red sand with some gravel and coal (?Cuckoo Oak Sand), overlain by 1.4 m of till and underlain by 1.9 m of a lower till. The sands of the main channel below Madeley Court are overlapped by till on both sides, the eastern margin of the buried sands following the A442 (Bridgnorth–Dawley) Road. Excavations proved widespread Cuckoo Oak Sands, as well as varved sands and clays, below this till. Figure 48c shows the section through boreholes sunk for the

Tweedale No. 3 Sewer tunnel under the tip from Madeley Court Pits; a section in the tunnel [6985 0496] revealed pebbly, sandy, pale grey clay, passing down into clayey sands and coarse sandy gravels; a fallen pine tree lying at the base of the clay was dated at 3685 ± 100 years BP (Welin et al., 1973, p.302). A temporary section [6992 0485] revealed:

	Thickness m
Head; sandstone boulders and cobbles in sand matrix, few erratics	0–1.2
Till, red-brown, green and yellowish; blocks of Coalport Formation to 0.6 m across, sand pods near clear-cut base	2–2.5
Sand, brown, cross-bedded, well sorted to poorly sorted and pebbly; much coal debris; interbedded with clean well-sorted gravel	0.9–1.1
Sandstone (Coalport Formation)	—

A further temporary section [6995 0492] revealed similar head and till overlying dark grey laminated clay, and an adjacent borehole [6993 0493] proved 4.8 m of Cuckoo Oak Sands beneath these clays and down to 86.3 m above OD.

Extensive drilling has provided details of the drift complex around Cuckoo Oak. Figure 49 shows two sections across this area along the realigned Shifnal–Madeley Road [7037 0468 to 7100 0469] and along the Tweedale No. 2 Sewer [7064 0434 to 7092 0447]. The lowest deposit in the local sequence is a stiff pebbly red-brown till, up to 4 m in thickness. It is overlain by laminated clay and gravelly sand (Figure 49a), or by thick sandy

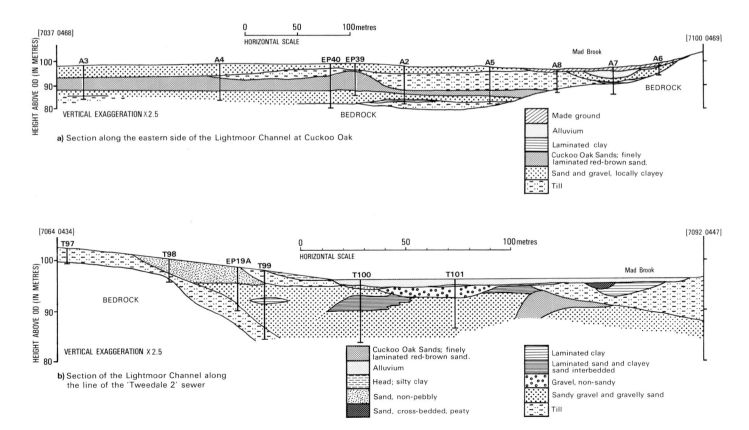

Figure 49   Sections through the drift deposits of the Lightmoor Channel. Boreholes shown as vertical lines.

and clayey gravels, fine to coarse, interbedded with coarse gravelly sand, cross-bedded and largely composed of Permo-Trias-derived sand (Figure 49b). Within these gravels lies a seam of brownish grey pebbly laminated clay 1 m thick. Typical Cuckoo Oak Sands locally occur within these deposits (Figure 49b), but were proved much more widely elsewhere in this area (Figure 49a). They were best exposed in an underpass excavation [7049 0466] where 3.5 m of very uniform Permo-Trias-derived sand, finely laminated but not cross-bedded, contained finely ground coal (also one clast 70 mm across) and was overlain unconformably by 2.0 m of coarse gravel with sandstone boulders up to 0.5 m long. In a similar exposure [7026 0462] the gravel contained sandstone boulders to 1.3 m long and passed up into till. At the old Hills Lane Sand Pit, Wills (1924, p.284) recorded a similar sequence with 2.4 m of till resting on cross-bedded gravel overlying horizontal sand; Prestwich (1840, p.462) recorded this sand thinning from 27 m to 2 m in a distance of 91 m, testifying to the steep sides of the buried channel. The upper till overlaps the Cuckoo Oak Sands in the north and south (at the Hills Lane Sand Pit) and over the whole of the Cuckoo Oak area east of the A442 road; this is thickest (at least 7.62 m) at a borehole [7085 0463], but thins rapidly east of the Mad Brook as it oversteps on to Keele and Enville beds. The sands shown on the Telford map east of the A442 and either side of the Madeley–Shifnal road overlie this till and form a wide, shallow spread disgorging from the late-glacial channel of the Mad Brook. They are up to 4.6 m thick (Figure 49a) and comprise clean well-sorted brown sand, generally cross-bedded, and gravels with pebbles (up to 7 cm across) of Coal Measures sandstones and coal, Bunter quartzite, Uriconian basalt and northern igneous rocks. South-east of these deposits a further sequence of sands, gravels and laminated clays cuts down to a lower level and follows the present north–south course of the Mad Brook. Along the line of Figure 49a these fill a relatively narrow channel, with laminated clay overlying and underlying sands and gravels. The latter were proved to be 4.3 m thick beneath alluvium [7084 0450]. Along the section depicted in Figure 49b, 2.5 m of well-sorted gravel with a matrix of greenish brown and yellow mottled clayey sand rested on till and earlier channel deposits. Beside the channel to the west, the till is overlain by 1.3 m of sandy clay head, and to the east by 1.3 m of laminated clay, underlying 1.3 m of clean coarse-grained grey-green sand and black peaty sand, all cross-bedded. A rootlet bed truncated below the sand has been dated at 9410 ± 120 years BP, a log in the peaty sand at 3180 ± 100 years BP and a rootlet bed in the sand truncated below alluvium is dated at 1400 ± 100 years BP (Welin et al., 1972).

Along the line of section in Figure 49b the buried channel is only 220 m wide; it follows the Mad Brook south-eastwards past Brockton, with till overlapping the channel sands on both sides. Past Brockton the channel widens and the river follows the north side of the channel, then the channel splits and the Mad Brook flows eastward past Harrington Hall [742 021]. Along this course it cuts down deeply into Bridgnorth Sandstone, but glacial sands survive as terraces on either side of the gorge and these pass under till to the south. The sands are level with the third terrace deposits on the River Worfe, which correlate with the third terrace of the Severn — two patches of this terrace appear on the Telford map east of Harrington Hall, wrongly labelled as Higher Terraces. The main buried channel continues south-eastwards between Sutton Maddock and New House, where the drift is much thicker than in the valley of the Worfe past Harrington Hall, as a borehole at the edge of the channel [7221 0191] records 1.5 m of till on 25.9 m of fine to coarse angular gravel down to 56.1 m above OD. A gravity survey and an expanding-probe restivity survey along the road from [SO 729 997] near Stockton Church to past Astol

(Chapter 8) indicate a channel filled mainly with sand and gravel, up to 36 m deep and cutting down to 37 m above OD [7395 0025].

Homer, Sheinton, Buildwas, Leighton

The lowest drift deposits in the local sequence, and the most renowned in the Telford district, are the **Buildwas Sands**. These were deposited in thin cross-stratified units, and are largely composed of clean Permo-Trias-derived sand, with little other material except for scattered clasts and thin beds of coal debris. They occur on both sides of the Ironbridge Gorge, at between 22 m and 95 m above OD, between Strethill Farm [661 041] and Buildwas Abbey [643 043], and in smaller patches farther upstream. The hillocks of sand give the appearance of being the remnants of an early, eroded deposit. In the pit south-east of Buildwas Abbey they are overlain unconformably by coarse assorted gravels which pass up into till. The Buildwas Sands are overlain by till north-east of Strethill Farm [659 042] and at Brook's Hill [636 037]. North of the river, blanket till is widespread on the higher slopes leading up to the Wrekin and Little Wenlock. The till south of the river is overlain locally by mounds and ridges of sand between Homer [62 01] and Belswardyne, and by laminated clays at Brook's Hill. Finally, head is developed below Wenlock Edge [600 000 to 627 027].

Rushton, Cluddley, Wrockwardine, Wellington, Dothill

Till is ubiquitous except where it thins out against the Precambrian inliers of the Wrekin, Rushton and Wrockwardine. It thickens north-eastwards to a recorded maximum of 11 m at Dothill [6437 1273]. Erratics include coal, Wenlock Limestone, Comley Sandstone, angular (?Wrekin) quartzite, and Bridgnorth Sandstone. Around the Precambrian inliers till rests directly on bedrock, but in the valley running from Aston to Wellington it is underlain by a complex of interbedded sands and laminated clays. At Aston this laminated clay, with scattered pebbles and shell fragments, rests either on Keele Beds or on gravelly sands. Near Wrockwardine and at Dothill the till is underlain by at least 11.9 m and 12.8 m respectively of interbedded sand and laminated clay. Sands also overlie the till from Cluddley to Aston, at Dothill and around Whitefields Farm [6040 1175], where fine-grained clayey sands pass up into coarse sandy gravel and then into pale brown soft silty laminated clays. Further laminated clays are known bevelled into the upper sands [6325 1090] north of Cluddley, and resting on till and lower sands north of Wrockwardine Bank. Mounds of sand at Dothill reach a thickness of at least 5.9 m [643 127] and laminated clays are also recorded there.

Allscott, Rushmoor, Eyton, Hadley, Donnington

The principal lithologies around Allscott, Rushmoor and Bratton are laminated clay and coarse-grained red or orange sands and gravels. The clays are pale brown, soft and silty to sandy and were formerly widely worked for brick making. Two lithologically similar deposits may be of quite different ages. The main area of clay stretching from Rushmoor to Wheelwright Cottages [643 145] is presumed to be a late-glacial feature, as such a large flat area of soft clay is not likely to have survived the passage of an ice sheet; however, a smaller area of similar clay at Allscott is overlain by till and must be older. Coarse-grained red sands with much fine rounded gravel are exposed over large areas both north and south of the Tern. Most or all of these must predate the till which overlies sands at Allscott, Admaston and Dothill.

Farther east, sands occur widely around Leegomery and Hadley, passing below till to the south. A power auger borehole at Leegomery House Farm recorded 3.0 m of sand on 3.4 m of till, underlain by 1.8 m of laminated clay and sand (not bottomed). Large areas of laminated clay between Eyton and Donnington [651 148 to 704 149] are a late feature. Sands younger than the blanket till are encountered again farther east in the area around Trench Farm [691 132]. A series of six BGS boreholes between Trench, Hoo Hall and Donnington revealed the following succession:

	Thickness m
Clay, soft, unbedded, sandy, ?lacustrine	0.9
Sand, clayey, with lumps of sandy clay and pebbles to 0.4 m diameter	1.2
Till, chocolate-brown; pebbles include Precambrian rocks and shell debris	0.8–4.0
Laminated clay, purple-brown, ?lacustrine	0.6–2.4
Sand, largely Permo-Trias-derived, pebbles to 0.05 m	2.9–10.7+
Till, hard, brown, very sandy	0.9–2.7
Laminated clay, purple-brown, laminated, ?lacustrine	0.9

Lilleshall, Muxton, St Georges

The area of rising ground flanking the major watershed of the Enville Beds escarpment is partially covered by a relatively thin sequence of sands and laminated clays. Till crops out in very few areas. A power auger borehole [7240 1448] proved till underlain by stoneless laminated clay on fine-grained clayey sand. The laminated clay extends from Lilleshall Grove [730 137] to near Honnington Grange [722 148] at heights from 100 m above OD down to 75 m above OD; it appears to be a relatively old and dissected deposit. The underlying fine-grained clayey sands, which contain few pebbles, cover large areas around Sulpher Piece Plantation [724 141], Freehold Colliery [7179 1347] and Muxton [717 144]. Sands and laminated clays around Honnington [724 149] and Lilleshall Abbey [738 142] are terraced, with flats of clay separated by slopes of sand; they do not appear to have been overridden by ice, and they rest upon till [742 148, 740 143, 733 133]. Laminated clays postdating the ice retreat also rest in the valley bottom and on valleyside benches between Honnington Grange [722 150] and Donnington [713 144]. Lacustrine rhythmites (alternating laminae of clay and sand) are overlain by sand at Honnington Grange [7243 1487]. Isolated areas of sand and till are found in the south-east of the area, one of the sand deposits [732 128] forming a conspicuous knoll on the escarpment: 22 species of marine shells have been found here.

Ketley

A deeply incised postglacial valley cuts through thick deposits of drift in this area. In sandpits north and south of the A5 road, Pocock et al. (1938, pp.184–185) record dull purple and brown till with striated boulders, overlying laminated clay and loam, laminated and cross-bedded sands, and coarse-grained sand with stringers and lenticles of gravel.

Boreholes for the Ketley (M54) Interchange revealed a more complex sequence (Figure 50). Sands and laminated clays up to at least 23.2 m thick are both overlain and underlain by till, the deposits infilling a valley that falls northwards. Later sands overlie the upper till at Arleston [666 104]. The deposits proved in the boreholes are considered to represent a lacustrine sequence between two tills.

RIVER TERRACES

Upstream of the Ironbridge Gorge three terraces of the River Severn are recognised (Figure 51); these correspond respectively to the Atcham, Cressage and Uffington terraces of the Shrewsbury area (Pocock et al., 1938, p.208). They lie 3 m to 6 m, 6 m to 12 m and 12 m to 18 m above the Severn. Terrace gravel deposits beside the Severn downstream from Ironbridge [702 020, 710 010] are presumed to correlate with the first (Atcham) terrace upstream of the gorge. The Atcham and Cressage terraces are present (Figure 51) on the River Tern, but the Uffington Terrace is not known.

Two patches of gravel in the south-east of the area [750 020] at around 73 m above OD are terraces of the Mad Brook, not far above its junction with the Worfe. They appear to correlate downstream with the Main Terrace of the Worfe, Severn and Stour, and upstream they coalesce with sands and gravels which are overlain by till. The Main Terrace thus must predate the maximum advance of the Devensian ice, and this accords with evidence outside the area, as equivalent gravels in the valley of the Salwarpe (another tributary of the Severn) rest upon organic deposits dated at 41 500 and 41 900 years (Coope et al., 1961). The Main Terrace of the Severn does not extend into the Telford district because the Ironbridge Gorge is a later feature (Hamblin, 1986). The Dean Brook is believed to be the preglacial headwater of the Severn; patches of sand and gravel between The Vineyards and Deancorner (Figure 47) grade down into the Main Terrace of the Severn at Apley Lawn, south of the district.

ALLUVIUM AND PEAT

Apart from that flanking the River Severn upstream of Ironbridge, alluvium is not well developed in the area. A few small areas of peat are known (Figure 51), of which those north of Wappenshall [664 148, 661 148] and at Donnington army depot [697 147] form the southern limit of the Weald Moors (Whitehead et al., 1928, p.200). The alluvium of the district is mostly silty sandy clay, composed of local material derived largely from older drift deposits.

The strip of alluvium [723 136] 400 m long near Muxtonbridge Farm is a soft bright red silty clay derived from the local Keele Beds. Alluvium and peat mapped at Hollinswood [704 091] has been largely removed during land reclamation, as has alluvium near Telford town centre [6984 0871]. Where the Nedge–Stafford Park sewer crosses the Nedge Brook [7123 0788] the alluvium is 3 m thick, consisting of grey peaty clay with gastropod shells and beds of peat. In a tributary of the Nedge Brook, a borehole [7100 0741] penetrated 0.9 m of peat at the surface. Another borehole [7104 0560] in the alluvium along the Mad Brook proved 1.7 m of stiff silty dark grey clay, overlying 2.5 m (not bottomed) of pale brown and grey firm sandy clay with layers of peat.

Radiocarbon data from the Tweedale Sewer [7084 0444] have already been published (Welin et al., 1972,

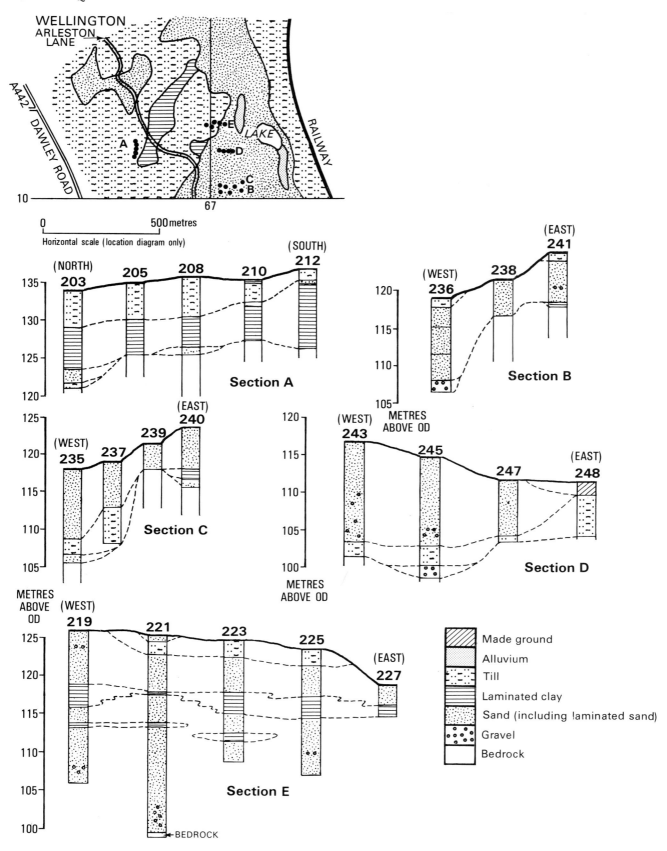

Figure 50 Borehole sections through the drift at the Ketley Interchange (M54 motorway), revealing upper and lower tills separated by a complex of sands and laminated clays.

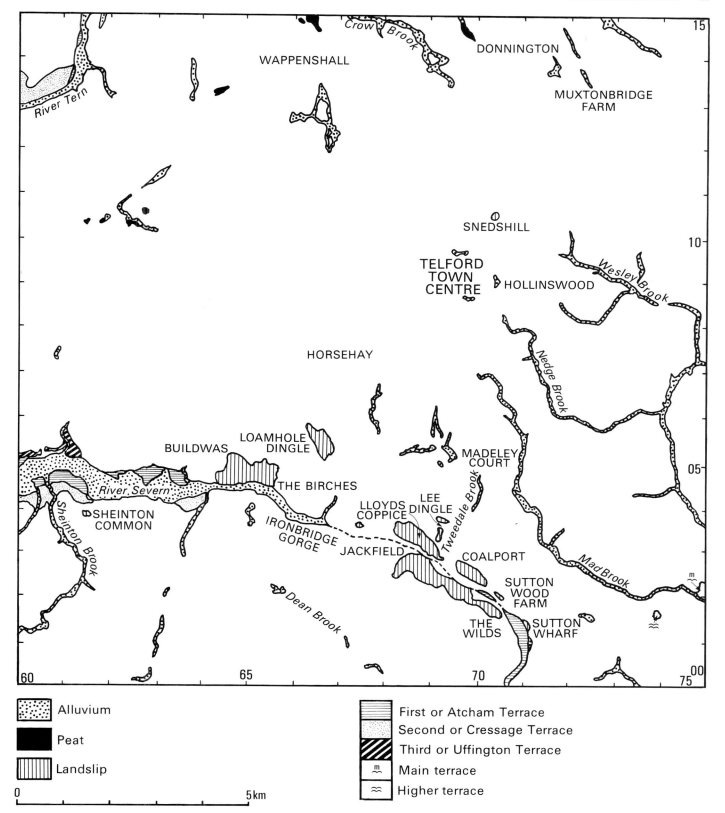

Figure 51 River terraces; alluvium and peat; and landslips.

p.333) and are given above. Near Madeley Court [6949 0511], a sample of wood dated at 720 ± 100 years BP was obtained from 1.3 m below the top of a bed of soft grey alluvial clay 2 m thick.

LANDSLIPS

Landslips are common along the banks of the Severn, and reflect the immature nature of this recent valley; they are, however, very variable in their nature. The large area of slipped Wenlock Shale adjacent to Buildwas (Figure 51) appears from its subdued form to be a relatively old slip, and apart from reactivation of its south-western and south-eastern extremities, it has not moved in historic times (Gostelow et al., 1991). The slipped mass is at least 32 m thick and is underlain by up to 45 cm of soft, pebbly bentonitic clay. Bentonites occur as thin layers at many horizons within the Wenlock Shale and render this formation particularly liable to slipping. Up to 200 m north of the River Severn, the slip was found to have overridden the gravel which underlies the alluvium of the river at a level of 31 m above OD. The south-western corner of the main slip, immediately north of Buildwas Bridge, is apparently still active, as the bridge itself and nearby buildings show signs of movement. At the south-eastern end of the main slip, a catastrophic slide occured in May 1773 at the Birches [654 046]. From a contemporary plan held by the Ironbridge Museum Trust, this appears to be a translational failure: the Wenlock Shale dips at about 15° to the south-east and a large mass of it has slid down-dip. The turnpike road was displaced, a bridge destroyed, and chasms up to 11 m deep appeared behind the slip; the River Severn was blocked and cut a new course around the toe of the slip.

Less is known about the slip in Loamhole Dingle [Figure 51; 666 055] except that again the Wenlock Shale has moved down-dip; this slip is currently active and causes problems with the Coalbrookdale–Horsehay road. The road across Sheinton Common [615 038] is similarly affected by active slipping of the Shineton Shales.

Shallow-seated downhill movement in the surface layers of made ground and weathered Coal Measures has affected the village of Ironbridge over a long period, resulting in deformation and cracking of buildings on the steep slopes above the Severn and of the Iron Bridge itself. The first recorded catastrophic failure occurred in 1969, when fill material forming the flat playground behind a school [6745 0351] became waterlogged and slipped; this loaded the weathered Coal Measures on the steep slope below and caused a rotational slip which extended down to the Ironbridge–Madeley road. A programme of drilling and testing by BGS outlined the area of actual or potential slipping. The instability below the school is caused by water draining out of the Big Flint Rock along the axis of a syncline close to the school, softening the argillaceous beds of the Lower Coal Measures. The effect was probably exacerbated by the extent of old workings in these measures and the lack of mains drainage in Ironbridge.

Farther downstream, at Lloyds Coppice (Figure 51), a large area of the Coalport Formation is actively moving as a series of rotational slips and surface slides. Crags of Thick Rock sandstone have moved down from their outcrop near the top of the hill, bringing with them the overlying thick till. The Coalport Formation is particularly susceptible to degradation in this area as it includes more silty strata and less sandstone than elsewhere. The Lees Farm boreholes revealed only 10.4 m of Thick Rock and 5.0 m of Sulphur Rock; the former drains freely into the Tweedale Brook, but the latter does not come to crop to the east and hence drains water at the foot of the Coppice and causes continued slipping. Although the slipping is thus most active lower on the slopes, it does not appear to extend down to river level.

Areas of slip occur on either side of Lee Dingle; both have clear back scarps but their lower limits are not easily defined. The southern area, and the western part of the northern area, comprise a series of shallow slip structures extending through the drift and the weathered zone of the Coalport Formation. The eastern part of the northern slip apparently represents one or two larger rotational slips. Instability in this area is caused by a combination of factors: the steep sides of the hill, the softness and low permeability of the drift deposits, and the argillaceous nature of the Coalport Formation. Waterlogging and easy weakening of the strata are the result.

On the north side of the Severn at Coalport (Figure 51) a further large area of slipping similarly comprises a series of shallow structures. The slipping is wholly contained within argillaceous Coalport Formation above the Top Rock, although it has also brought down large masses of Brookside Rock (Keele Beds); a smaller area of slipping below Sutton Wood Farm [705 020] is in an identical situation, and similar slipping has occurred in Coalport mudstones between the Top Rock and Priorslee Rock at a low level in the gorge beyond Sutton Wharf [711 014].

In the Coalport Formation outcrop south of the Severn, an area of active translational and rotational slipping stretches from Jackfield to The Wilds (Figure 51), and includes the famous Jackfield slip described by Henkel and Skempton (1954) and Skempton (1964). This slip was clearly not caused primarily by the dip of the strata, which is to the south-east, or by underground workings. It was a translational shear with its base wholly within the weathered zone (at a depth of 5.2 m) and parallel to the slope of the hill. The first sign of movement came with a broken water main in 1950, and the major movement occurred in the winter of 1951/52; a sheet of material 183 m long moved through 18 m at its centre but only 9 m at the river bank, causing bulging and cracking of the surface, with damage to houses, railway and mains services. By April 1953 the length and width of the slide had increased to 213 m and 200 m; the horizontal movement was 24 m at the centre and 14 m at the river bank. The slide had extended uphill by means of minor rotational slips, and the River Severn had been narrowed from 38 m to 24 m.

Away from the River Severn little landslipping is evident, but active shallow-seated movements were noted at Snedshill, on the steep slopes west of the reservoir [701 105]; again the movement has effected the weathered zone in an area steepened by Pleistocene erosion; in this case the bedrock material is mudstone of the Hadley Formation.

REFERENCES

Most of the references listed below are held in the Library of the British Geological Survey at Keyworth, Nottingham. Copies of the references can be purchased subject to the current copyright legislation.

ARBER, E A N. 1914. On the fossil floras of the Wyre Forest, with special reference to the geology of the coalfield and its relationships to the neighbouring Coal Measure areas. *Philosophical Transactions of the Royal Society of London*, Series B, Vol. 204, 363–445.

— 1916. On the fossil floras of the Coal Measures of South Staffordshire. *Philosophical Transactions of the Royal Society of London*, Series B, Vol. 208, 127–155.

— 1917. The structure of the South Staffordshire Coalfield, with special reference to the concealed areas and the neighbouring fields. *Transactions of the Institute of Mining Engineers*, Vol. 52, 35–70.

AUDLEY-CHARLES, M G. 1970. Triassic palaeogeography of the British Isles. *Quarterly Journal of the Geological Society of London*, Vol. 126, 49–89.

BAGNOLD, R A. 1941. *The physics of blown sand and desert dunes.* (London: Methuen.)

BAILEY, E B. 1926. Subterranean penetration by a desert climate. *Geological Magazine*, Vol. 58, 276–280.

BARROW, G. 1913. On the *Spirorbis* limestone of North Warwickshire. *Report of the British Association, Birmingham*, 472–473. Also: *Geological Magazine*, Decade 5, Vol. 10, 463–465.

BASSETT, M G, COCKS, L R M, HOLLAND, C H, RICKARDS, R B, and WARREN, P T. 1975. The type Wenlock Series. *Report of the Institute of Geological Sciences*, No. 75/13.

BESLY, B M. 1988. Palaeogeographic implications of late Westphalian to early Permian red-beds, Central England. 200–221 in *Sedimentation in a synorogenic basin complex*. BESLY, B M, and KELLING, G (editors). (Glasgow and London: Blackie.)

BOLTON, H. 1921. A new species of blattoid (*Archimylacris*) from the Keele Group (Radstockian) of Shropshire. *Quarterly Journal of the Geological Society of London*, Vol. 77, 23–29.

BROOKS, M. 1966. A study of density variations in New Red Sandstones from the English Midlands. *Geological Magazine*, Vol. 103, No. 1, 61–69.

CALEF, C E, and HANCOCK, N J. 1974. Wenlock and Ludlow marine communities in Wales and the Welsh borderland. *Palaeontology*, Vol. 17, 779–810.

CALLAWAY, C. 1884. On a new metamorphic area in Shropshire. *Geological Magazine*, Vol. 21, 362–366.

CAMPBELL-SMITH, W. 1963. Descriptions of the igneous rocks represented among pebbles from the Bunter Pebble-Beds of the Midlands of England. *Bulletin of the British Museum, Mineralogy*, Vol. 2, 1–17.

CANTRILL, T C. 1895. *A contribution to the geology of the Wyre Forest Coalfield.* (Kidderminster: T Mark.)

— 1909. *Spirorbis*-limestones in the 'Permian' of the South Staffordshire and Warwickshire Coalfields. *Geological Magazine*, Decade 5, Vol.6, 447–454.

CLARKE, W J. 1901. The unconformity in the Coal Measures of the Shropshire Coalfield. *Quarterly Journal of the Geological Society of London*, Vol. 57, 86–95.

COBBOLD, E S. 1913. Two species of *Paradoxides* from Neve's Castle (Shropshire). *Quarterly Journal of the Geological Society of London*, Vol. 69, 45–50.

— 1921. The Cambrian horizons of Comley (Shropshire) and their Brachiopoda, Pteropoda, Gasteropoda, etc. *Quarterly Journal of the Geological Society of London*, Vol. 76, 325–386.

— and POCOCK, R W. 1934. The Cambrian area of Rushton (Shropshire). *Philosophical Transactions of the Royal Society of London*, Series B, Vol. 223, 305–409.

COCKIN, G M. 1906. On the occurrence of limestone of the Lower Carboniferous Series in the Cannock Chase portion of the South Staffordshire Coalfield. *Quarterly Journal of the Geological Society of London*, Vol. 62, 523–529. Also *Geological Magazine*, Decade 5, Vol. 8, 237.

COCKS, L R M, WOODCOCK, N H, RICKARDS, R B, TEMPLE, J T, and LANE, P D. 1984. The Llandovery Series of the type area. *Bulletin of the British Museum of Natural History, (Geology)*, Vol. 38, 131–182.

— and RICKARDS, R B. 1969. Five boreholes in Shropshire and the relationships of shelly and graptolitic facies in the Lower Silurian. *Quarterly Journal of the Geological Society of London*, Vol. 124, 213–238.

— and WALTON, G. 1968. A large temporary exposure in the Lower Silurian of Shropshire. *Geological Magazine*, Vol. 105, 390–397.

COOK, A H, and THIRLAWAY, H I S. 1955. The geological results of measurements of gravity in the Welsh Borders. *Quarterly Journal of the Geological Society of London*, Vol. 111, 47–70.

COOPE, G R, SHOTTON, F W, and STRACHAN, I. 1961. A late Pleistocene fauna and flora from Upton Warren, Worcestershire. *Philosophical Transactions of the Royal Society of London*, Vol. B244, 379–421.

COPE, J C W, and GIBBONS, W. 1987. New evidence for the relative age of the Ercall Granophyre and its bearing on the Precambrian–Cambrian boundary in southern Britain. *Geological Journal*, Vol. 22, 53–60.

COWIE, J W, RUSHTON, A W A, and STUBBLEFIELD, C J. 1972. A correlation of Cambrian rocks in the British Isles. *Special Report of the Geological Society of London*, No. 2.

COX, L R. 1926. *Anthracopupa britannica* sp. nov., a land gastropod from the red beds of the uppermost Coal Measures of Northern Worcestershire. *Quarterly Journal of the Geological Society of London*, Vol. 82, 401–410.

DIX, E, and TRUEMAN, A E. 1931. Some non-marine lamellibranchs from the upper part of the Coal Measures. *Quarterly Journal of the Geological Society of London*, Vol. 87, 180–211.

DUNHAM, K C. 1953. Red colouration in desert formations of Permian and Triassic age in Britain. *Compte Rendu, 19th Session, International Geological Congress, Algiers*, Vol. 7, 25–32.

EARP, J R. 1961. Exploratory boreholes in the North Staffordshire Coalfield. *Bulletin of the Geological Survey of Great Britain*, No. 17, 153–190.

ETHERIDGE, R. 1880. A contribution to the study of the British Carboniferous tubicolar annelida. *Geological Magazine*, Decade 2, Vol. 7, 109–115, 171–174, 215–222, 258–266, 304–307, 362–369.

FITCH, F J, MILLER, J A, and THOMPSON, D B. 1966. The palaeogeographic significance of isotopic age determination on detrital micas from the Triassic of the Stockport–Macclesfield district, Central England. *Palaeogeography, Palaeoclimatology, Palaeoecology*, Vol. 2, 281–312.

FLEET, W F. 1923. Notes on the Triassic sands near Birmingham with special reference to their heavy detrital minerals. *Proceedings of the Geologists' Association*, Vol. 34, 114–119.

— 1925. The chief detrital minerals in the rocks of the English Midlands. *Geological Magazine*, Vol. 62, 98–128.

— 1927. The heavy minerals of the Keele, Enville, 'Permian', and Lower Triassic rocks of the Midlands, and the correlation of these strata. *Proceedings of the Geologists' Association*, Vol. 38, 1–48.

— 1929. Petrography of the Upper Bunter Sandstone of the Midlands. *Proceedings of the Birmingham Natural History and Philosophical Society*, Vol. 15, 213–217.

FORSTER, A. 1972. Density, porosity, sonic velocity and magnetic susceptibility determinations on selected rock types from the Telford area, Shropshire. *Institute of Geological Sciences, Geophysics Laboratory Report*, No. 17.

FORTEY, R A, and OWENS, R M. 1991. A trilobite fauna from the highest Shineton Shales in Shropshire, and correlation of the latest Tremadoc. *Geological Magazine*, Vol. 128, 437–464.

GEORGE, T N, JOHNSON, G A L, MITCHELL, M, PRENTICE, J E, RAMSBOTTOM, W H C, SEVASTOPULO, G D, and WILSON, R B. 1976. A correlation of Dinantian rocks in the British Isles. *Special Report of the Geological Society of London*, No. 7.

GIBSON, W. 1901. On the character of the Upper Coal Measures of North Staffordshire, Denbighshire, South Staffordshire, and Nottinghamshire, and their relation to the Productive Series. *Quarterly Journal of the Geological Society of London*, Vol. 57, 251–266.

GOSTELOW, T P, HAMBLIN, R J O, HARRIS, D I, and HIGHT, D W. 1991. The influence of Late and Post Glacial slope development on the engineering geology of Wenlock Shale, near Ironbridge, Salop. 349–359 *in* Quaternary engineering geology. FORSTER, A, CULSHAW, M G, CRIPPS, J C, LITTLE, J A, and MOON, C F (editors). *Special Publication of the Geological Society Engineering Geology*, No. 7.

GREIG, D C, WRIGHT, J E, HAINS, B A, and MITCHELL, G H. 1968. Geology of the country around Church Stretton, Craven Arms, Wenlock Edge and Brown Clee. *Memoir of the Geological Survey of Great Britain*.

GRESLEY, W S. 1886. On the occurrence of fossiliferous haematite nodules in the Permian breccias in Leicestershire, together with some account of their economic value, &c. *Midland Naturalist*, Vol. 9, 1–8, 33–37, 64–69, 92–99.

GUION, P D, and FIELDING, C R. 1988. Westphalian A and B sedimentation in the Pennine Basin, U.K. 153–177 in

Sedimentation in a synorogenic basin complex. BESLY, B M, and KELLING, G (editors). (Glasgow and London: Blackie.)

HAMBLIN, R J O. 1986. The Pleistocene sequence of the Telford district. *Proceedings of the Geologists' Association*, Vol. 97, No. 4, 365–377.

— BROWN, I J, and ELLWOOD, J. 1989. Mineral resources of the Coalbrookdale Coalfield — basis of the Industrial Revolution. *Mercian Geologist*, Vol. 12, 9–27.

HENKEL, D J, and SKEMPTON, A W. 1954. A landslide at Jackfield, Shropshire, in a heavily over-consolidated clay. *Geotechnique*, Vol. 5, No. 2, 131–137.

HOARE, R H. 1959. Red beds in the Coal Measures of the West Midlands. *Transactions of the Institution of Mining Engineers*, Vol. 119,185–198.

HOLLAND, C H, LAWSON, J D, and WALMSLEY, V G. 1963. The Silurian rocks of the Ludlow District, Shropshire. *Bulletin of the British Museum of Natural History*, Geology, Vol. 8, 93–171.

HOLLIS, J M, and REED, A H. 1981. The Pleistocene deposits of the Southern Worfe Catchment. *Proceedings of the Geologists' Association*, Vol. 92, 59–74.

HORTON, A, and HAINS, B A. 1972. Development of porcellanous rocks and reddening of the Coal Measures in the South Derbyshire, Leicestershire and Warwickshire coalfields. *Bulletin of the Geological Survey of Great Britain*, No. 42, 51–77.

HULL, E. 1860. On the new subdivisions of the Triassic rocks of the Central Counties. *Transactions of the Manchester Geological Society*, Vol. 2, 22–34.

— 1869. On the evidence of a ridge of Lower Carboniferous rocks crossing the plain of Cheshire beneath the Trias, and forming the boundary between the Permian rocks of the Lancashire type on the north, and those of the Salopian type on the south. *Quarterly Journal of the Geological Society of London*, Vol. 25, 171–184.

INSTITUTE OF GEOLOGICAL SCIENCES. 1978. Telford. Sheet SJ60, Solid and Drift. 1:25 000 series, classical areas of British geology. (Southampton: Ordnance Survey for Institute of Geological Sciences.)

JONES, D. 1871. On the correlation of the Carboniferous deposits of Cornbrook, Brown Clee, Harcott and Coalbrookdale. *Geological Magazine*, Vol. 8, 363–371.

— 1872. The correlation of the Coalbrookdale and South Staffordshire coalfields: a paper read before the Institute 5-8-72. *Transactions of the South Midland Institute of Mining, Mechanical and Civil Engineers*, Vol. 3, pamphlet, p.14.

— 1894, 1895. The structure of the Forest-of-Wyre Coalfield. *Transactions of the Federated Institution of Mining Engineers*, Vol. 7, 287–300, 577–580; also Vol. 8, 356–360.

JUKES, J B. 1859. South Staffordshire Coalfield. 2nd edition. *Memoir of the Geological Survey of Great Britain*.

KING, W W. 1899. The Permian conglomerates of the Lower Severn Basin. *Quarterly Journal of the Geological Society of London*, Vol. 55, 97–128, also *Geological Magazine*, Decade 4, Vol. 6, 48.

— 1921. The plexography of South Staffordshire in Avonian times. *Transactions of the Institution of Mining Engineers*, Vol. 61, 151–168.

— and LEWIS, W J. 1913. The basal Carboniferous beds at Lye, in South Staffordshire. *Geological Magazine*, Decade 5, Vol. 10, 521–522.

LAMONT, A. 1946. Fossils from Middle Bunter pebbles collected around Birmingham. *Geological Magazine*, Vol. 83, 39–44.

LAWSON, J D. 1975. Ludlow benthonic assemblages. *Palaeontology*, Vol. 18, 509–525.

MITCHELL, G F, PENNY, L F, SHOTTON, F W, and WEST, R G. 1973. A correlation of Quaternary deposits in the British Isles. *Special Report of the Geological Society of London*, No. 4.

MITCHELL, G H, POCOCK, R W, and TAYLOR, J H. 1961. The geology of the country around Droitwich, Abberley and Kidderminster. *Memoir of the Geological Survey of Great Britain.*

— STUBBLEFIELD, C J, and CROOKALL, R. 1945. The geology of the northern part of the South Staffordshire Coalfield (Cannock Chase region) in New Series One-Inch Sheets 140, 153, 154. *Memoir of the Geological Survey, Wartime Pamphlet*, No. 43.

MITCHELL, M, and REYNOLDS, M J. 1981. Early Tournaisian rocks at Lilleshall, Shropshire. *Geological Magazine*, Vol. 118, No. 6, 699-702.

MOORE, L R, and TRUEMAN, A E. 1939. The structure of the Bristol and Somerset coalfields. *Proceedings of the Geologists' Association*, Vol. 50, 46–67.

MURCHISON, R I. 1832. On the sedimentary rocks which occupy the western parts of Shropshire and Herefordshire, and are prolonged from north-east to south-west, through Radnor, Brecknock, and Caermarthonshires, with descriptions of the accompanying rocks of intrusive or igneous characters. *Proceedings of the Geological Society of London*, Vol. 1, 470–474.

— 1834. On the structure and classification of the Transition rocks of Shropshire, Herefordshire and part of Wales, and on the lines of disturbance which have affected that series of deposits, including the Valley of Elevation of Woolhope. *Proceedings of the Geological Society of London*, Vol. 2, 13–18.

— 1834. A general view of the New Red Sandstone Series, in the counties of Salop, Stafford, Worcester and Gloucester. *Proceedings of the Geological Society of London*, Vol. 2, No. 38, 115–118.

— 1835. On the Silurian system of rocks. *London, Edinburgh and Dublin Philosophical Magazine*, Vol. 7, No. 3, 46–52.

— 1839. *The Silurian System, founded on geological researches in the counties of Salop, Hereford, Radnor, Montgomeryshire, Carmarthen, Brecon, Pembroke, Monmouth, Gloucester, Worcester and Stafford; with descriptions of the coalfields and overlying formations.* (London: John Murray.)

— 1854. (1st edition); 1867 (3rd edition). *Siluria* (see below).

— 1872. (4th edition) *Siluria, a history of the oldest rocks in the British Isles and other countries; with sketches of the origin and distribution of native gold, the general succession of geological formations, and the changes of the earth's surface.* (London: John Murray.)

MYERS, J. 1954. On the occurrence of *Anthraconauta tenuis* (Davies and Trueman) in North Staffs. *Geological Magazine*, Vol. 91, 171–173.

MYKURA, W. 1951. The age of the Malvern folding. *Geological Magazine*, Vol. 88, 386–392.

PARASNIS, D S. 1952. A study of rock densities in the English Midlands. *Monthly notices of the Royal Astronomical Society.*

PATCHETT, P J, GALE, N H, GOODWIN, R, and HUMM, M J. 1980. Rb-Sr whole-rock isochron ages of late Precambrian to Cambrian igneous rocks from southern Britain. *Journal of the Geological Society of London*, Vol. 137, 649–656.

POCOCK, R W, WHITEHEAD, T H, WEDD, C B, and ROBERTSON, T. 1938. Shrewsbury district including the Hanwood Coalfield. *Memoir of the Geological Survey of Great Britain.*

— and WRAY, D A. 1925. The geology of the country around Wem. Explanation of Sheet 138. *Memoir of the Geological Survey of Great Britain.*

POOLE, E G. 1970. Trial boreholes in Coal Measures at Dudley, Worcestershire. *Bulletin of the Geological Survey of Great Britain*, No. 33, 1–41.

— 1975. Correlation of the Upper Coal Measures of Central England and adjoining areas and their relationship to the Stephanian of the Continent. *Bulletin de la Société Belge de Géologie*, Vol. 84, No. 1, 57–66.

— and CALVER, M A. 1966. Trial boreholes on the site of a reservoir at Eymore Farm near Bewdley, Worcestershire. *Bulletin of the Geological Survey of Great Britain*, No. 24, 131–156.

— and WHITEMAN, A J. 1966. Geology of the country around Nantwich and Whitchurch. *Memoir of the Geological Survey of Great Britain.*

PRESTWICH, J. 1840. On the geology of Coalbrook Dale. *Transactions of the Geological Society of London*, Series 2, Vol. 5, 413–495.

PURTON, W. 1865. On the geology of Coalbrookdale. *Geological Magazine*, Vol. 2, 514–515.

RAMSAY, A C. 1855. On the occurrence of angular, sub-angular, polished and striated fragments and boulders in the Permian breccia of Shropshire, Worcestershire, etc.; and on the probable existence of glaciers and icebergs in the Permian epoch. *Quarterly Journal of the Geological Society of London*, Vol. 11, 185–205. Also: *Report of the British Association (Liverpool) for 1854*, 93–94.

RAMSBOTTOM, W H C, CALVER, M A, EAGAR, R M C, HODSON, F, HOLLIDAY, D W, STUBBLEFIELD, C J, and WILSON, R B. 1978. A correlation of Silesian Rocks in the British Isles. *Special Report of the Geological Society of London*, No. 10.

— and MITCHELL, M. 1980. The recognition and division of the Tournaisian Series in Britain. *Journal of the Geological Society of London*, Vol. 137, 61–63.

RANDALL, J. 1873. On the northerly extension of the Old Red Sandstone to Linley, and other geological features of the valley of Linley Brook. *Geological Magazine*, Vol. 10, 494–500.

RASTALL, R H. 1925. On the tectonics of the Southern Midlands. *Geological Magazine*, Vol. 62, 193–222.

RAW, F. 1936. Mesonacidae of Comley in Shropshire, with a discussion of classification within the family. *Quarterly Journal of the Geological Society of London*, Vol. 92, 236–293.

ROYAL COMMISSION ON COAL SUPPLIES. 1905. *Digest of evidence given before the Royal Commission on Coal Supplies, volume 1.* (London: Chichester Press.)

RUSHTON, A W A, HAMBLIN, R J O, and Strong, G E. 1988. The Croft Borehole in the Lilleshall Inlier of North Shropshire. *Report of the British Geological Survey*, Vol. 19, No. 3.

SCOFFIN, T P. 1971. The conditions of growth of the Wenlock reefs of Shropshire (England). *Sedimentology*, Vol. 17, 173–219.

SCOTT, M. 1861. On the 'Symon Fault' in the Coalbrook-Dale Coalfield. *Quarterly Journal of the Geological Society of London*, Vol. 17, 457–467.

SELWOOD, E B, EDWARDS, R A, SIMPSON, S, CHESHER, J A, HAMBLIN, R J O, HENSON, M R, RIDDOLLS, B W, and WATERS, R A. 1984. Geology of the country around Newton Abbot. *Memoir of the British Geological Survey.*

SHAW, J. 1972. Sedimentation in the ice-contact environment, with examples from Shropshire, England. *Sedimentology*, Vol. 18, 23–62.

SHERGOLD, J H, and BASSETT, M G. 1970. Facies and faunas at the Wenlock/Ludlow boundary of Wenlock Edge, Shropshire. *Lethaia*, Vol. 3, 113–142.

SHERLOCK, R L. 1926. A correlation of the British Permo-Triassic rocks. Part 1: North England, Scotland, and Ireland. *Proceedings of the Geologists' Association*, Vol. 37, 1–72.

SHOTTON, F W. 1937. The lower Bunter sandstones of North Worcestershire and East Shropshire. *Geological Magazine*, Vol. 74, 534–553.

— 1956. Some aspects of the New Red desert in Britain. *Liverpool and Manchester Geological Journal*, Vol. 1 (5), 450–465.

— (editor). 1977. *The English Midlands*. Guidebook for excursion A2, International Union for Quaternary Research. (Norwich: Geo Abstracts Ltd.)

SKEMPTON, A W. 1964. Long term stability of clay slopes (Rankine lecture). *Geotechnique*, Vol. 14, No. 2, 77–102.

SMITH, D B, BRUNSTROM, R G W, MANNING, P I, SIMPSON, S, and SHOTTON, F W. 1974. A correlation of Permian rocks in the British Isles. *Special Report of the Geological Society of London*, No. 5.

SMITH, N J P, and RUSHTON, A W A. 1993. Cambrian and Ordovician stratigraphy related to structure and seismic profiles in the western part of the England Midlands. *Geological Magazine*, Vol. 130, 665–671.

SMITH, S. 1930. Valentian corals from Shropshire and Montgomeryshire, with a note on a new stromatoporoid. *Quarterly Journal of the Geological Society of London*, Vol. 86, 291–330.

SMITH, T. 1846. *The Miner's Guide*. (Tipton: T Smith.).

SMYTH, W W. 1862. The iron-ores of Great Britain, Part IV. The iron-ores of the Shropshire and North Staffordshire Coalfields. *Memoir of the Geological Survey of Great Britain*.

STOBBS, J T. 1906. The value of fossil mollusca in Coal Measure stratigraphy. *Transactions of the Institution of Mining Engineers*, Vol. 30, 443–465; also discussion, Vol. 31, 485.

STONEHOUSE, T H. 1950. Recent provings of concealed extensions of the coalfield of Shropshire and South Staffordshire. *Transactions of the Institution of Mining Engineers*, Vol. 110, 289–300.

STUBBLEFIELD, C J. 1930. A new Upper Cambrian section in South Shropshire. *Summary of Progress of the Geological Survey of Great Britain for 1929*, part 2, 54–62.

— and BULMAN, O M B. 1927. The Shineton Shales of the Wrekin District. *Quarterly Journal of the Geological Society of London*, Vol. 83, 96–146.

— and TROTTER, F M. 1957. Divisions of the Coal Measures on Geological Survey maps of England and Wales. *Bulletin of the Geological Survey of Great Britain*, Vol. 13, 1–5.

TAYLOR, B J, PRICE, R H, and TROTTER, F M. 1963. The geology of the country around Knutsford and Stockport. *Memoir of the Geological Survey of Great Britain*.

THORPE, R S, BECKINSALE, R D, PATCHETT, P J, PIPER, A, DAVIES, G R, and EVANS, J A. 1984. Crustal growth and late Precambrian-early Palaeozoic plate tectonic evolution of England and Wales. *Journal of the Geological Society of London*, Vol. 141, 521–536.

TOWNSON, R. 1799. *Tracts and observations in natural history and physiology*. (London: R Townson.)

TROTTER, F M. 1939. Reddened Carboniferous beds in the Carlisle Basin and Edenside. *Geological Magazine*, Vol. 76, 408–416.

— 1953. Reddened beds of Carboniferous age in north-west England and their origin. *Proceedings of the Yorkshire Geological Society*, Vol. 29, 1–20.

— 1954. Reddened beds in the Coal Measures of South Lancashire. *Bulletin of the Geological Survey of Great Britain*, No. 5, 61–80.

TRUEMAN, A E. 1940. The lamellibranch zones of the South Staffordshire Coalfield. *Geological Magazine*, Vol. 77, 28–41.

— 1946. Stratigraphical problems in the Coal Measures of Europe and North America. *Quarterly Journal of the Geological Society of London*, Vol. 102, xlix–xciii.

— 1948 (for 1947). Stratigraphical problems in the coalfields of Great Britain. *Quarterly Journal of the Geological Society of London*, Vol. 103, lxv–civ.

— and WEIR, J. 1951. British Carboniferous non-marine lamellibranchia. *Memoir of the Palaeontographical Society*, Vol. 105, No. V, 101–152.

TUCKER, R D, and PHARAOH, T C. 1991. U-Pb zircon ages for Late Precambrian igneous rocks in southern Britain. *Journal of the Geological Society of London*, Vol. 148, 435–443.

WAGNER, R H. 1983. A lower Rotliegend flora from Ayrshire. *Scottish Journal of Geology*, Vol. 19, 135–155.

WARRINGTON, G, AUDLEY-CHARLES, M G, ELLIOTT, R E, EVANS, W B, IVIMEY-COOK, H C, KENT, P, ROBINSON, P L, SHOTTON, F W, and TAYLOR, F M. 1980. A correlation of Triassic rocks in the British Isles. *Special Report of the Geological Society of London*, No. 13.

WATKINS, R. 1979. Benthic community organisation in the Ludlow Series of the Welsh Borderland. *Bulletin of the British Museum of Natural History, Geology*, Vol. 31, 175–280.

WATTS, W W. 1925. The geology of South Shropshire, and excursion to South Shropshire. *Proceedings of the Geologists' Association*, Vol. 36, 321–405.

WELIN, E, ENGSTRAND, L, and VACZY, S. 1972. Institute of Geological Sciences radiocarbon dates III. *Radiocarbon*, Vol. 14, No. 2, 331–335.

— 1973. Institute of Geological Sciences radiocarbon dates IV. *Radiocarbon*, Vol. 15, No. 2, 299–302.

WHITE, D E. 1974. The boundary between the Wenlock and Ludlow Series. *Geological Magazine*, Vol. 111, 448–449.

— 1981. The base of the Ludlow Series in the graptolitic facies. *Geological Magazine*, Vol. 118, No. 5, 566.

— and COPPACK, B C. 1977. A new section showing the junction between the Ludlow and Downton Series in the Much Wenlock area, Shropshire. *Bulletin of the Geological Survey of Great Britain*, No. 62, 25–32.

WHITE, D E, and LAWSON, J D. 1989. The Přídolí Series in the Welsh Borderland and south-central Wales. 131–140 in *A global standard for the Silurian system*. HOLLAND, C H, and BASSETT, M G (editors). (Cardiff: National Museum of Wales, Geological Series No. 9.)

WHITEHEAD, T H. 1922. The subdivisions of the red rocks formerly classed as Permian in South Staffordshire and the neighbouring counties. *Summary of Progress of the Geological Survey of Great Britain for 1921*. Appendix VII, 169–173.

— ROBERTSON, T, POCOCK, R W, and DIXON, E E L. 1928. The country between Wolverhampton and Oakengates. *Memoir of the Geological Survey of Great Britain*.

WHITTARD, W F. 1928. The stratigraphy of the Valentian rocks of Shropshire. The main outcrop. *Quarterly Journal of the Geological Society of London*, Vol. 83, 737–759.

— 1952. A geology of South Shropshire. *Proceedings of the Geologists' Association*, Vol. 63, 143–197.

WILLIAMS, D H. 1846. Sections illustrative of the Coal Measures in the vicinity of Coalbrook-Dale, Shropshire. Vertical sections, Sheet No. 23. *Geological Survey of Great Britain.*

WILLS, L J. 1924. The development of the Severn Valley in the neighbourhood of Ironbridge and Bridgnorth. *Quarterly Journal of the Geological Society of London*, Vol. 80, 274–314.

— 1929. *The physiographical evolution of Britain.* (London: Edward Arnold.)

— 1935. An outline of the palaeogeography of the Birmingham country. *Proceedings of the Geologists' Association*, Vol. 46, 211–246.

— 1948. *The palaeogeography of the Midlands.* (Liverpool: Liverpool University Press.)

— 1950. *Geology of the Birmingham area.* British Association for the Advancement of Science Handbook, 15–36.

— 1956. *Concealed coalfields.* (London: Blackie & Son.)

— 1970. The Triassic succession in the Central Midlands in its regional setting. *Quarterly Journal of the Geological Society of London*, Vol. 126, 225–283.

— 1973. A palaeogeological map of the Palaeozoic floor below the Upper Permian and Mesozoic formations in England and Wales, with inferred and speculative reconstructions of the Palaeozoic outcrops in adjacent areas as in Permo-Trias times. *Memoir of the Geological Society of London*, No. 7.

WILSON, A A, REES, J G, CROFTS, R G, HOWARD, A S, BUCHANAN, J G, and WAINE, P J. 1992. Stoke-on-Trent: a geological background for planning and development. *British Geological Survey Technical Report* WA/91/01.

WILSON, G V. 1926. The concealed coalfield of Yorkshire and Nottinghamshire (2nd edition). *Memoir of the Geological Survey of England and Wales.*

ZIEGLER, A M, COCKS, L R M, and MCKERROW, W S. 1968. The Llandovery transgression of the Welsh Borderland. *Palaeontology*, Vol. 11, 736–782.

— MCKERROW, W S, BURNE, R V, and BAKER, P E. 1969. Correlation and environmental setting of the Skomer Volcanic Group, Pembrokeshire. *Proceedings of the Geologists' Association*, Vol. 80, 409–439.

APPENDIX 1

BGS boreholes

Six cored boreholes were drilled to elucidate, in conjunction with geophysical surveys, the structure of the Bridgnorth Sandstone, Keele Beds and Precambrian rocks north of the Boundary Fault. In all cases boreholes were cored from as near surface as possible. Three of the holes were terminated on entering Uriconian rocks, but the Hoo Hall Borehole failed to penetrate the Keele Beds; the Rushton and Wrekin Buildings boreholes were continued well into the Precambrian rocks. In addition, the Coed-yr-Allt Beds and Ruabon Marl were proved at Wrekin Buildings.

Full details are available in the BGS archives, held by the National Geosciences Data Centre, Keyworth. Abbreviated summaries are given below.

1 Hoo Hall Borehole (1970), SJ61SE/23

Site: 720 m SE of St Lawrence's Church, Preston upon the Weald Moors.
National Grid reference [6231 0871], surface level 63 m above OD

	Depth m
Glacial deposits (open hole to 1.98 m)	to 11.28
Bridgnorth Sandstone	to 45.79
Keele Beds	seen to 91.44

2 Kinley Farm Borehole (1971), SJ61SE/24

Site: 1100 m on bearing 237° from St Lawrence's Church, Preston upon the Weald Moors.
National Grid reference [6716 1478], surface level 56.4 m above OD

	Depth m
Glacial deposits (open hole to 3.20 m)	to 9.50
Keele Beds	to 39.19
Uriconian rocks	seen to 45.72

3 Leegomery House Farm Borehole (1971), SJ61SE/25

Site: 125 m on bearing 160° from Leegomery House Farm.
National Grid reference [6638 1268], surface level 76.0 m above OD

	Depth m
Glacial deposits (open hole)	to 17.50
Bridgnorth Sandstone (open hole to 21.79 m)	to 24.99
Keele Beds	to 118.74
Uriconian rocks	seen to 119.35

4 Lodge Farm (Trench) Borehole (1971), SJ61SE/26

Site: 190 m on bearing 055° from Trench (disused) Railway Station.
National Grid reference [6887 1297], surface level 73 m above OD

	Depth m
Glacial deposits and Bridgnorth Sandstone (open hole to 7.87 m)	to 71.83
Keele Beds	to 88.47
Uriconian rocks	seen to 91.44

5 Rushton Borehole (1973), SJ60NW/6

Site: 770 m on bearing 208° from Woodgreen Crossroads.
National Grid reference [6069 0822], surface level 123.8 m above OD

	Depth m
Rushton Schists (open hole to 3.05m)	seen to 152.45

6 Wrekin Buildings Borehole (1972), SJ60NW/7

Site: 780 m on bearing 320° from the Wrekin Summit.
National Grid reference [6231 0871], surface level 167.9 m above OD

	Depth m
Hillwash on Bridgnorth Sandstone (open hole to 4.90 m)	to 74.32
Keele Beds	to 120.10
Coed-yr-Allt Beds	to 138.15
Ruabon Marl	to 151.00
Granodiorite	seen to 196.52

APPENDIX 2

List of mine shafts, pits and collieries

Some 132 shafts, pits and collieries are listed here and shown in Figure 52. A further 95 sites for which there is only a little information are not listed, as are many hundreds of mine shafts for which BGS has no information other than a reference to their existence.

Notes

(1) BGS registered number — this consists of the 1:10 000 quarter sheet number followed by an accession number.

(2) Sources of information:
Unprefixed numbers and those prefixed WM or R refer to Mine Abandonment Plans held by British Coal.
Numbers prefixed P refer to a page in Prestwich (1840).
Numbers prefixed S refer to a page in Scott (1861).

'W' indicates Geological Survey Vertical Section Sheet 23 (Williams, 1846).
No entry indicates details obtained from some other source.

(3) Strata recorded are abbreviated as follows:
D — Drift
W — Wildmoor Sandstone
S — Kidderminster Conglomerate
B — Bridgnorth Sandstone
E — Enville Beds
K — Keele Beds
C — Coalport Formation or Coed-yr-Allt Beds
H — Hadley Formation or Ruabon Marl
P — Lower and Middle Coal Measures
U — Strata older than Lower and Middle Coal Measures

Name	National Grid reference	BGS registered number (1)	Source of information (2)	Strata (3)
Amies Field Pit	c.6915 0195	SJ60SE/372	P478	CHP
Arleston Pit	67017 09797	SJ60NE/640	14405, 14406	P
Ash Tree Pits	6771 0558	SJ60NE/1378–1379	8222	H
Barker's Yard Pits	688 066	SJ60NE/501–503	W	CHP
Barnyard Pits	7201 1271	SJ71SW/360–361	9695	P
Belle Vue Colliery	6960 1126	SJ61SE/708–709	7359,8936,13505	P
Belle Vue No. 3 Shaft	6951 1141	SJ61SE/710	13505	P
Benthall Level	668 024	SJ60SE/186–190	9659	P
Benthall Potteries Pits 1–9	665 011	SJ60SE/300–308	7494	DP
Benthall Potteries (unnamed shaft)	66250 02168	SJ60SE/181		P
Best Fireclay Mine	6772 0765	SJ60NE/1050	6236, WM128	P
Blists Hill Pits	6946 0348	SJ60SE/73–74	8461	CHP
Boundary Pit	69708 12060	SJ61SE/538	4286	P
Brandlee Colliery No. 1 Shaft	67720 07653	SJ60NE/1050	6236, WM128	P
Brandlee Colliery No. 1 + 2(nth)	678 077	SJ60NE/1132–1133	6235	P
Brandlee Colliery No. 3	67811 07642	SJ60NE/1052	WM128	P
Brick Kiln Leasowe Pit	6841 0423	SJ60SE/2–5		P
Brickyard Pit	71156 11598	SJ71SW/564	5367	P
Bridge House Pit	69373 10533	SJ61SE/771		P
Bridge Pit	688 112	SJ61SE/1007–1008	9578	P
Broseley Wood Green Pit	6756 0266	SJ60SE/415	7493	H
Buckatree Colliery	662 081	SJ60NE/778–786	7367	P
Bye Pit	6909 1194	SJ61SE/617	W	HP
Castle Green (trial pit)	c.674 045	Not registered	P,475	P
Castle Pits	688 063	SJ60NE/504–507	W	DCHP
Caughley	c.698 008	?SJ60SE/402–407	W	CHP
Charles Hay Pits	c.6816 0759	Not registered		P
Cliff Pits	681 094	SJ60NE/871–873	10384	P

Figure 52
Distribution of mine shafts, pits and collieries in the Telford district.

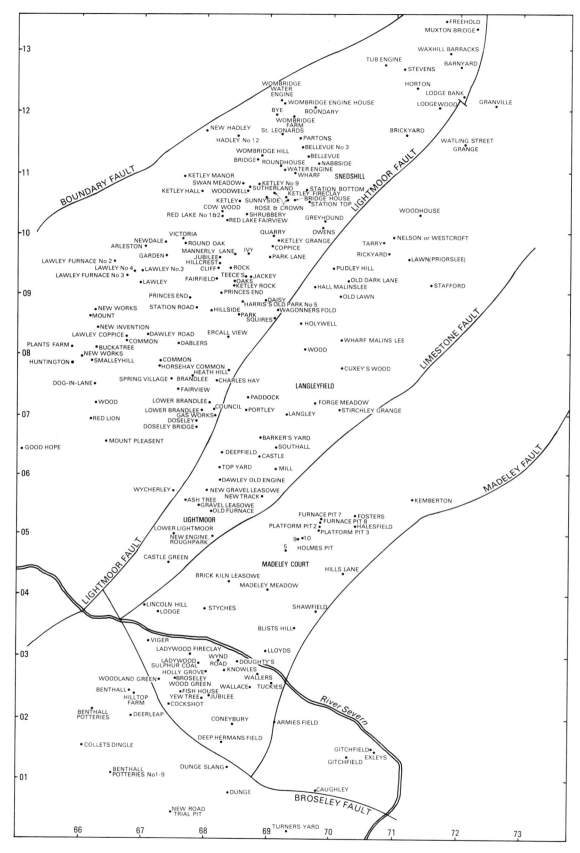

Name	National Grid reference	BGS registered number (1)	Source of information (2)	Strata (3)
Cockshot Pits	674 022	SJ60SE/222–225	W	CHP
Colley's Dingle	66105 01600	SJ60SE/336		P
Common Colliery	667 082	SJ60NE/803–814	WM12	P
Common Colliery	6727 0793	SJ60NE/1038	13224	P
Coneybury Pit	6848 0190	SJ60SE/351	3552	C
Coppice Pits	690 097	SJ60NE/330–331	9052	P
Coppice Pits	691 096	SJ60NE/332–333	4106	P
Council Colliery	6810 0711	SJ60NE/1142	8003	P
Cow Wood Pits (Red Lake Colliery)	682 103	SJ61SE/923–932	4835	P
Crow Hayes Shaft	7402 1568	SJ71NW/15	P479	KCPU
Cuxeys Wood Pits	701 078	SJ70NW/190–193	S,991	CHP
Dablers Pit (Dawley Colliery)	6754 0820	SJ60NE/1009	4069	P
Daisy Pit (Old Park No. 9)	6894 0890	SJ60NE/409	4107	P
Dawley Old Engine Shaft	?682 059	SJ60NE/531–535	3356	CHP
= Old Work in Dawley			P480, P482,	
= Dawley Parva/Dawley Pit			W	
Dawley Road Pits	670 083	SJ60NE/929–931	WM41, 9811	P
Deep Pit (Herman's Field Pit)	683 016	SJ60SE/338–340	13371, P481	DCHP
Deepfield Pit	6828 0638	SJ60NE/1337–1338	W	CHPU
Deerleap Mine	6688 0203	SJ60SE/185	14178	P
Dog in Lane Colliery (No. 4 Pit)	66220 07552	SJ60NE/1197	14147	P
Doseley Mine	678 069	SJ60NE/1323–1325	9061	P
Doseley Bridge Pits	678 068	SJ60NE/1320–1321	9044	P
		SJ60NE/1326–1327	9044	P
Doughty's Mine	685 029	SJ60SE/230–231	4599	H
Dunge No. 7 Pits	684 008	SJ60SE/344–349	5128	CH
Dunge No. 7 Pits No. 3 shaft	68380 00740	SJ60SE/346	5128	CH
Dunge Colliery, Slang shaft	68405 01220	SJ60SE/350		CHP
Ercall View Pits	683 083	SJ60NE/943–950	5803	P
Exley's Pit	707 014	SJ70SW/617–618		DCHPU
Fairfield Colliery	681 092	SJ60NE/858–859	10447, 7324	P
Fairview Colliery (No. 2 Brandlee) No.4	67535 07467	SJ60NE/1060	12722	P
Fish House Colliery	676 024	SJ60SE/193–194	4088	P
Forge Meadow Pits	6971 0722	SJ60NE/496–497	P482	CH
Fosters Pit, Halesfield	704 053	SJ70NW/198–200	4513, WM166, 134, 171, 372, 389,369	KCHP
Freehold Pit	7179 1347	SJ71SW/71–74	9386	P
Garden Pits	673 096	SJ60NE/713–714	7607	P
Gas Works Colliery	681 070	SJ60NE/1138–1140	8010	P
Gitchfield, unnamed shaft	70309 01374	SJ70SW/619		CH
Gitchfield Level	70704 01481	SJ70SW/616		CHP
Good Hope Colliery	65102 06452	SJ60NE/1244	WM160	P
Granville Colliery No. 2 Shaft	72547 12057	SJ71SW/10	5964 WM135, WM170	KCHPU
Gravel Leasowe Pits	679 055	SJ60NE/1356–1360	12687	CHP
Greyhound Pits	69869 10210	SJ61SE/792		P
Hadley Colliery No. 12 shaft	68477 11607	SJ61SE/1014		HP

Name	National Grid reference	BGS registered number (1)	Source of information (2)	Strata (3)
Halesfield Pits	704 051	SJ70NW/201–207	W,S, WM166, 134, 171, 372, 389, 369	CHP
Hall Pits, Malins Lee	696 091	SJ60NE/362–365	W	CHP
Harris's Pit (Old Park No. 5)	68542 08868	SJ60NE/419	14493	P
Heath Hill Colliery	683 077	SJ60NE/1147–1149	7576, 7580	HP
Herman's Field Pits (Deep Pit)	683 016	SJ60SE/338–340	13371, P481	DCHP
Hillcrest Colliery	68188 09512	SJ60NE/870	8727	P
Hillside Colliery	680 087	SJ60NE/922–924	7880	P
Hills Lane Pit	7022 0435	SJ70SW/9–10	P485,W,2919	CHP
Hilltop Farm, Day level	66922 02432	SJ60SE/190?		P
Holly Grove Level	6809 0277	SJ60SE/244	6970	H
Holywell Pits	695 085	SJ60NE/448–453	P482, 3305	CHP
Horsehay Common Colliery	672 078	SJ60NE/1023–1034	13224, WM82	P
Horsehay Common Colliery No. 3	6728 0778	SJ60NE/1025	13224, WM82	P
Horton Pits	7132 1238	SJ71SW/287–290		CHP
Huntington Colliery	659 079	SJ60NE/758–765	13390	P
Ivy No. 2 Pit	6865 0956	SJ60NE/374	12894	P
Jackey Pit	68688 09271	SJ60NE/382	6405	P
Jubilee Colliery	6819 0960	SJ60NE/848, 849	5440	P
Jubilee Colliery	6814 0959	SJ60NE/869	6373	P
Jubilee Pit	68108 02348	SJ60SE/248	5804	H
Kemberton Pit, Inside shaft	71292 05569	SJ70NW/209	10081, WM166, 134, 171, 372, 389, 369	KCHP
Ketley Colliery	685 105	SJ61SE/851–864	3435	P
Ketley Colliery Rock Pits	684 091	SJ60NE/391–392	3345	P
Ketley No. 9 Pit	6882 1081	SJ61SE/853	3435	P
Ketley Fireclay Mine	6923 1057	SJ61SE/778 or 779	7142	P
Ketley Fireclay Mine	6901 1054	SJ61SE/781		P
Ketley Grange Pits	691 099	SJ60NE/318, 320	3913	P
Ketley Hall Colliery	67940 10705	SJ61SE/819	11209	HP
Ketley Manor Pit	676 109	SJ61SE/823–825	4522	P
Knowles Pit	683 028	SJ60SE/235–236	10448	H
Ladywood Fireclay Pit	67818 03066	SJ60SE/616	12723	HP
Ladywood Sulphur Coal levels	679 029	SJ60SE/191–192		P
Langleyfield Pits	69 07	SJ60NE/470–497	5322, P481	CHP
"Langley" Pit	692 070?	SJ60NE/487–490?	P480	CHP
Lawley Colliery	6697 0921	SJ60NE/574	2610A	P
Lawley Colliery No. 3 Pit	6699 0939	SJ60NE/609	14405, 14406, 14407	P
Lawley Colliery No. 4 Pit	6686 0939	SJ60NE/608		P
Lawley Coppice Colliery	c.667 082	SJ60NE/798–814	WM12	P
Lawley Furnace No. 2 Pit	665 095	SJ60NE/586–598	7109, 7110	P
Lawley Furnace No. 3 Pit	667 093	SJ60NE/599–602	7112	P
Lawn Pit (Priorslee)	7120 0956	SJ70NW/164–166		P
Lightmoor Whimsey Pit	Not known	Not registered	P475	CHPU
Lincoln Hill Limestone Pit	67060 03845	SJ60SE/102	P480	DPU
Little Dawley — see Dawley Parva				
Lloyds Water Engine Air Pit	69002 03110	SJ60SE/70		P
Lodge Pit	?67302 03762	SJ60SE/108	P477	DHP

Name	National Grid reference	BGS registered number (1)	Source of information (2)	Strata (3)
Lodge Bank Pits	720 122	SJ71SW/362–367		P
Lodgewood Pits	716 120	SJ71SW/312–313	P479	P
Lower Brandlee Colliery	6793 0711	SJ60NE/1093	6234	P
Lower Brandlee Colliery	680 072	SJ60NE/1124–1125	5491	P
Lower Lightmoor Colliery	675 050	SJ60NE/1351–1353	3356, 6052, 12686	HP
Madeley Court No. 2 ⎤ Platform	69856 05117	SJ60NE/526	5921	DCHP
Madeley Court No. 3 ⎦ Pits	69850 05105	SJ60NE/527		
Madeley Court No. 5 (Holmes' Pit)	69308 04753	SJ60SE/49	W	DCHP
Madeley Court No. 7 ⎤ Furnace	69863 05200	SJ60NE/522	W,5921	DCHP
Madeley Court No. 8 ⎦ Pits	69868 05208	SJ60NE/520		
Madeley Court No. 9	69512 04933	SJ60SE/58	3223,W	CP
Madeley Court No. 10	69525 04940	SJ60SE/59		
Madeley Meadow Pit	690 040	SJ60SE/6–8	7119, P484	CHPU
Malins Lee Hall Pits	696 091	SJ60NE/362–365	W	CHP
Mannerley Lane Colliery	684 096	SJ60NE/862–864	4452	P
Mill Pit	691 061	SJ60NE/513–514	W	DCHP
Mount Pit	661 086	SJ60NE/794–797	11210	P
Mount Pleasant Colliery	6644 0657	SJ60NE/1306–1307	3974	P
Muxton Bridge Pits	722 133	SJ71SW/75–83	9386	P
Nabbside Pit (Wombridge Colliery)	697 111	SJ61SE/703–706	3008, 4286	P
Nelson Pit	7096 0992	SJ70NW/138–139	W	CHP
New Dale Colliery	673 098	SJ60NE/715–718	7275	P
New Engine Pit, Roughpark	6814 0499	SJ60SE/1		DHP
New Gravel Leasow	680 057	SJ60NE/559–562	8222	CH
New Hadley Pits	67984 11675	SJ61SE/840	P481	HP
New Invention Colliery	6628 0846	SJ60NE/787	8538	P
New Road Trial Pit, Broseley	c.6751 0149	SJ60SE/337		P
New Track Pits	6894 0565	SJ60NE/528		DCHP
New Works Colliery	660 079	SJ60NE/755–757	10109, 7029	P
New Works Colliery	662 087	SJ60NE/820–821	8060	P
Oaks Colliery	684 092	SJ60NE/388–389	10411	P
Old Dark Lane Pits	7024 0922	SJ70NW/158–159	W	C
Old Furnace Colliery Air Pit	68121 05393	SJ60NE/558	12687	DCH
Old Lawn Pits (Malins Lee)	701 089	SJ70NW/172–174	W,5322, 2675	CHP
Old Park Colliery, Park Pits	6848 0866	SJ60NE/417–418	3205	HP
Old Park No.5, Harris's Pit	6854 0887	SJ60NE/419	14493	P
Owens Pit	6984 1008	SJ61SE/737		P
Paddock Pits	686 073	SJ60NE/462–465	W	DCHP
Park Pits, Old Park Colliery	6848 0866	SJ60NE/417–418	3205	HP
Park Lane Pit	6898 0959	SJ60NE/371	9053	P
Partons Pit (Wombridge Coll)	6945 1155	SJ61SE/713–714	4549	P
Plants Farm Colliery	658 081	SJ60NE/1689–1693		P
Portley Pit	686 071	SJ60NE/466–468	W	CHP
Princes End Pits	681 090	SJ60NE/889–891	14408	P
Princes End Pits	677 089	SJ60NE/893–902	14408	P
Pudley Hill Pits	700 094	SJ70NW/160–161	R399A, S322, S323	CHP
Quarry Pits	6905 0995	SJ60NE/322–329		P
Red Lake Colliery Nos. 1 & 2 Pits	682 103	SJ61SE/933–934	8610	P

Name	National Grid reference	BGS registered number (1)	Source of information (2)	Strata (3)
Red Lake Colliery				
Fairview Pits	683 102	SJ61SE/937–940	4584, 5110	P
Red Lake Colliery Quarry Pits (see Cow Wood Pits)				
Red Lion Colliery	6617 0699	SJ60NE/1258	13119	P
Rickyard Pit	7089 0966	SJ70NW/140–141	W,13382, 13039	CHP
Rock Colliery No. 1 Pit	6840 0950	SJ60NE/830	WM361	P
Rock Pits	683 094	SJ60NE/830–845 SJ60NE/850–853	WM361, 3965, 3925 4125	P P
Rose & Crown Colliery	6928 1055	SJ61SE/776	10412	P
Rose & Crown Colliery No. 1 Pit	6905 1066	SJ61SE/782	5138	P
Rough Park, New Engine Pit	6814 0499	SJ60SE/1		DHP
Roundhouse Pit	6915 1109	SJ61SE/719	3195	P
Round Oak Colliery	676 098	SJ60NE/705–712	9182	P
St. Leonard's Colliery	6917 1162	SJ61SE/620–621	10334	P
Shawfield Pits	6982 0374	SJ60SE/77–78	3553	P
Shrubbery Colliery	686 103	SJ61SE/917–918	9051	DP
Smalleyhill No. 2	6617 0794	SJ60NE/772	WM99	P
Smiths Pit, in the Lloyds	Not Known	Not registered		P
Snedshill	Not Known	Not registered	P478	P
Southall Pits	691 064	SJ60NE/511–512	W	CHP
Spring Village Pits	674 076	SJ60NE/1180	4069	P
Squires Pits	6908 0859	SJ60NE/439–440	3535	P
Stafford Pits	7156 0915	SJ70NW/167–171	9205	KCHP
Station Bottom Pits	6957 1070	SJ61SE/728–729	4834	P
Station Road Colliery	678 087	SJ60NE/906–908	9374	P
Station Top Pits	696 105	SJ61SE/731–733	4834	P
Stevens Water Engine Air Pit	711 126	SJ71SW/235–237		P
Stirchley Grange Pits	701 071	SJ70NW/194–196	S,3183	CHP
Styches Pit	680 038	SJ60SE/61–62		P
Sunnyside Colliery	6892 1057	SJ61SE/790–791	9729	P
Sutherland Colliery	686 107	SJ61SE/914–916	9291	P
Swan Meadow Pits	685 108	SJ61SE/920–922	11594	P
Tarry Pits	7078 0984	SJ70NW/136–137		CHP
Teece's Pit	6863 0926	SJ60NE/384	10018	P
Top Yard Pit	6824 0614	SJ60NE/1343–1344	W	CHP
Tub Engine Pit	7081 1274	SJ71SW/666	P483	P
Tuckies Pit	691 025	SJ60SE/298–299	7662	CH
Turner's Yard Colliery	693 002	SJ60SE/390–397	WM105, WM4	HP
Victoria Colliery	6761 0993	SJ60NE/719	9933	DP
Viger Drift	6713 0328	SJ60SE/114	15130	P
Waggoner's Fold Pit	691 087	SJ60NE/441–442	3182	P
Wallace Shafts	687 025	SJ60SE/253–255	12791	CH
Wallers Pits	688 027	SJ60SE/232–234	3477	CH
Water Engine Pit	692 110	SJ61SE/717–718	4286, 3091	P
Watling Street Grange Pit	720 114	SJ71SW/600–602	WM170, WM135	KCHP
Waxhill Barracks Pit	718 129	SJ71SW/252–257		P
Wellington Road Colliery No. 4 (=Dog-in-Lane Colliery)	66220 07552	SJ60NE/1197	14147	P

Name	National Grid reference	BGS registered number (1)	Source of information (2)	Strata (3)
Westcroft Pit	708 099	SJ70NW/136–137 or SJ70NW/138–139		CHP
Wharf Pit	69369 10984	SJ61SE/722		P
Wharf Pit Malins Lee	701 082	SJ70NW/178–182	W,S	CHP
Wombridge Engine House Pit	69220 12116	SJ61SE/612		P
Wombridge Farm Mine	693 119	SJ61SE/625–630	8364	P
Wombridge Hill Pits	688 112	SJ61SE/1005–1006	5589	P
Wombridge Water Engine Pit	69204 12127	SJ61SE/613	P475, 4286	CHPU
Wood Pits	6955 0808	SJ60NE/455–456		P
Wood Pits	662 072	SJ60NE/1201–1227	11353	P
Wood Pits No. 4	66216 07172	SJ60NE/1218	11353	P
Woodhouse Pits	713 103	SJ71SW/659–663	13039, 13382, 9206, 12475	P
Woodland Green Mine	673 026	SJ60SE/411–412	6374	H
Woodwell Pits	686 107	SJ61SE/912–913	8004	P
Wycherley Pits	6753 0573	SJ60NE/1347–1350	5051, 4365	CP
Wynd Road Pits	682 029	SJ60SE/239–240	6053	H
Yew Tree Pit	6799 0233	SJ60SE/211	P481	CHP
(Name of shaft not known)	6995 1229	SJ61SE/590		P

APPENDIX 3

Details of the more important boreholes in BGS archives

Name	National Grid reference	BGS registered number See note(1), Appendix 2	Strata See note(3), Appendix 2
Aston A2	6162 0944	SJ60NW/17	DK
Brickkiln Plantation	74692 13520	SJ71SW/6	EKCHP
Brookside 95	70182 06156	SJ70NW/314	C
Brookside 137	70180 06036	SJ70NW/321	C
Childpit Lane	75608 15196	SJ71NE/6	EKCHP
Cluddley A1	6397 1080	SJ61SW/76	DBK
Cluddley A2	6376 1095	SJ61SW/77	DK
Cluddley A3	6377 1074	SJ61SW/78	DK
Cluddley A4	6333 1030	SJ61SW/79	DK
Court Works	69879 05266	SJ60NE/1925	DC
Croft, Lilleshall	7284 1505	SJ71NW/16	U
D'Arcy Exploration Co. G1	7094 0104	SJ70SW/40	DCHU
D'Arcy Exploration Co. G2	7221 0191	SJ70SW/39	DBEKCHU
D'Arcy Exploration Co. G3	6956 0295	SJ60SE/409	KCHPU
Dawley By-Pass DBP 7	68132 07221	SJ60NE/1876	DP
Dawley–Donnington DDD 1	68687 08669	SJ60NE/60	DHP
Dawley–Donnington DDD 2	68708 08567	SJ60NE/61	DHP
Dawley–Donnington DDD 3	68690 08460	SJ60NE/62	DH
Dawley–Donnington DDD 4	68681 08355	SJ60NE/63	DH
Dawley–Donnington DDD 6	68641 08148	SJ60NE/64	DH
Dawley–Donnington DDD 8	68520 07966	SJ60NE/65	DHP
Dawley–Donnington DDD 9	68440 07930	SJ60NE/66	DHP
Dawley–Donnington DDD10	68365 07865	SJ60NE/67	DHP
Dawley–Donnington DDD11	68215 07855	SJ60NE/68	DP
Dawley–Donnington DDH10	69928 12161	SJ61SE/385	DP
Dawley–Donnington DDH16	69444 12023	SJ61SE/391	P
Dawley–Donnington DDD(N)12	69252 12028	SJ61SE/440	CH
Dawley–Donnington DDD(N)12a	69343 12067	SJ61SE/441	CH
Dawley–Donnington DDD(N)13	69431 12006	SJ61SE/442	P
Dawley–Donnington DDD(N)13a	69474 12012	SJ61SE/443	P
Dawley–Donnington DDN(N)17a	69674 12121	SJ61SE/445	DH
Dawley–Donnington DDD(N)18a	69902 12140	SJ61SE/447	DP
Dawley–Donnington DDD(N)19	69932 12169	SJ61SE/448	DP
Dawley–Donnington DDD(N)21	70142 12236	SJ71SW/688	DP
Dawley–Donnington DDD(N)22	70253 12263	SJ71SW/689	DP
Dawley–Donnington DDD(N)23	70351 12300	SJ71SW/690	DP
Dawley–Donnington DDD(N)25	70501 12430	SJ71SW/692	DP
Dawley–Donnington DDD(N)26	70755 12612	SJ71SW/693	P
Dawley North-West 7	68463 07800	SJ60NE/199	DP
Dawley North-West 11	68285 07968	SJ60NE/203	DP
Dawley North-West 17	68134 08046	SJ60NE/208	DP
Dean	6799 0006	SJ60SE/619	U
Donnington A2	7122 1438	SJ71SW/35	DB
Eastern Central Primary Road North			
ECPR(N)1	69970 09735	SJ60NE/75	DC
ECPR(N)2	69926 09800	SJ60NE/76	DP
ECPR(N)4	69905 10004	SJ61SE/504	P
ECPR(N)5	69900 10102	SJ61SE/505	P
ECPR(N)6	69953 10212	SJ61SE/506	DP
ECPR(N)7	69990 10318	SJ61SE/507	DP
ECPR(N)8	69990 10415	SJ61SE/508	DP
ECPR(N)8a	7006 1043	SJ71SW/685	DP
ECPR(N)9	7000 1053	SJ71SW/686	P
ECPR(N)10	69995 10606	SJ61SE/509	P

Name	National Grid reference	BGS registered number See note(1), Appendix 2	Strata See note(3), Appendix 2
ECPR(N)12	69909 10762	SJ61SE/511	DP
ECPR(N)14	69822 10931	SJ61SE/513	DP
Eastern Interceptor Sewer ES10	71258 06420	SJ70NW/574	DK
Eastern Primary Road EP47A	70428 05381	SJ70NW/371	DKC
Eyton	6495 1384	SJ61SW/224	DB
Freehold Colliery Underground borehole	7215 1382	SJ71SW/669	P
Granville Colliery Underground borehole	72865 12772	SJ71SW/670	P
Granville Colliery Underground No. 3	73885 14205	SJ71SW/9	P
Grindle Forge	7524 0348	SJ70SE/1	DB
Hadley Park 1	6720 1322	SJ61SE/294	DBKU
Hadley Park 2	6798 1281	SJ61SE/295	DBKU
Hadley Park 3	6738 1361	SJ61SE/296	DBKU
Hadley Park 4	6775 1349	SJ61SE/297	DKU
Hadley Park 5	6884 1353	SJ61SE/1108	DBKU
Harrington Pumping Station	7477 0156	SJ70SW/646	WS
Hinksman's Brewery	7473 0788	SJ70NW/1404	DB
Hollybank Wood	74576 11999	SJ71SW/7	EKCHP
Holmer Farm A	70927 05752	SJ70NW/373	DC
Holmer Farm B	70878 05693	SJ70NW/374	DKC
Holmer Farm C	70825 05643	SJ70NW/375	DKC
Holmer Farm D	70972 05813	SJ70NW/376	DC
Holmer Farm E	71003 05881	SJ70NW/381	DKC
Honnington A1	7240 1448	SJ71SW/36	DP
Hoo Hall A2	6884 1439	SJ61SE/290	DB
Hoo Hall A3	6911 1386	SJ61SE/291	DB
Hoo Hall Borehole	6861 1488	SJ61SE/23	DBK
Hugh's Bridge	74000 14963	SJ71SW/8	KCHP
Ironbridge Church	67223 03551	SJ60SE/600	P
Isombridge Farm	6106 1374	SJ61SW/218	DB
Jocky Bank 1	67894 03585	SJ60SE/601	HP
Jocky Bank 2	67867 03493	SJ60SE/602	DP
Kinley Farm	6696 1474	SJ61SE/1109	DK
Kinley Farm	6689 1466	SJ61SE/1110	DK
Kinley Farm (BGS)	6716 1478	SJ61SE/24	DKU
Leegomery House Farm	6638 1268	SJ61SE/25	DBKU
Lees Farm 1	68736 03727	SJ60SE/891	DCH
Lees Farm 1A	68704 03739	SJ60SE/892	DCHP
Lees Farm 2	68686 03676	SJ60SE/893	DC
Lees Farm 4	69183 03630	SJ60SE/620	C
Lees Farm 4A	69126 03585	SJ60SE/621	DC
Lees Farm 6	69217 03746	SJ60SE/623	DC
Lilleshall A1	7286 1495	SJ71SW/33	P
Lilleshall 1	7427 1385	SJ71SW/2	EKCHP
Lilleshall 2	7564 1429	SJ71SE/2	DEKCHP
Lilleshall 3, 3A	75700 15985	SJ71NE/2	EKCHP
Lilleshall 4	7543 1296	SJ71SE/3	EKCHP
Lilleshall 5	7688 1095	SJ71SE/4	SBEKCHPU
Lilleshall 6	7770 1395	SJ71SE/1	SBEKCHP
Lilleshall 7A	74000 12735	SJ71SW/1	EKCHP
Lodge Farm	67566 03704	SJ60SE/20	HPU
Lodge Farm, Trench	6887 1297	SJ61SE/26	DBKU
M54 No. 2B	70984 09376	SJ70NW/29	DC
M54 No. 3	7122 0937	SJ70NW/30	C
M54 No. 4	71480 09335	SJ70NW/34	K
M54 No. 19	73758 08934	SJ70NW/68	DE
M54 No. 27	73711 08982	SJ70NW/77	E
Mad Brook Valley Sewer M71	71093 05799	SJ70NW/560	DK
Madeley Wood 1	7387 0876	SJ70NW/16	EKCHP
Madeley Wood 2	7311 0878	SJ70NW/12	EKCHP
Madeley Wood 3	7464 0906	SJ70NW/13	BEKCHP
Madeley Wood 4	7332 0657	SJ70NW/14	EKCHPU
Madeley Wood 5	7500 0628	SJ70NE/1	DBEKCHP

Name	National Grid reference	BGS registered number See note(1), Appendix 2	Strata See note(3), Appendix 2
Madeley Wood 6	7427 0698	SJ70NW/15	BEKCHP
Madeley Wood 7	7357 0834	SJ70NW/22	EKCHP
Madeley Wood 8	7364 0855	SJ70NW/26	EKCHP
Madeley Wood Underground 5	72402 07333	SJ70NW/17	P
Madeley Wood Underground 6	73092 07717	SJ70NW/18	P
Madeley Wood Underground 7	73179 07870	SJ70NW/19	P
Madeley Wood Underground 8	73387 08064	SJ70NW/20a	P
Madeley Wood Underground 9	73387 08064	SJ70NW/20b	P
Madeley Wood Underground 10	73407 08091	SJ70NW/21a	PH
Madeley Wood Underground 11	73407 08091	SJ70NW/21b	P
Madeley Wood Underground 12	73430 08127	SJ70NW/23	P
Madeley Wood Underground 13	72531 07176	SJ70NW/24	P
Madeley Wood Underground 14	72557 07144	SJ70NW/25	P
Malinslee 1	68520 08395	SJ60NE/39	HP
Malinslee 2	68900 08570	SJ60NE/41	HP
Malinslee 3	68942 08725	SJ60NE/42	DHP
Malinslee 4	69180 08830	SJ60NE/40	HP
Malinslee 6	68647 08154	SJ60NE/43	DHP
Naird Farm 1	71723 07601	SJ70NW/1343	E
Naird Farm 2	71837 07607	SJ70NW/1344	E
Naird Farm 5	71769 07857	SJ70NW/1347	E
Naird Farm 6	71909 07861	SJ70NW/1348	E
Naird Farm 7	72051 07835	SJ70NW/1349	E
Nedge Valley N41	71358 08000	SJ70NW/718	DK
Nedge Valley N42	71383 08057	SJ70NW/719	DK
Nedge Valley N43	71399 08115	SJ70NW/720	DKC
Nedge Valley N44	71413 08174	SJ70NW/721	DKC
Nedge Valley N45	71437 08230	SJ70NW/722	DKC
Nedge Valley N46	71461 08283	SJ70NW/723	DKC
Nedge Valley N47	71480 08335	SJ70NW/724	DKC
Nedge Valley N48	71524 08382	SJ70NW/725	DK
Nedge Valley N49	71569 08424	SJ70NW/726	DK
Nedge Valley N50	71624 08464	SJ70NW/727	DK
Nedge Valley N51	71682 08490	SJ70NW/728	DK
Nedge Valley N64	71150 06568	SJ70NW/738	DKC
Nedge Valley N65	71181 06642	SJ70NW/739	DK
North-Eastern Primary Road NEPR B3	69662 11300	SJ61SE/478	P
North-Eastern Primary Road NEPR 2	69741 11133	SJ61SE/495	P
North-Eastern Primary Road NEPR 3	69700 11224	SJ61SE/496	DP
North-Eastern Primary Road NEPR 4	69633 11349	SJ61SE/497	DP
North-Eastern Primary Road NEPR 5	69582 11440	SJ61SE/498	P
North-Eastern Primary Road NEPR 6	69515 11533	SJ61SE/499	DP
North-Eastern Primary Road NEPR 7	69445 11608	SJ61SE/500a	DP
North-Eastern Primary Road NEPR 8	69357 11653	SJ61SE/501	DP
North-Eastern Primary Road NEPR 9	69235 11731	SJ61SE/502	DP
Oakengates Ring Road ORR2A	69749 10848	SJ61SE/40	DP
Oakengates Ring Road ORR4	69749 10991	SJ61SE/37	DP
Oakengates Ring Road ORR5A	69727 11019	SJ61SE/38	DP
Oakengates Ring Road ORR6	69700 11050	SJ61SE/39	DP
Old Park 1002	69653 09500	SJ60NE/1713	P
Old Park 1021	69357 09596	SJ60NE/1716	P
Old Park 1046	68902 08948	SJ60NE/1727	P
Old Park OP1	69807 09672	SJ60NE/30	P
Old Park OP2	69427 09759	SJ60NE/31	DP
Old Park OP3	69160 09432	SJ60NE/32	P
Old Park OP4	69312 09260	SJ60NE/33	P
Old Park OP5	68892 08958	SJ60NE/34	P
Randley By-Pass Sewer RL1 to RL19	70055 07509 to 70543 08075	SJ70NW/1074 to SJ70NW/1092	C
Rushton	6069 0822	SJ60NW/6	U
Shifnal Manor A1 to A6	737 067	SJ70NW/125-130	DB
Slang Lane No. 2	6448 1163	SJ61SW/209	DK

Name	National Grid reference	BGS registered number See note(1), Appendix 2	Strata See note(3), Appendix 2
Stafford Park 213	71937 09081	SJ70NW/999	DK
Stirchley S67	70096 06991	SJ70NW/487	C
Telford-Wolverhampton Motorway 2B	70984 09376	SJ70NW/29	DC
Telford-Wolverhampton Motorway 3	7122 0937	SJ70NW/30	C
Telford-Wolverhampton Motorway 4	71480 09335	SJ70NW/34	K
Telford-Wolverhampton Motorway 19	73758 08974	SJ70NW/68	DE
Telford-Wolverhampton Motorway 27	73711 08982	SJ70NW/77	E
Town Centre TC1	69971 08989	SJ60NE/1553	DC
Town Centre TC2	69916 09029	SJ60NE/1554	DC
Town Centre TC3	69926 08959	SJ60NE/1555	DC
Town Centre TC21	69847 08948	SJ60NE/1506	C
Town Centre TC22	69734 09287	SJ60NE/1503	C
Town Centre TC25	69402 08835	SJ60NE/1507	C
Town Centre TC27	69935 08528	SJ60NE/1509	C
Town Centre TC31	70195 09036	SJ70NW/1040	C
Town Centre TC34	70351 08787	SJ70NW/1043	C
Town Centre TC35	70298 08527	SJ70NW/1044	C
Town Centre TC36	70572 08764	SJ70NW/1045	C
Town Centre TC37	70667 08294	SJ70NW/1046	C
Town Centre TC44	68864 09247	SJ60NE/51	DP
Town Centre TC46	68746 09414	SJ60NE/53	DP
Town Centre TC54	66782 10200	SJ61SE/517	DP
Town Centre TC59	70299 08399	SJ70NW/958	DC
Town Centre TC61	70268 08257	SJ70NW/960	DC
Town Centre TC62	70379 08325	SJ70NW/961	DC
Town Centre TC63	70517 08345	SJ70NW/962	DC
Town Centre TC82	69448 08902	SJ60NE/1545	DC
Town Centre TC83	69527 08851	SJ60NE/1546	DC
Town Centre TC86	69794 08709	SJ60NE/1549	C
Town Centre TC94	70277 08722	SJ70NW/1371	C
Trench, Lodge Farm	6887 1297	SJ61SE/26	DBKU
Messrs. C & W Walker's Midland Ironworks	7096 1424	SJ71SW/731	DB
Wellington By-Pass 6/3R	66687 10242	SJ61SE/206	DP
Wellington By-Pass 6/7R	66685 10198	SJ61SE/211	DP
Wesley Brook B3	73898 08697	SJ70NW/121	DE
Woodside W0601–W0619	c. 682 045	SJ60SE/706-723	DC
Woodside W0626	68899 04813	SJ60SE/704	DC
Woodside W0627	68911 04812	SJ60SE/705	DC
Wrekin Buildings	6231 0871	SJ60NW/7	BKCHU

APPENDIX 4

List of opencast coal and fireclay sites

All sites known to have been worked by opencast methods for coal and/or fireclay up to 1975 are listed here and their approximate extent indicated on Figure 53.

Opencast site	National Grid reference	BGS registered number
Arleston Hill	664 092	SJ60NE/1
Benthall Hall	6595 0245	SJ60SE/12
Broseley	664 022	SJ60SE/421
Candles	666 080	SJ60NE/16
Candles North	668 084	SJ60NE/16
Candles South	664 075	SJ60NE/16
Candles South 2	6635 0725	SJ60NE/16
Caughley	6915 0015	Not registered
Clares Lane	688 090	SJ60NE/1849
Clay Colliery	665 065	SJ60NE/1686
Coalmoor	654 072	SJ60NE/18
Dingle	658 060	SJ60NE/2
Doseley	660 092	Not registered
Dog-in-Lane	664 078	SJ60NE/28
Ganey	688 000	SJ60SE/11
Greenfields	662 072	SJ60NE/1625
Holywell Lane	674 055	SJ60NE/20
Horsehay Flats	665 069	SJ60NE/1626
Huntington Heath	655 083	SJ60NE/3
Huntington Heath D	6585 0770	SJ60NE/3
Huntington Heath E	6605 0735	SJ60NE/3
Huntington Heath No. 5	661 083	SJ60NE/3
Ketley Grange	690 100	SJ60NE/12
Lackey	659 086	SJ60NE/21
Lawley	679 083	SJ60NE/1601
Lawley Bank	673 085	SJ60NE/15
Lawley Common	678 085	SJ60NE/13
Leasowes A	654 063	SJ60NE/19
Leasowes B	653 061	SJ60NE/19
Limekiln Lane	656 099	SJ60NE/1600
Linley Green No. 1	SO 6865 9925	SO69NE/2
Maddocks Hill	651 085	SJ60NE/4
Malthouse Farm	653 072	SJ60NE/1623
Mannerly Lane	681 102	SJ61SE/1
Mannerly Lane Extension	6820 1015	SJ61SE/1
Monroe	673 098	SJ60NE/11
Moors Farm	651 058	SJ60NE/1628
Mossey Green	685 095	SJ60NE/1602
Old Park	690 090	SJ60NE/1850
Princes End	679 091	SJ60NE/6
Red Lion	661 070	SJ60NE/1624
Rudgewood No. 1	SO 684 993	SO69NE/1
Rudgewood No. 2	SO 682 993	SO69NE/1
Smalleyhill	663 083	SJ60NE/1687
Spread Eagles	652 068	SJ60NE/17
Spring Village	672 077	SJ60NE/8
Spring Village North	671 080	SJ60NE/10
Stocking Farm	675 058	SJ60NE/7
Stoneyhill	668 060	SJ60NE/1688
Swann Farm	649 063	SJ60NW/1
Swann Farm West	645 062	SJ60NW/2
Trough	670 094	SJ60NE/9
Wellington Road	670 081	SJ60NE/10

Willey Park	675 009	SJ60SE/10
Willowmoor	645 078	SJ60NW/3
Willowmoor South	6445 0745	SJ60NW/3
Woodside	674 046	Not registered

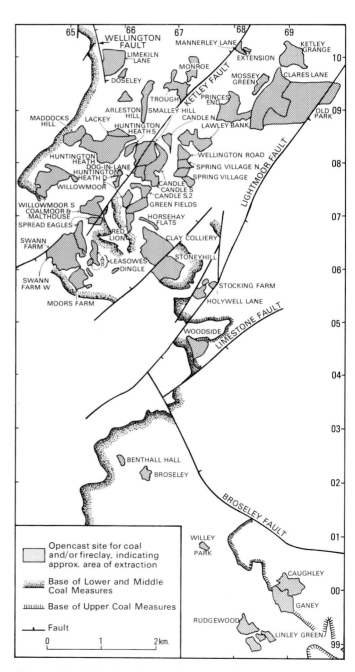

Figure 53 Distribution and extent of opencast coal and fireclay sites in the Telford district.

APPENDIX 5

Glossary of old mining terms

Bass (or black bass)	black shale
Bastard seatearth	seatearth that has no overlying coal seam
Bind(s)	fissile sandstone, sandy shale or siltstone
Bind bass	black sandy or silty shale
Bind rock	bedded sandstone
Black slums	coaly shale or clay
Blue bind	bluish grey sandy shale or siltstone
Blue clod	bluish grey mudstone or shale
Calaminker	red clay
Clod	grey mudstone or shale
Clunch	rooty mudstone; fireclay; seatearth; may be silty
Gob	backfill to old workings
Linseed earth	dark grey fireclay with ironstone nodules
Pitchy bass	black bituminous shale
Pricking	seatearth ('pricked out' before the overlying coal was worked)
Quoiceneck	seatearth showing shining listric surfaces when broken open (quoice is the local name for a pigeon)
Rock	sandstone
(Rock(y) binds or rough binds)	fissile sandstone
Wild ground	probably red measures, possibly faulted ground

APPENDIX 6

Geological Survey photographs

Photographs illustrating the geology of the Telford district are deposited for reference in the headquarters of the British Geological Survey, Keyworth, Nottingham NG12 5GG; in the library at the BGS, Murchison House, West Mains Road, Edinburgh EH9 3LA; and in the BGS Information Office at the Natural History Museum Earth Galleries, Exhibition Road, London SW7 2DE. They belong to the A series and were taken up to 1974. The photographs depict details of the various rocks and sediments exposed and also include general views and scenery. A list of titles can be supplied on request. The photographs can be supplied as black and white or colour prints and colour transparencies, at an advertised tariff.

FOSSIL INDEX

GENERAL INDEX

BRITISH GEOLOGICAL SURVEY

Keyworth, Nottingham NG12 5GG
0115-936 3100

Murchison House, West Mains Road, Edinburgh
EH9 3LA   0131-667 1000

London Information Office, Natural History Museum
Earth Galleries, Exhibition Road, London SW7 2DE
0171-589 4090

The full range of Survey publications is available through the
Sales Desks at Keyworth and at Murchison House, Edinburgh,
and in the BGS London Information Office in the Natural
History Museum (Earth Galleries). The adjacent bookshop
stocks the more popular books for sale over the counter. Most
BGS books and reports can be bought from HMSO and
through HMSO agents and retailers. Maps are listed in the
BGS Map Catalogue, and can be bought together with books
and reports through BGS-approved stockists and agents as well
as direct from BGS.

*The British Geological Survey carries out the geological survey of Great
Britain and Northern Ireland (the latter as an agency service for the
government of Northern Ireland), and of the surrounding continental
shelf, as well as its basic research projects. It also undertakes
programmes of British technical aid in geology in developing countries
as arranged by the Overseas Development Administration.*

*The British Geological Survey is a component body of the Natural
Environment Research Council.*

HMSO publications are available from:

HMSO Publications Centre
(Mail, fax and telephone orders only)
PO Box 276, London SW8 5DT
Telephone orders 0171-873 9090
General enquiries 0171-873 0011
Queuing system in operation for both numbers
Fax orders 0171-873 8200

HMSO Bookshops
49 High Holborn, London WC1V 6HB
(counter service only)
0171-873 0011   Fax 0171-831 1326
68–69 Bull Street, Birmingham B4 6AD
0121-236 9696   Fax 0121-236 9699
33 Wine Street, Bristol BS1 2BQ
0117-9264306   Fax 0117-9294515
9 Princess Street, Manchester M60 8AS
0161-834 7201   Fax 0161-833 0634
16 Arthur Street, Belfast BT1 4GD
01232-238451   Fax 01232-235401
71 Lothian Road, Edinburgh EH3 9AZ
0131-228 4181   Fax 0131-229 2734

HMSO's Accredited Agents
(see Yellow Pages)

And through good booksellers